S0-ACD-404

United States

STAMPS
& STORIES

Illustrated Stories of Important People, Places,
and Events — With a Catalogue of All Postage
Stamps of the U. S. and the United Nations.

Editor	Elena Marzulla
Associate Editors	Bill Beal
	Duane Hillmer
	Rose Pickford
Art Director	Edward G. Mueller
Artists	Larry D. Cahill
	Barbara Ehlers
	John Graham
	Linda A. Steckelberg
	William J. Sudyka
Stamp Curator	Gene Lachowski
Consultant	Norman S. Hubbard, Ph.D.
Cover Art	Harry Knox
	Jack Pardue

Stamp Quotations from Scott's 1972 Standard
Postage Stamp Catalogue.

Editor-in-Chief	James B. Hatcher
Associate Editor	
for U.S. and U.N.	Irving Koslow

**This Exploration Volume is edited and published
for the United States Postal Service by**

Scott Publishing Co.

Headquarters and Plant
10102 F Street
Omaha, Nebraska 68127

Catalogue Editorial Offices
604 Fifth Avenue
New York, N. Y. 10020

The United States Postal Service sells only commemoratives released during the past few years and current regular and special stamps and postal stationery. A list of stamps and postal stationery available at face value from the USPS may be obtained by sending a stamped addressed envelope to the Philatelic Sales Unit, Washington, D. C. 20036.

Prices listed in this handbook are called "catalogue prices" by collectors and serve only as a guide to market prices for fine specimens when offered by an informed dealer to an informed buyer. They are taken from the 1972 Scott Catalogue whose editors have based these values on the current stamp market. Comments concerning them should be directed to the Scott Publishing Co.

The Scott numbering system for stamps is used in this book since it is the identification system used by most stamp dealers and collectors in the United States.

Note: When minimum catalogue price of a used stamp is fixed by Scott at 3 cents it reflects dealer's labor and service costs. The sum of these minimum prices does not properly indicate the value of an accumulation of stamps consisting only of cheaper stamps. Prices of actual stamps are dependent upon supply and demand, changes in popularity, local custom, quality of the stamp itself and many other factors.

Dedicated...

To those people whose main purpose in life is service to others, and who pursue that purpose by diligent and courageous public service.

May they continue their devoted work to achieve the ideal of a better world. May their spirit be undaunted by rebuke, their resolution be not reduced by censure, and may their effort be undiluted by criticism.

Let us recognize the loyal service of all who work for the public good. Let us appreciate the worthwhile accomplishments of the many people who do so much to help mankind.

STAMPS AND STORIES

THE UNITED STATES

On this unique journey through the pages of American history, postage stamps are your guide. Illustrated stories of the famous people and events shown on stamps recreate the building of a nation from its founding to the present day.

Biographies of presidents, pioneers, and inventors appear along with stories about authors, explorers, and many others. Boy Scouts, suffragettes, and artists stand with George Washington, Lewis and Clark, and Frank Lloyd Wright in their contributions to the American way of life. The achievements of peace — the building of the transcontinental railroad or the Panama Canal — follow the smoke of the epic battles of the Civil War, Lexington and Concord or Bataan and Corregidor.

The voyages of Christopher Columbus, the explorations of Apollo astronauts, the feats of Daniel Boone and Davy Crockett — all are brought to life in this book.

In addition, the stamps of United States territories and former possessions are included: the Canal Zone, Guam, Hawaii, Philippine Islands, and Puerto Rico. The history of these lands and peoples adds yet another dimension to the diversity of the U. S. heritage.

The stamps of the United Nations are also represented. This special section gives historic and philatelic variety to the book. The story of the founding of the U. N. and brief stories on some of its agencies are important additions to the history of man's achievements. *Shown at left are three U. N. Secretaries General: Trygve Lie, Dag Hammarskjöld, and U Thant.*

A special feature, "How to Be a Happy Stamp Collector", includes fascinating facts on stamps and stamp collecting — from how they are made to helpful tips for the beginner. Another story, "Hidden Opportunities in Stamp Collecting", tells the always interesting tale of treasure hunting for valuable rarities. These lively and informative articles, plus an easy-to-read glossary of philatelic terms, an index of U. S. commemorative issues, and a complete index to story subjects will enlarge your interest in the stimulating, educational, and entertaining world of stamp collecting.

TABLE OF CONTENTS

The chronology of this book is according to the date of issue of United States and other postage stamps. Stories, indicated in light type below, relate to stamps and follow this chronology.

HOW TO USE THIS BOOK . . .

...which will help you enjoy learning about history and stamps.

All U. S. postage stamps are listed in chronological order according to date of issue. Each listing contains the following:

Scott Catalogue Number	Denomination	Common Name of Stamp
1163	.08	.04 4c Boys' Clubs of America	Oct. 18
Unused Price	Used Price	First Day of Issue

1163

When year of issue, perforati or watermark is mentioned, description applies to all succe ing listings until a change is no

"Sia" Numbers

Duplicated designs are sho once, with later stamps referen by a number (sia — same illus tion as) which is the number of stamp shown.

New Issue Listings

New stamps are regularly lis in the Scott Monthly Journal.

645

U. S. Government regulations specify onl cancelled stamps be shown actual size in colo Stamps in this book are about 70% of actu size. This may alter the effects intended b designers and diminish the beauty from that o the actual stamps. Color fidelity not guarantee

Shown at left are actual and 70% sizes. Fu size, *unused* stamps are more attractive tha smaller size reproductions.

Scott Publishing Co. Does Not Sell Stamps — How to Order from Others

Identify items wanted by country of issue, Scott No., and condition. For example, request "U. S. No. 1163 unused" when ordering the 4c Boys' Club Stamp of 1960.

Condition is an important factor of price.

Unused prices are for stamps in fine con tion. Off-center, heavily cancelled, fade or stained stamps usually sell at large d counts. Values in italics indicate lat auction prices, infrequent sales, or fluc ating market value.

Abbreviations Used (Clockwise from Upper Left)

bis. brn. (bistre brown)	org. (orange)
blk. (black)	ultra. (ultramarine)
brt. bl. (bright blue)	verm. (vermilion)
brn. (brown)	vio. (violet)
car. (carmine)	yel. (yellow)
dk. bl. (dark blue)	Imperf. (Imperforate)
dp. bl. (deep blue)	Perf. (Perforated)
dp. vio. (deep violet)	
grn. (green)	sia (same illustration as)
lt. grn. (light green)	Wmk. (Watermark)
multi. (multicolored)	Unwmkd. (Unwatermarked)

THE UNITED STATES

GOVT. — Republic.
AREA — 3,615,211 sq. mi.
POP. — 203,184,772 (1970).
CAPITAL — Washington, D. C.
100 Cents — 1 Dollar
In addition to the 50 States and the District of Columbia, the Republic includes Guam, the

Commonwealth of Puerto Rico, the Virgin Islands, American Samoa, Wake, Midway and a number of small islands in the Pacific Ocean, all of which use stamps of the United States.

Included also is the Panama Canal Zone which issues its own stamps.

1	2	3	4

Issues of 1847 to 1894 are Unwatermarked
Issue of 1847, Imperf.

400.00	67.50	5c Benjamin Franklin
1850.00	225.00	10c George Washington

Issue of 1875, Reproductions of 1 & 2

Actually, official imitations made from new plates by order of the Post Office Department. Issued without gum.

235.00	5c Franklin
325.00	10c Washington

Reproductions. The letters R. W. H. & E. at the ·ttom of each stamp are less distinct on the reproduc-·ns than on the originals.

5c. On the originals the left side of the white shirt frill touches the oval on a level with the top of the "F" of "Five." On the reproductions it touches the oval about on a level with the top of the figure "5."

10c. On the reproductions, line of coat at left points to right tip of "X" and line of coat at right points to center of "S" of CENTS. On the originals, line of coat points to "T" of TEN and between "T" and "S" of CENTS. On the reproductions the eyes have a sleepy look, the line of the mouth is straighter, and in the curl of hair near the left cheek is a strong black dot, while the originals have only a faint one.

See also No. 948

GEORGE WASHINGTON (1732-99)

Let me now . . . warn you in the most solemn manner against the baneful effects of the spirit of party. Farewell Address, 1796

Following a triumphant procession from Mount Vernon, George Washington arrived in New York City on April 30, 1789 for his inauguration as the first president of the United States. Standing on the balcony of Federal Hall, the man who had led the Continental Army to victory in the Revolution took the oath of office and the crowd lining Wall Street broke into cheers of confidence and approval.

Washington's two terms in office (1789-97) justified the faith of his countrymen. Despite his fears that he faced "an ocean of difficulties without that competency of political skill, abilities, and inclinations which is necessary to manage the helm," he proved an able executive. Ignoring the antagonism that existed between Thomas Jefferson and Alexander Hamilton he made Jefferson secretary of state, Hamilton secretary of the treasury, and then utilized both men's talents to the fullest. His administration saw the establishment of national credit, the setting up of an effective working government where none had been before, and a new era of strength for the nation he served so well in war and peace.

Portraits of George Washington have consistently appeared on U. S. stamps from 1847 to the present.

Haiti Scott No. C11.

Detail of 5 Type I
Has curved, unbroken lines outside labels.
Scrollwork is complete, forms little balls at bottom.

Detail of 6 Type Ia
Top ornaments and outer line partly cut away.
Lower scrollwork is complete.

Detail of 8 Type III
Outer lines broken in the middle.
Side ornaments are complete.

Detail of 8A Type IIIa
Outer lines broken top or bottom but not both.

5

Detail of 9 Type IV
Outer lines recut top, bottom, or both.

Detail of 7 Type II
Lower scrollwork incomplete (lacks little balls).
Side ornaments are complete.

BENJAMIN FRANKLIN (1706-90)

Do not squander time, for that is the stuff life is made of. Poor Richard's Almanac, 1757.

Benjamin Franklin served his country for fifty years as inventor, philosopher, statesman, diplomat, author, and scientist. As a statesman he helped draft the Declaration of Independence and was one of its signers. As a diplomat he served for many years as the American representative to France, where he enlisted financial and military support for the American Revolutionary cause.

A Bostonian by birth and a Philadelphian by choice, Franklin was also an accomplished printer. He helped develop the first circulating library and the first post office; invented the Franklin stove, the lightning rod, and bifocal glasses; organized police and fire departments; wrote *Poor Richard's Almanac* and his famous *Autobiography*.

The first U. S. Postmaster-General, Franklin has appeared on more U. S. stamps than any other public figure except Washington.

U.S.S.R. Scott No. 1875

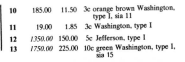

	Issue of 1851-56, Imperf.			**10**	185.00	11.50	3c orange brown Washington, type I, sia 11
	16.500.00	*5750.00*	1c Franklin, type I				
	Nos. 6-9: Franklin, sia 5			**11**	19.00	1.85	3c Washington, type I
	1750.00	*600.00*	1c dark blue, type 1a	**12**	*1350.00*	150.00	5c Jefferson, type I
	110.00	25.00	1c blue, type II	**13**	*1750.00*	225.00	10c green Washington, type I, sia 15
	1000.00	*285.00*	1c blue, type III				
A	300.00	140.00	1c pale blue, type IIIa				
	75.00	22.50	1c blue, type IV				

Detail of **11**
THREE CENTS.
Type I. There is an outer frame line at top and bottom.

Detail of **12**
FIVE CENTS.
Type I. There are projections on all four sides.

10c Washington Types I-IV of 1855

Detail of **13**
Type I. The "shells" at the lower corners are practically complete. The outer line below the label is very nearly complete. The outer lines are broken above the middle of the top label and the "X" in each upper corner.

15

Detail of **14**
Type II. The design is complete at the top. The outer line at the bottom is broken in the middle. The shells are partly cut away.

Detail of **15**
Type III. The outer lines are broken above the top label and the "X" numerals. The outer line at the bottom and the shells are partly cut away, as in Type II.

Detail of **16**
Type IV. The outer lines have been recut at top or bottom or both.
Types I, II, III and IV have complete ornaments at the sides of the stamps and three pearls at each outer edge of the bottom panel.

17

37

38

39

Detail of 24
ONE CENT FRANKLIN
Type V. Similar to type III of 1851-56 but with side ornaments partly cut away.

Detail of 26
THREE CENTS WASHINGTON
Type II. The outer frame line has been removed at top and bottom. The side frame lines were recut so as to be continuous from the top to the bottom of the plate.

Detail of 35
TEN CENTS WASHINGTON
(Two typical examples).
Type V. Side ornaments slightly cut away. Outer lines complete except over right X.

30A

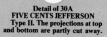

Detail of 30A
FIVE CENTS JEFFERSON
Type II. The projections at top and bottom are partly cut away.

14	265.00	45.00	10c green, type II, sia 15	32	225.00	26.50	10c green, type II
15	265.00	45.00	10c Washington, type III	33	225.00	26.50	10c green, type III
16	*2000.00*	325.00	10c green, type IV, sia 15	34	*1900.00*	225.00	10c green, type IV
17	260.00	40.00	12c Washington	35	33.50	13.00	10c green, type V
				36	60.00	19.00	12c black Washington, sia 17
	Issue of 1857-61, Perf. 15			37	115.00	60.00	24c Washington
	Nos. 18-24: Franklin, sia 5			38	120.00	70.00	30c Franklin
18	200.00	120.00	1c blue, type I	39	400.00	*1000.00*	90c Washington
19	1250.00	375.00	1c blue, type Ia			120.00	90c Same, with pen cancel
20	110.00	40.00	1c blue, type II				

Note: Beware of forged cancellations of 39. Genuine cancellations are extremely rare.

21	425.00	125.00	1c blue, type III		**1875: Government Reprints, Perf. 12**		
22	110.00	42.50	1c blue, type IIIa		**White Paper, Without Gum**		
23	575.00	70.00	1c blue, type IV	40	160.00		1c bright blue Franklin, sia 5
24	20.00	8.00	1c blue, type V	41	800.00		3c scarlet Washington, sia 11
	Nos. 25-26: Washington, sia 11			42	300.00		5c orange brown Jefferson, sia 30A
25	110.00	6.00	3c rose, type I				
26	8.00	1.00	3c dull red, type II	43	550.00		10c blue green Washington, sia 15
	Nos. 27-29: Jefferson, sia 12						
27	800.00	125.00	5c brick red, type I	44	600.00		12c greenish black Washington, sia 17
28	*525.00*	75.00	5c red brown, type I				
28A	*1750.00*	300.00	5c Indian red, type I	45	675.00		24c blackish violet Washington, sia 37
29	175.00	52.50	5c brown, type I				
30	85.00	110.00	5c orange brown Jefferson, type II, sia 30A	46	950.00		30c yel. org. Franklin, sia 38
30A	90.00	37.50	5c Jefferson, type II	47	1300.00		90c deep blue Washington, sia 39
	Nos. 31-35: Washington, sia 15						
31	*1500.00*	135.00	10c green, type I				

THOMAS JEFFERSON (1743-1826)

Third President of the United States, legislator, diplomat, and author; scientist, musician, and inventor; architect, philosopher, and planter, Thomas Jefferson was a Renaissance man born into the Age of Reason.

The son of a well-to-do Virginia planter, Jefferson attended the College of William and Mary and received his law degree before serving in the legislature of Virginia. By the time the Second Continental Congress met in Philadelphia he was well-known as a politician, as a firm, outspoken advocate of Locke's philosophy of man's inherent right to liberty, as a gifted writer, and as a strong supporter of the rebels' cause in the Revolution. It was only natural that he became a member of the five-man committee charged with drafting the Declaration of Independence.

The Declaration, adopted by the Continental Congress on July 4, 1776, was largely the work of Jefferson, then thirty-three. It was for this accomplishment, for the drafting of Virginia's Statute for Religious Freedom and for founding the University of Virginia that the "Sage of Monticello" wished to be remembered.

Americans today also remember that he designed and built Monticello, his Virginia home, that he authorized the Louisiana Purchase, and that he believed in an agrarian nation in which all men would share in the choice of government.

See Scott No. 12, 30A , 1318

Scott No. 1318 shows the Jefferson Memorial in Washington, D. C.

Issue of 1861, First Designs

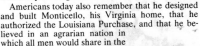

Detail of 55

Detail of 56

55

56

Detail of 57

Detail of 58

57

58

59

Detail of 62

62

Issue of 1861-62: Second Designs

1c. A dash has been added under the tip of the ornament at right of the numeral in upper left corner.

3c. Ornaments at corners have been enlarged and end in a small ball.

5c. A leaflet has been added to the foliated ornaments at each corner.

10c. A heavy curved line has been cut below the stars and an outer line has been added to the ornaments above them.

12c. Ovals and scrolls have been added to the corners.

		Issue of 1861: First Designs. Perf. 12		
55	12,000.00		1c Franklin	
56	225.00		3c Washington	
57	7000.00		5c brown Jefferson, sia 67	
58	1400.00	200.00	10c Washington	
59	25,000.00		12c Washington	
60	1300.00	150.00	24c violet Washington, sia 7	
61	9000.00		30c red org. Franklin, sia 7	
62	11,000.00		90c dull blue Washington, sia 72	

The paper of Nos. 55 to 62 inclusive is thin and se transparent, that of the following issues is thicker a more opaque.

		Issue of 1861-62: Second Designs, Perf. 12	
63	27.50	6.00	1c Franklin
64	875.00	100.00	3c Washington
65	9.00	.45	3c rose Washington, sia 64
66	550.00		3c lake Washington, sia 64
67	650.00	60.00	5c Jefferson
68	35.00	6.50	10c Washington
69	62.50	10.00	12c Washington
70	150.00	16.00	24c Washington
71	90.00	15.00	30c Franklin
72	250.00	48.50	90c Washington

Of Nos. 55-62, 58 and 60 were valid for postag hence the cancelled prices. Of Nos. 63-72, only 66 w not valid for postage; hence the absence of a cancell price.

Issue of 1861-66, Perf. 12

Following the outbreak of the Civil War, the U.S government re-designed all postage stamps to preven their usage by the South.

73	32.50	7.00	2c Andrew Jackson ("Black Jack")
74	1200.00		3c scarlet Washington, sia 64
75	185.00	37.50	5c red brown Jefferson, sia 67

90c. Parallel lines form an angle above the ribbon with "U. S. Postage"; between these lines a row of dashes has been added and a point of color to the apex of the lower pair.

Grill

70

71

73

77

76	42.50	10.00	5c brn. Jefferson, sia 67
77	125.00	17.50	15c Abraham Lincoln
78	45.00	12.50	24c lilac Washington, sia 70

No. 74 was not regularly issued.

Grills on U. S. Stamps

Between 1867 and 1870, postage stamps were embossed with grills to prevent people from re-using cancelled stamps. The pyramid-shaped grills absorbed cancellation ink, making it virtually impossible to chemically remove a postmark.

Issue of 1867, With Grills, Perf. 12
Grills A, B, C: Points Up
A. Grill Covers Entire Stamp

79	800.00	225.00	3c rose Washington, sia 64
80		27,500.00	5c brn. Jefferson, sia 67
81		25,000.00	30c org. Franklin, sia 71

B. Grill 18x15 mm.

| 82 | | | 3c rose Washington, sia 64 |

C. Grill about 13x16 mm.

| 83 | 250.00 | 57.50 | 3c rose Washington, sia 64 |

Grills D, Z, E, F: Points Down
D. Grill about 12x14 mm.

| 84 | 675.00 | 200.00 | 2c blk. Jackson, sia 73 |
| 85 | 350.00 | 50.00 | 3c rose Washington, sia 64 |

Z. Grill about 11x14 mm.

85A		25,000.00	1c bl. Franklin, sia 63
85B	260.00	60.00	2c blk. Jackson, sia 73
85C	850.00	200.00	3c rose Washington, sia 64
85D		15,000.00	10c green Washington, sia 68
85E	450.00	125.00	12c black Washington, sia 69
85F		22,500.00	15c blk. Lincoln, sia 77

ANDREW JACKSON (1767-1845)

There are no necessary evils in government. Its evils exist only in its abuses. Message Vetoing the Bank Bill, July 10, 1832

Andrew Jackson, founder of the Democratic party and hero of the Battle of New Orleans, was the first U. S. president not born of the Virginia or Massachusetts aristocracy. In 1828 the once-poor soldier hero of the War of 1812 defeated venerable John Quincy Adams for the presidency and the aspirations of the common man were given voice in Washington.

During "Old Hickory's" two terms in office (1828-36) the nation entered a new era of expansion under "Jacksonian Democracy". An enemy of "money power", the president vetoed the re-charter of the Bank of the United States in 1832. Under his policy of fiscal reform the public debt was paid for the first time. In 1837 Jackson, more popular than when elected, retired to the Hermitage, his home in Tennessee.

See Scott Stamp Nos. 73, 1037

Detail of 118
FIFTEEN CENTS.
Type I. Picture unframed.

Detail of 119
Type II. Picture framed.
Type III. Same as type I but without fringe of brown shading lines around central vignette.

112

113

114

115

116

118

120

117

121

122

E. Grill about 11x13 mm.			
86	90.00	31.50	1c blue Franklin, sia 63
87	45.00	12.00	2c black Jackson, sia 73
88	22.50	1.85	3c rose Washington, sia 64
89	165.00	22.50	10c grn. Washington, sia 68
90	175.00	22.50	12c blk. Washington, sia 69
91	500.00	57.50	15c black Lincoln, sia 77
F. Grill about 9x13 mm.			
92	50.00	17.50	1c blue Franklin, sia 63
93	27.50	7.75	2c black Jackson, sia 73
94	15.00	1.20	3c red Washington, sia 64
95	225.00	55.00	5c brown Jefferson, sia 67
96	72.50	13.00	10c yellow green Washington, sia 68
97	80.00	15.00	12c black Washington, sia 69
98	87.50	16.00	15c black Lincoln, sia 77
99	250.00	90.00	24c gray lilac Washington, sia 70

100	325.00	55.00	30c orange Franklin, sia 71
101	575.00	175.00	90c black Washington, sia 72
Reissues of 1875, Without Grill, Perf. 12			
102	145.00	95.00	1c blue Franklin, sia 63
103	725.00	450.00	2c blue Jackson, sia 73
104	925.00	500.00	3c brown red Washington, sia 64
105	650.00	425.00	5c light brown Jefferson, sia 67
106	750.00	400.00	10c grn. Washington, sia 68
107	975.00	450.00	12c blk. Washington, sia 69
108	800.00	400.00	15c black Lincoln, sia 77
109	950.00	475.00	24c deep violet Washington, sia 70
110	1400.00	650.00	30c brownish orange Franklin, sia 71
111	1650.00	750.00	90c black Washington, sia 72

119b

120b

121b

HIDDEN OPPORTUNITIES IN STAMP COLLECTING

For the beginning collector or the seasoned expert the chance discovery of a rare and valuable stamp can be the excitement of a lifetime. As is the case with most other collector's items, it is the desirability and the rarity of a stamp which can make it worth thousands of dollars. An interesting case in point concerns the first U. S. pictorial stamps, which were issued in 1869 and were the forerunners of modern commemoratives. Due to a printing error, portions of the designs of three of these stamps were printed upside down. These inverted varieties of the 15c, 24c and 30c denominations are now among the most valuable of all U. S. stamps.

The inverts were discovered while the 1869 stamps were still in circulation, but they received no spectacular notice in the writings of the day. Long after, copies of the stamps started to turn up. During the 1930's a New York stamp dealer visiting in Portland, Oregon, stumbled onto a copy of the 30c with inverted flags. The stamp was included in a dealer's regular stock and had evidently been in several collections before that. None of its owners had noticed that the flags were upside-down! A used copy of this stamp is now worth $20,000, and an unused copy $32,000.

See Scott Stamp Nos. 112-122, 119b, 120b, 121b

Issue of 1869, With Grill Measuring 9-1/2x9 mm. Perf. 12			
112	67.50	20.00	1c Franklin
113	40.00	8.50	2c Post Horse & Rider
114	21.00	1.75	3c Locomotive
115	125.00	21.50	6c Washington
116	135.00	21.50	10c Shield and Eagle
117	125.00	21.50	12c S. S. Adriatic
118	400.00	90.00	15c Columbus Landing, type I
119	145.00	27.00	15c brown and blue Columbus Landing, type II, sia 118
119b	*35,000.00*	*6000.00*	Center inverted
120	350.00	110.00	24c Declaration of Independence
120b	*23,500.00*	*5000.00*	Center inverted
121	400.00	60.00	30c Shield, Eagle and Flags
121b	*32,000.00*	*20,000.00*	Flags inverted
122	900.00	260.00	90c Lincoln
Reissues of 1875, Without Grill Hard White Paper, Perf. 12			
123	115.00	75.00	1c buff, sia 112
124	160.00	80.00	2c brown, sia 113
125	850.00	500.00	3c blue, sia 114
126	325.00	165.00	6c blue, sia 115
127	365.00	200.00	10c yellow, sia 116
128	425.00	200.00	12c green, sia 117
129	500.00	200.00	15c brown and blue Columbus Landing, type III, sia 118
130	400.00	200.00	24c grn. & vio., sia 120
131	600.00	300.00	30c bl. & car., sia 121
132	1000.00	600.00	90c cat. & blk., sia 122
Reissues of 1880, Soft, Porous Paper, Perf. 12			
133	95.00	90.00	1c buff, sia 112

15

134   135   136   137   138   139   140   141   142   143   144

PATRICK HENRY (1736-99), "TONGUE OF THE REVOLUTION"

English poet Lord Byron called Patrick Henry the "Forest-born Demosthenes," an apt description of the best-known orator of the American Revolutionary War. Henry's forensic skill in the Virginia legislature helped spur colonial revolt in the South. His famous "Give me liberty or give me death!" speech was made to his state's assembly in 1775 in support of armed resistance to the British.

In addition to serving in the legislature, Henry also served as governor of Virginia several times. An Antifederalist, he refused election to the Constitutional Convention of 1787, but subsequently fought for the addition of the Bill of Rights. Throughout his life he was a hero of Virginia.

See Scott Stamp Nos. 1052, 1142

1873: Printed by the Continental Bank Note Co.
Designs of the 1870-71 Issue with secret marks on the values from 1c to 15c as described and illustrated below.

156
1c. In the pearl at the left of the numeral "1" there is a small crescent.

157
2c. Under the scroll at the left of "U. S." there is a small diagonal line. This mark seldom shows clearly. The stamp, No. 157, can be distinguished by its color.

158
3c. The under part of the upper tail of the left ribbon is heavily shaded.

159
6c. The first four vertical lines of the shading in the lower part of the left ribbon have been strengthened.

160
7c. Two small semi-circles are drawn around the ends of the lines which outline the ball in the lower right hand corner.

161
10c. There is a small semi-circle in the scroll at the right end of the upper label.

162
12c. The balls of the figure "2" are crescent shaped.

163
15c. In the lower part of the triangle in the upper left corner two lines have been made heavier forming a "V". This mark can be found on some of the Continental and American (1879) printings, but not all stamps show it.

Secret marks were added to the dies of the 24c, 30c and 90c but new plates were not made from them. The various printings of these stamps can be distinguished only by the shades and paper.

Issue of 1870-71			
With Grill, White Wove Paper, Perf. 12			
134	100.00	12.50	1c Franklin
135	75.00	9.00	2c Jackson
136	50.00	1.65	3c Washington
137	250.00	45.00	6c Lincoln
138	235.00	45.00	7c Edwin M. Stanton
139	350.00	90.00	10c Jefferson
140	*4000.00*	575.00	12c Henry Clay
141	265.00	90.00	15c Daniel Webster
142		*5250.00*	24c Winfield Scott
143	850.00	200.00	30c Alexander Hamilton
144	1450.00	150.00	90c Commodore O. H. Perry

Without Grill			
White Wove Paper, Perf. 12			
145	23.00	1.65	1c ultra. Franklin, sia 134
146	12.50	1.25	2c red brn. Jackson, sia 135
147	9.50	.15	3c green Washington, sia 136
148	55.00	3.50	6c carmine Lincoln, sia 137
149	75.00	12.50	7c verm. Stanton, sia 138
150	60.00	4.00	10c brown Jefferson, sia 139
151	120.00	12.50	12c dull violet Clay, sia 140
152	82.50	12.50	15c bright orange Webster. sia 141
153	90.00	15.00	24c purple W. Scott, sia 142
154	210.00	25.00	30c black Hamilton, sia 143
155	285.00	45.00	90c carmine Perry, sia 144

White Wove Paper, Thin to Thick

156	13.50	.50	1c Franklin
157	19.00	1.50	2c Jackson
158	6.00	.08	3c Washington
159	50.00	2.00	6c Lincoln
160	87.50	15.00	7c Stanton
161	45.00	3.00	10c Jefferson
162	140.00	12.00	12c Clay
163	125.00	12.00	15c Webster
164			24c W. Scott, sia 142
165	120.00	11.50	30c Hamilton, sia 143
166	225.00	45.00	90c Perry, sia 144

It is generally accepted as fact that the Continental Bank Note Co. printed and delivered a quantity of 24c stamps. They are impossible to distinguish from those printed by the National Bank Note-Co.

Issue of 1875
Special Printing
Hard, White Wove Paper, Without Gum

167	2400.00	1c ultra. Franklin, sia 156
168	1500.00	2c dark brown Jackson, sia 157
169	3500.00	3c dark green Washington, sia 158
170	3000.00	6c dull rose Lincoln, sia 159
171	1300.00	7c reddish vermilion Stanton, sia 160
172	2500.00	10c pale brown Jefferson, sia 161
173	1450.00	12c dark violet Clay, sia 162
174	2400.00	15c bright orange Webster, sia 163
175	1200.00	24c dull purple W. Scott. sia 142
176	2600.00	30c greenish black Hamilton, sia 143
177	2600.00	90c violet car. Perry, sia 144

Although perforated. these stamps were usually cut apart with scissors. As a result. the perforations are often much mutilated and the design is frequently damaged.

Yellowish Wove Paper

178	40.00	1.25	2c vermilion Jackson, sia 157
179	35.00	2.75	5c Zachary Taylor, Jun. 21

Special Printing
Hard, White Wove Paper, Without Gum

180	8000.00	2c carmine verm. Jackson, sia 157
181	9500.00	5c bright blue Taylor, sia 179

Issue of 1879. Printed by the American Bank Note Company. Soft, porous paper, varying from thin to thick.

182	28.50	.55	1c dark ultramarine Franklin, sia 156
183	11.50	.50	2c vermilion Jackson, sia 157
184	5.50	.08	3c green Washington, sia 158
185	35.00	2.00	5c blue Taylor, sia 179
186	95.00	3.00	6c pink Lincoln, sia 159

187	150.00	3.25	10c brown Jefferson, sia 139 (no secret mark)
188	72.50	2.85	10c brown Jefferson, sia 161 (with secret mark)
189	25.00	4.25	15c red orange Webster, sia 163
190	82.50	6.50	30c full black Hamilton, sia 143
191	235.00	45.00	90c carmine Perry, sia 144

Issue of 1880, Special Printing
Soft, Porous Paper, Without Gum

192	3750.00	1c dark ultramarine Franklin, sia 156
193	2750.00	2c black brown Jackson, sia 157
194	4000.00	3c blue green Washington, sia 158
195	3200.00	6c dull rose Lincoln, sia 159
196	1600.00	7c scarlet vermilion Stanton, sia 160
197	3250.00	10c deep brown Jefferson, sia 161
198	2450.00	12c blackish purple Clay, sia 162
199	3000.00	15c orange Webster, sia 163
200	1100.00	24c dark violet W. Scott, sia 142
201	2750.00	30c greenish black Hamilton, sia 143
202	3000.00	90c dull car. Perry, sia 144
203	7500.00	2c scarlet vermilion Jackson, sia 157
204	9500.00	5c deep blue Taylor, sia 179

Issue of 1882

205	21.00	1.65	5c James Garfield, Apr. 10

Special Printing. Soft, Porous Paper, Without Gum

205C	8000.00	5c gray brown, sia 205

Issue of 1881-82, Designs of 1873 Re-engraved.

206	5.25	.30	1c Franklin
207	8.50	.08	3c Washington
208	52.50	12.00	6c Lincoln
209	12.00	1.00	10c Jefferson

Issue of 1883

210	3.50	.05	2c Washington, Oct. 1
211	17.00	2.00	4c Jackson, Oct. 1

Special Printing. Soft, Porous Paper.

211B	175.00	2c pale red brown Washington, sia 210
211D	7000.00	4c deep blue green Jackson, sia 211, no gum

Issue of 1887

212	9.00		1c Franklin
213	2.35	.05	2c grn. Washington, sia 210
214	10.00	7.50	3c vermilion Washington, sia 207

Detail of 206
1c. Upper vertical lines have been deepened, creating a solid effect in parts of background. Upper arabesques have lines of shading.

206

Detail of 207
3c. Shading at sides of central oval is half its previous width. A short horizontal dash has been cut below the "TS" of "CENTS"

207

Detail of 208
6c. Has three vertical lines instead of four between the edge of the panel and the outside of the stamp.

208

Detail of 209
10c. Has four vertical lines instead of five between left side of oval and edge of the shield. Horizontal lines in lower part of background have been strengthened.

209

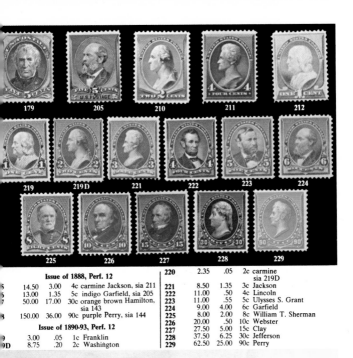

179	205	210	211	212
219	219D	221	222	223	224
225	226	227	228	229

Issue of 1888, Perf. 12

14.50	3.00	4c carmine Jackson, sia 211
13.00	1.35	5c indigo Garfield, sia 205
50.00	17.00	30c orange brown Hamilton, sia 143
150.00	36.00	90c purple Perry, sia 144

Issue of 1890-93, Perf. 12

3.00	.05	1c Franklin
8.75	.20	2c Washington

220	2.35	.05	2c carmine sia 219D
221	8.50	1.35	3c Jackson
222	11.00	.50	4c Lincoln
223	11.00	.55	5c Ulysses S. Grant
224	9.00	4.00	6c Garfield
225	8.00	2.00	8c William T. Sherman
226	20.00	.50	10c Webster
227	27.50	5.00	15c Clay
228	37.50	6.25	30c Jefferson
229	62.50	25.00	90c Perry

THE MEXICAN WAR – FROM BUENA VISTA TO THE HALLS OF MONTEZUMA

A secure Texas and the addition of California, New Mexico, and most of Utah, Nevada, Arizona, and Colorado to U. S. territory were the results of the Mexican War, which was precipitated by the admission of Texas to the Union in 1845. Since Mexico had never recognized Texan independence, annexation by the United States was considered an act of war. When negotiations failed to settle the dispute, President James Polk ordered General Zachary Taylor to the Rio Grande. Clashes between American and Mexican forces followed, and in May of 1846 the U. S. declared war. Polk then sent General Stephen Kearney into New Mexico and California, while Taylor invaded Mexico. "Old Rough and Ready" Taylor's victory over Santa Ana at Buena Vista early in 1847 put new fighting spirit into the troops of General Winfield Scott, who captured Mexico City on September 14. Under the terms of the 1848 Treaty of Guadalupe Hidalgo, Mexico gave up her claim to Texas and ceded the Southwest to the United States.

See Scott Stamp Nos.
142, 179, 944

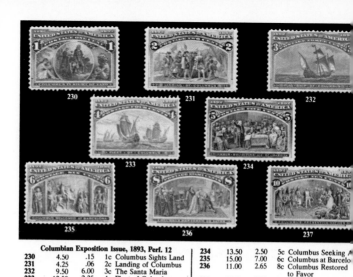

THE VOYAGES OF CHRISTOPHER COLUMBUS (1451?-1506)

Christopher Columbus found America by chance while looking for the Indies. Today Columbus is regarded as a great explorer; in his own time, he was often thought of as a dreamer and a fool.

When Columbus first decided that the riches of the Indies could be reached by sailing west from Europe, kings and princes scoffed at him. But the stubborn Columbus was not easily denied. He persisted in his dream until the Queen of Spain, Isabella, intervened to help him.

Outfitted by Isabella and King Ferdinand with a crew of ninety and a fleet of tiny ships — the *Nina, Pinta,* and *Santa Maria* — the intrepid navigator left Spain on August 3, 1492 on "the most important voyage in all history." On October 12, 1492

San Marino Scott No. 315

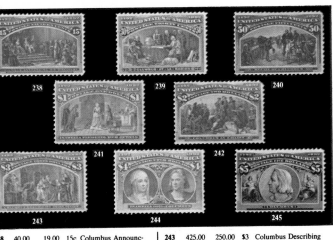

238	40.00	19.00	15c	Columbus Announcing His Discovery
239	55.00	27.50	30c	Columbus at La Rabida
240	85.00	40.00	50c	Recall of Columbus
241	250.00	145.00	$1	Isabella Pledging Jewels
242	290.00	135.00	$2	Columbus in Chains

243	425.00	250.00	$3	Columbus Describing His Third Voyage
244	600.00	300.00	$4	Isabella and Columbus
245	650.00	350.00	$5	Portrait of Columbus

The World's Columbian Exposition was held in Chicago in 1893 to celebrate the 400th anniversary of the discovery of America by Christopher Columbus.

he landed on an island named San Salvador (in the Bahamas), where he was greeted by a group of peaceful Arawaks. Convinced that he had found the Indies, Columbus named these natives "Indians."

When Columbus and his crew returned to Spain they were greeted with a hero's welcome. But the glory of the journey did not last. Although three more voyages were made, the Indies failed to yield the riches Spain was looking for, the colonies Columbus tried to found were failures, and the government of Spain became convinced that his discoveries were worthless.

Nor did it listen when Columbus countered, "By...Divine Will I have placed under the sovereignty of the King and Queen an Other World, whereby Spain, which was reckoned poor, is to become the richest of all countries." Neglected and alone, Columbus died in poverty before his prophecy came true.

See Scott Stamp Nos. 230-245.

DANIEL WEBSTER (1782-1852)

I speak today for the preservation of the Union. Hear me for my cause.
Senate debate of the Clay Compromise, March 7, 1850

Twice secretary of state and twenty years a senator, Daniel Webster was an eloquent spokesman for the Union in the years before the Civil War. In 1832, when South Carolina challenged the exercise of federal laws within its boundaries, Webster supported his old enemy, President Andrew Jackson, against the states' righters. In 1850 the New England lawyer was again embroiled in the defense of the Union. In his last great Senate speech he rose to answer John C. Calhoun during a heated debate over the Clay Compromise. Webster's impassioned argument was instrumental in the passage of Henry Clay's brainchild, a stopgap solution to the slavery question that postponed the Civil War for eleven years.

Webster is also known for his successful argument of several landmark Supreme Court cases including the Dartmouth College Case of 1819, which held that a state cannot violate a contract.

See Scott Stamp Nos. 258, 259, 725, 1380, O31

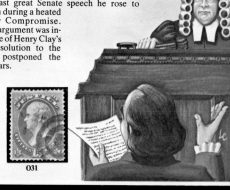

O31

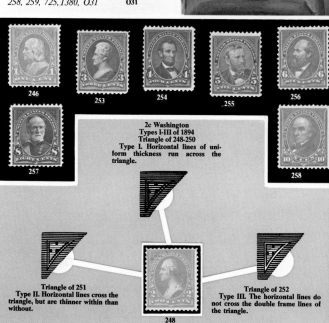

246

253

254

255

256

257

258

**2c Washington
Types I-III of 1894
Triangle of 248-250**
Type I. Horizontal lines of uniform thickness run across the triangle.

Triangle of 251
Type II. Horizontal lines cross the triangle, but are thinner within than without.

Triangle of 252
Type III. The horizontal lines do not cross the double frame lines of the triangle.

248

259   **260**   **262**   **263**

$1 Perry
Types of 1894

Detail of 261
Type I. The circles enclosing $1
are broken.

Detail of 261 A
Type II. The circles enclosing $1
are complete.

261

Bureau Issues

Starting in 1894, the Bureau of Engraving and Printing at Washington has produced all U.S. postage stamps except Nos. 909-921 (Overrun Countries), 1335 (Eakins painting), 1355 (Disney), 1410-1413 (Anti-Pollution), and 1414-1418 (Christmas, 1970). Bureau-printed stamps are engraved except Nos. 525-536, which are offset, and certain combinations of lithography and engraving, such as No. 1275.

Issue of 1894, Perf. 12 Unwmkd.

246	3.50	.85	1c Franklin
247	4.50	.35	1c blue Franklin, sia 246
248	3.00	.65	2c Washington, type I

Nos. 249-252: Washington, sia 248

249	13.50	.25	2c carmine lake, type I
250	3.35	.08	2c carmine, type I
251	26.50	.60	2c carmine, type II
252	10.50	.90	2c carmine, type III
253	7.50	2.15	3c Jackson
254	9.50	.60	4c Lincoln
255	6.75	.85	5c Grant
256	9.50	3.25	6c Garfield
257	8.50	1.85	8c Sherman
258	18.50	1.50	10c Webster
259	36.50	10.00	15c Clay
260	42.50	18.50	50c Jefferson
261	135.00	57.50	$1 Commodore Perry, type I
261A	200.00	90.00	$1 black Perry, type II, sia 261
262	195.00	100.00	$2 James Madison
263	475.00	275.00	$5 John Marshall

JAMES MADISON (1751-1836)

I believe there are more instances of the abridgment of the freedom of the people by gradual and silent encroachments of those in power than by violent and sudden usurpations. Speech in the Virginia Convention, 1788

James Madison, fourth president of the United States, justly earned his title "Father of the Constitution", for he was the chief drafter of that document which is the bulwark of U. S. government. A co-author of the *Federalist Papers,* he also figured prominently in the drafting of the Bill of Rights, and was Jefferson's secretary of state from 1801 until 1809.

During Madison's administration (1809-17), the War of 1812 took place, the White House was burned, and Madison was forced to flee the capital, the only president to do so.

See Scott Stamp No. 262

TEN CENTS.

Type I. The tips of the foliate ornaments do not impinge on the white curved line below "TEN CENTS."

282C

Type II. The tips of the ornaments break the curved line below the "E" of "TEN" and the "T" of "CENTS."

283

Watermark 191

Wmkd.  (191)

266	6.00	.75	2c carmine, type II
267	.60	.03	2c carmine, type III
268	5.00	.45	3c purple Jackson, sia 253
269	6.00	.45	4c dark brown Lincoln, sia 25
270	5.25	.70	5c chocolate Grant, sia 255
271	10.50	1.25	6c dull brown Garfield, sia 25
272	4.50	.40	8c vio. brown Sherman, sia 25
273	8.00	.50	10c dk. green Webster, sia 25
274	28.50	2.25	15c dark blue Clay, sia 259
275	40.00	4.75	50c orange Jefferson, sia 260
276	110.00	16.00	$1 black Perry, type I, sia 26
276A	225.00	29.00	$1 black Perry, type II, sia 26
277	135.00	80.00	$2 brt. blue Madison, sia 262
278	310.00	85.00	$5 dk. green Marshall, sia 26

Issue of 1898, Perf. 12

279	1.20	.06	1c dp. green Franklin, sia 24
279B	.90	.05	2c red Washington, type I sia 248
280	4.00	.35	4c rose brown Lincoln, sia 25
281	3.65	.30	5c dark blue Grant, sia 255
282	6.50	.75	6c lake Garfield, sia 256
282C	25.00	.80	10c Webster, type I
283	18.50	.70	10c Webster, type II
284	24.00	2.25	15c olive green Clay, sia 25

Trans-Mississippi Exposition Issue, Jun. 17
Perf. 12

285	7.00	1.65	1c Marquette on Mississip
286	5.50	.60	2c Farming in the West
287	24.00	7.00	4c Indian Hunting Buffalo
288	23.00	7.00	5c Frémont on the Rocky Mountains
289	30.00	12.00	8c Troops Guarding Train
290	40.00	7.00	10c Hardships of Emigratio
291	145.00	32.50	50c Western Mining Prospector
292	350.00	175.00	$1 Western Cattle in Storr
293	475.00	225.00	$2 Mississippi River Bridge at St. Louis, Missouri

The Trans-Mississippi Exposition was held in Omaha, Nebraska from June 1 to November 1, 1898. For this reason, the above stamps have been nicknamed "Omahas."

Issue of 1895, Perf. 12

264	.75	.06	1c blue Franklin, sia 246

Nos. 265-267: Washington, sia 248

265	4.75	.20	2c carmine, type I

THE LEWIS AND CLARK EXPEDITION

On May 14, 1804 Meriwether Lewis (1744-1809), William Clark (1770-1838), thirty-two soldiers, and ten civilians climbed into a 55-foot keel boat and headed up the Missouri river on a perilous, 4,000 mile expedition through the vast Louisiana Territory. The goal of the expedition, which began at St. Louis, was to find a water route to the Pacific and to learn about the far West and its Indians.

After wintering among the Mandan Indians, Lewis and Clark were led across the Rockies by their Shoshone guide, Sacajawea (the Bird Woman). On November 15, 1805, when they canoed down the Columbia to the Pacific, a new route had been found for the Northwest and the United States was able to add Oregon to its western claims. This vast territory included the present states of Oregon, Washington, Idaho, and parts of Montana and Wyoming.

See Scott Stamp Nos. 323-327, 1020, 1063

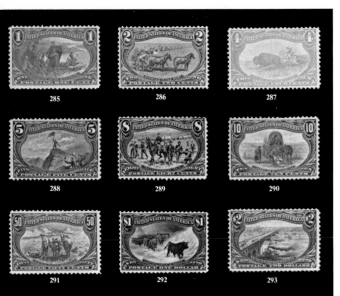

285   286   287

288   289   290

291   292   293

THE OPENING OF THE WEST

The first pioneers who traveled west followed in the footsteps of well-known explorers. In 1806 Zebulon Pike explored the Southwest as far as Colorado, and in 1842 John Frémont blazed a trail to Oregon.

By 1843 scores of covered wagons had moved into Oregon. In 1847 Brigham Young led his Mormon followers into Utah. St. Louis, then a fur trading center, became the starting point for a steady stream of Conestoga wagons moving westward on the Santa Fe, Mormon, and Oregon trails.

The discovery of gold in California (1848) brought 90,000 prospectors and miners to the West. Muddy mining towns sprang up overnight, permanent settlements took root, and California soon demanded entrance to the Union.

See Scott Stamp Nos. 285-293,
783, 837, 950, 954, 964

San Marino Scott No. C75

25

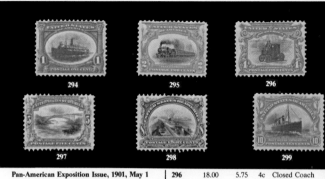

294 295 296

297 298 299

Pan-American Exposition Issue, 1901, May 1

Wmkd. **USPS** (191)

Perf. 12.

294	4.00	1.35	1c	Great Lakes Streamer
294a	*3500.00*	*1500.00*	1c	Center inverted
295	4.00	.40	2c	An Early Locomotive
295a	*18,000.00*	*6000.00*	2c	Center inverted
296	18.00	5.75	4c	Closed Coach Automobile
296a	*5750.00*		4c	Center inverted
297	18.00	6.50	5c	Bridge at Niagara Falls
298	23.50	14.00	8c	Sault Ste. Marie Canal Locks
299	35.00	9.00	10c	American Line Steamship

The Pan-American Exposition was held in Buffalo, New York in 1901. It stressed engineering progress in the Western hemisphere in the nineteenth century.

HENRY FORD

Henry Ford (1863-1947) was a Michigan farm boy whose vision changed a nation. He was not the first automobile manufacturer, nor was he the first to use mass production methods, but his idea that everyone could own an inexpensive automobile was revolutionary, as was his use of conveyor belts to speed assembly lines. The famous black 1909 Model T was the result.

Later Ford innovations were profit-sharing with employees and higher wages for shorter hours. When America took to the highways in Ford's Model T, a billion-dollar industry began to grow.

See Scott Stamp Nos. 296, 1286A

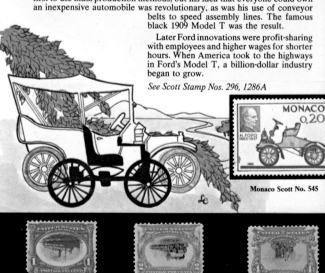

Monaco Scott No. 545

294a 295a 296a

Regular Issue of 1902-03			
Wmkd. USPS (191)			
Perf. 12.			
300	1.10	.05	1c Franklin
300b	45.00	27.50	Booklet pane of six
301	1.35	.05	2c Washington
301c	35.00	25.00	Booklet pane of six
302	6.25	1.00	3c Jackson
303	6.25	.40	4c Grant
304	6.25	.35	5c Lincoln
305	8.00	.85	6c Garfield
306	5.00	.55	8c Martha Washington
307	8.75	.55	10c Webster
308	5.00	3.00	13c Benjamin Harrison
309	25.00	2.00	15c Clay
310	67.50	6.50	50c Jefferson
311	125.00	12.00	$1 David G. Farragut

| 312 | 185.00 | 50.00 | $2 Madison |
| 313 | 360.00 | 185.00 | $5 Marshall |

For listings of 312 and 313 with Perf. 10, see Nos. 479 and 480.

Issues of 1906-08
Imperf.

314	5.25	4.00	1c blue green Franklin, sia 300
314A	5500.00	3100.00	4c brown Grant, sia 303
315	160.00	125.00	5c blue Lincoln, sia 304

No. 314A was issued imperforate, but all copies were privately perforated with large oblong perforations at the sides. (Schermack type III).

Coil Stamps
Perf. 12 Horizontally

316			1c blue green pair Franklin, sia 300
317	1350.00		5c blue pair Lincoln, sia 304

JOHN MARSHALL (1755-1835)

John Marshall, a man of extraordinary vision, opened a new age of jurisprudence in America. The fourth Chief Justice of the United States, he gave the Constitution its first, historic interpretation and established the right of the Supreme Court to review the constitutionality of state and Federal laws.

Born in Virginia of a frontier family, Marshall was a member of the Virginia convention which debated the ratification of the Constitution. He was appointed Chief Justice of the Supreme Court by President Thomas Jefferson in 1801 and served in the post for thirty-four years.

See Scott Stamp No. 313

323   324   325   326   327   328   329   330

Perf. 12 Vertically

318	*1150.00*		1c bl. grn., pr. Franklin, sta 300	

With this series the Post Office Department began issuing stamps in coils for use in vending and affixing machines. The stamps in coils are perforated on two sides only, either horizontally or vertically, and are imperforate on the other two sides.

Collectors are warned that imperforate stamps are being fraudulently perforated to resemble coil stamps and part perforate varieties.

Issue of 1903, Perf. 12

Wmkd. USPS (191)

Shield-shaped Background

319	.95	.04	2c Washington	Nov. 12

319g	6.25	4.00	Booklet pane of six	

Issue of 1906

Nos. 320-322: Washington, sta 319

Imperf.

320	6.00	4.75	2c carmine,	Oct.

Issue of 1908, Coil Stamps

Perf. 12 Horizontally

321	6500.00		2c carmine pair	

Perf. 12 Vertically

322	1250.00		2c carmine pair	

Issue of 1904. Perf. 12

Wmkd. USPS (191)

Louisiana Purchase Exposition Issue, Apr. 30

323	8.25	2.25	1c Robert R. Livingston
324	6.50	.60	2c Thomas Jefferson
325	20.00	11.00	3c James Monroe
326	25.00	7.25	5c William McKinley
327	67.50	12.00	10c Map of Louisiana Purchase

The Louisiana Purchase Exposition was held in St Louis in 1904 in conjunction with the World's Fair o that year. President William McKinley (1843-1901) who died before the Exposition opened, authorized the Fair.

Issue of 1907, Perf. 12

Wmkd. USPS (191)

Jamestown Exposition Issue

328	4.00	1.75	1c Captain John Smith
329	5.00	.95	2c Founding of Jamestown
330	35.00	8.50	5c Pocahontas

The first permanent English settlement in North America was established in 1607, at Jamestown, Virginia

THE GAINING OF A NEW FRONTIER

Intricate diplomacy and power politics lay behind the Louisiana Purchase which, in 1803, more than doubled the size of the young United States at a cost of only $15 million.

Upon hearing that Louisiana had been ceded to Napoleon, President Thomas Jefferson, fearful for the country's safety, sent James Monroe to France with orders to assist Robert Livingston in buying Florida and New Orleans for $10 million. When Napoleon announced his willingness to sell the entire tract for $5 million more, Jefferson set aside his doubts about the constitutionality of such a purchase and had the Senate ratify the treaty before Bonaparte could change his mind.

So it was that in 1803 Louisiana became U. S. land. From it, thirteen states were carved; into it, in 1804, went Meriwether Lewis and William Clark to pave the way for future pioneers.

See Scott Stamp Nos. 323-327, 1020, 1063

France Scott No. B26

28

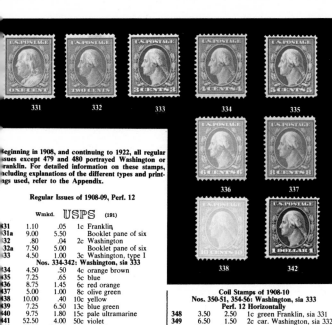

| | | | | 331 | 332 | 333 | 334 | 335 | 336 | 337 | 338 | 342 |

Beginning in 1908, and continuing to 1922, all regular issues except 479 and 480 portrayed Washington or Franklin. For detailed information on these stamps, including explanations of the different types and printings used, refer to the Appendix.

Regular Issues of 1908-09, Perf. 12

Wmkd. **USPS** (191)

331	1.10	.05	1c Franklin
331a	9.00	5.50	Booklet pane of six
332	.80	.04	2c Washington
332a	7.50	5.00	Booklet pane of six
333	4.50	1.00	3c Washington, type I

Nos. 334-342: Washington, sia 333

334	4.50	.50	4c orange brown
335	7.25	.65	5c blue
336	8.75	1.45	6c red orange
337	5.00	1.00	8c olive green
338	10.00	.40	10c yellow
339	7.25	6.50	13c blue green
340	9.75	1.80	15c pale ultramarine
341	52.50	4.00	50c violet
342	90.00	21.50	$1 violet brown

Imperf.

343	1.75	.85	1c green Franklin, sia 331
344	2.75	.85	2c car. Washington, sia 332

Nos. 345-347: Washington, sia 333

345	5.50	4.50	3c deep violet, type I
346	9.25	5.50	4c orange brown
347	16.00	10.00	5c blue

Coil Stamps of 1908-10
Nos. 350-51, 354-56: Washington, sia 333
Perf. 12 Horizontally

348	3.50	2.50	1c Franklin, sia 331
349	6.50	1.50	2c car. Washington, sia 332
350	15.00	12.00	4c orange brown
351	26.50	19.50	5c blue

1909, Perf. 12 Vertically

352	8.00	4.00	1c green Franklin, sia 331
353	6.50	1.50	2c car. Washington, sia 332
354	15.50	8.50	4c orange brown
355	23.50	13.50	5c blue
356	350.00	175.00	10c yellow

THE JAMESTOWN COLONY

Wee hope to build a nation where none before hath stood, Anonymous, 1610

On April 26, 1607 three small ships bearing some 120 English settlers arrived in Virginia. On May 14 the colonists disembarked at Jamestown; on May 26 they were attacked by Indians; within six months over fifty of them perished, victims of starvation and disease.

Despite this inauspicious start Jamestown survived, largely through the efforts of Captain John Smith, who made friends with the Indian Powhatan and his daughter, Pocahontas. Soon tobacco was a thriving industry, a landed gentry had developed, and the little colony could boast the New World's first elected legislature, the House of Burgesses.

See Scott Stamp Nos. 328-330

THE ALASKA PURCHASE

In 1867 President Andrew Johnson's secretary of state, William H. Seward, bought Alaska from the Russians at a cost of $7.2 million.

The purchase of the huge northern land mass seemed at first a poor bargain. Not only was Alaska difficult to reach, but it was also hard to live in, and appeared to have no strategic value.

Soon, however, people changed their thinking about "Seward's Folly". In 1896 gold was found in the Klondike region and droves of settlers poured into the land, once inhabited mainly by Eskimos and other Indians.

Since 1896 coal, oil, platinum, uranium, and tin have been discovered in Alaska, which also boasts a rich fur trade and a thriving fishing industry. In 1959 Alaska joined the Union as the forty-ninth state.

See Scott Stamp Nos. 370-371, 800, C53, C70

Issues of 1909, Bluish Paper Perf. 12
Nos. 359-366: Washington, sia 333

357	18.50	16.00	1c green Franklin, sia 331
358	17.50	15.00	2c car. Washington, sia 332
359	425.00	225.00	3c deep violet, type I
360	5500.00		4c orange brown
361	1550.00		5c blue
362	325.00	200.00	6c red orange
363	5500.00		8c olive green
364	365.00	200.00	10c yellow
365	775.00	260.00	13c blue green
366	300.00	180.00	15c pale ultramarine

Lincoln Memorial Issue, Feb. 12

Wmkd. ⓊⓈⓅⓈ (191)

367	2.75	1.00	2c Lincoln, Perf. 12
368	11.00	8.50	2c Lincoln, Imperf.
369	60.00	40.00	2c Lincoln, Perf 12, Bluish Paper

Issued on the 100th anniversary of the birth of Abraham Lincoln. The portrait on the stamps is from the statue by Saint-Gaudens.

Alaska-Yukon Pacific Exposition Issue

Wmkd. ⓊⓈⓅⓈ (191)

370	3.00	.85	2c William Seward,Perf. 12
371	13.00	7.00	2c William Seward, Imperf

William H. Seward (1801-72), Lincoln's Secretary State, bought Alaska for the U.S., in 1867.

Hudson-Fulton Celebration Issue, Sep. 25

Wmkd. ⓊⓈⓅⓈ (191)

372	3.00	1.25	2c Half Moon and Clermont, Perf. 12
373	13.00	8.50	2c Half Moon and Clermont, Imperf.

Henry Hudson discovered the New York River named for him in 1609. Robert Fulton's *Clermont* was first commercially successful steamboat.

367   368   369   370

372   373   371

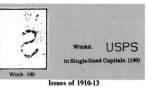

Wmkd. **USPS**

in Single lined Capitals. (190)

Wmk. 190

Issues of 1910-13
Nos. 376-82: Washington, sia 333
Perf. 12

74	1.20	.06	1c green Franklin, sia 331
74a	17.00	10.00	Booklet pane of six
75	.95	.03	2c car. Washington, sia 332
75a	5.00	2.50	Booklet pane of six
76	2.65	.60	3c deep violet, type I
77	3.75	.25	4c brown
78	3.75	.25	5c blue
79	7.75	.30	6c red orange
80	17.00	4.25	8c olive green
81	14.00	1.25	10c yellow
82	33.50	6.50	15c pale ultramarine

Imperf.

83	1.10	.75	1c green Franklin, sia 331
84	1.50	.50	2c car. Washington, sia 332

Coil Stamps
Perf. 12 Horizontally

85	4.25	3.00	1c green Franklin, sia 331
86	5.75	2.60	2c car. Washington, sia 332

Perf. 12 Vertically

87	8.75	6.25	1c green Franklin, sia 331

Perf. 8-1/2 Horizontally

388	70.00	18.50	2c car. Washington, sia 332
389	5000.00	1250.00	3c dp. vio. Washington, type I, sia 333

Stamps sold as 388 are sometimes privately perforated copies of 384.

Perf. 8-1/2 Horizontally

390	.50	.50	1c green Franklin, sia 331
391	8.25	1.80	2c car. Washington, sia 332

Perf. 8-1/2 Vertically
Nos. 394-396: Washington, sia 333

392	4.25	3.50	1c green Franklin, sia 331
393	8.50	.75	2c car. Washington, sia 332
394	11.50	8.50	3c deep violet, type I
395	11.50	6.00	4c brown
396	11.50	7.75	5c blue

Panama Pacific Exposition Issue
1913, Perf. 12

Wmkd. **USPS** (190)

397	3.25	.80	1c Balboa
398	4.00	.30	2c Locks, Panama Canal
399	22.00	4.00	5c Golden Gate
400	38.50	6.00	10c Discovery of San Francisco Bay
400A	72.50	4.25	10c orange, sia 400

1914-15, Perf. 10

401	7.25	2.40	1c green Balboa, sia 397
402	22.50	.45	2c car. Canal Locks, sia 398
403	58.50	4.75	5c blue Golden Gate, sia 399
404	285.00	20.00	10c orange Discovery of San Francisco Bay, sia 400

Spanish explorer Vasco Nuñez de Balboa discovered the Pacific Ocean in 1513. The Panama Canal, which links the Pacific and Atlantic Oceans, was opened in 1914.

397 398 399 400

405 406 414 420

Issues of 1912-14
Nos. 405-413: Washington, sia 333
Perf. 12

405	.95	.06	1c green
405b	3.50	2.00	Booklet pane of six
406	.75	.03	2c carmine, type I
406a	4.25	2.25	Booklet pane of six
407	15.50	2.75	7c black

Imperf.

408	.30	.25	1c green
409	.35	.25	2c carmine, type I

Coil Stamps

Perf. 8-1/2 Horizontally

410	1.00	.80	1c green
411	1.50	.75	2c carmine, type I

Perf. 8-1/2 Vertically

412	2.90	1.40	1c green
413	8.50	.20	2c carmine, type I

Perf. 12

414	6.00	.50	8c Franklin

Nos. 415-21: Franklin, sia 414

415	8.00	5.00	9c salmon red
416	5.50	.08	10c orange yellow
417	4.25	1.40	12c claret brown
418	12.00	1.20	15c gray
419	23.50	5.50	20c ultramarine
420	18.00	5.25	30c orange red
421	95.00	6.00	50c violet

Nos. 422-423: Franklin, sia 414, Perf. 12

Wmkd. **USPS** (191)

422	52.50	5.50	50c violet	Feb. 12
423	110.00	22.50	$1 violet brown	Feb. 12

Issues of 1914-15, Perf. 10

Wmkd. **USPS** (190)

Nos. 424-430: Washington, sia 333

424	.90	.06	1c green
424d	1.00	.65	Booklet pane of six
425	.40	.04	2c rose red, type I
425e	1.50	1.00	Booklet pane of six
426	2.65	.60	3c deep violet, type I
427	7.50	.18	4c brown
428	4.25	.20	5c blue
429	6.75	.40	6c red orange
430	11.00	1.50	7c black

Nos. 431-440: Franklin, sia 414

431	8.00	.65	8c pale olive green

432	9.00	3.00	9c salmon red
433	6.00	.06	10c orange yellow
434	4.00	2.40	11c dark green
435	4.00	1.50	12c claret brown
437	25.00	2.75	15c gray
438	32.50	1.30	20c ultramarine
439	42.50	4.00	30c orange red
440	150.00	4.50	50c violet

Coil Stamps, 1910 Washington, sia 333
Perf. 10 Horizontally

441	.25	.20	1c green
442	3.65	2.25	2c carmine, type I

Perf. 10 Vertically

443	2.65	1.20	1c green
444	8.25	.20	2c carmine, type I
445	58.50	30.00	3c violet, type I
446	28.50	8.75	4c brown
447	5.25	4.25	5c blue

Coil Stamps, Washington, sia 333
1915-16, Perf. 10 Horizontally

448	1.00	.75	1c green
449	4.00	40.00	2c red, type I
450	2.50	1.00	2c carmine, type III

1914-16, Perf. 10 Vertically

452	1.25	.60	1c green
453	27.50	1.75	2c red, type I
454	35.00	5.00	2c carmine, type II
455	.75	.35	2c carmine, type III
456	42.00	18.00	3c violet, type I
457	4.75	4.50	4c brown
458	4.75	4.00	5c blue

Issue of 1914 Washington, sia 333, Imperf.

459	80.00	80.00	2c carmine, type I Jun. 30

Issues of 1915, Perf. 10

Wmkd. USPS (191)

460	170.00	20.00	$1 violet black Franklin, sia 414 Feb. 8

Perf. 11

Wmkd. USPS (190)

461	17.00	15.00	2c red, type I, Washington. sia 333 Jun. 17

Privately perforated copies of No. 409 have been made to resemble No. 461.

From 1916 to date all postage stamps (except Nos. 519 and 832b) are on unwatermarked paper.

Issues of 1916-17, Unwmkd. Perf. 10
Nos. 462-469: Washington, sia 333

462	1.00	.15	1c green
462a	1.00	.60	Booklet pane of six
463	.50	.06	2c carmine, type I
463a	4.00	2.50	Booklet pane of six
464	15.00	4.25	3c violet, type I
465	6.50	.80	4c orange brown
466	12.00	.65	5c blue
467	175.00	175.00	5c car. (error in plate of 2c)
468	17.50	2.00	6c red orange
469	12.00	3.00	7c black

Nos. 470-78: Franklin, sia 414

470	12.00	2.00	8c olive green
471	8.50	4.50	9c salmon red
472	25.00	.50	10c orange yellow
473	6.00	5.00	11c dark green
474	9.00	2.00	12c claret brown
475	26.50	4.75	15c gray
476	33.50	4.50	20c light ultramarine
477	190.00	20.00	50c light violet
478	170.00	5.00	$1 violet black

Issues of 1917, Perf. 10, Mar. 22

479	60.00	11.00	$2 dk. bl. Madison, sia 312
480	52.50	13.00	$5 lt. grn. Marshall, sia 313

Issues of 1916-17, Washington, sia 333, Imperf.

481	.35	.30	1c green
482	.60	.60	2c carmine, type I
482A		3250.00	2c carmine, type Ia
483	4.25	4.00	3c violet, type I
484	3.00	2.75	3c violet, type II
485	3250.00		5c car. (error in plate of 2c)

Coil Stamps
1916-19, Washington, sia 333, Perf. 10 Horiz.

486	.15	.10	1c green
487	3.00	1.00	2c carmine, type II
488	.50	.50	2c carmine, type III
489	.55	.50	3c violet, type I

1916-22, Perf. 10 Vertically
Nos. 490-96: Washington, sia 333

490	.12	.08	1c green
491	450.00	60.00	2c carmine, type I

ALEXANDER HAMILTON (1757-1804)

In 1772 Alexander Hamilton left his birthplace in the West Indies and came to New York where he became an attorney and joined the struggle for American independence. After serving at the Constitutional Convention, he, James Madison, and John Jay wrote the *Federalist Papers,* which were instrumental in the ratification of the Constitution.

As Washington's secretary of the treasury, his organizational brilliancy and financial wizardry were invaluable to the new nation. He instituted a plan to pay the national debt, established the Bank of the United States, and began the mint. As a Federalist he believed in a strong centralized government composed of an aristocracy of landowners and industrialists which would lead the new country into an urban, industrialized future.

In 1804 Hamilton's political and personal rivalry with Aaron Burr ended in the tragic duel at Weehawken, N. J. in which Hamilton was killed at the height of his career.   *See Scott Stamp No. 1086*

St. Kitts-Nevis Scott No. 157

JOHN ADAMS (1735-1826), SECOND PRESIDENT OF THE U. S.

One of the most scholarly and brilliant presidents, John Adams was also one of the most candid. Adams' frankness made him a poor diplomat but served him well in other spheres.

During the stormy era of the Revolution he was a staunch, outspoken patriot who took part in both Continental Congresses, argued for the Declaration of Independence, and was responsible for Washington's appointment as commander-in-chief of the Continental Army. A Federalist and the first president to occupy the White House, Adams served as Chief Executive from 1797 until 1801. Like Jefferson he died on the fiftieth anniversary of the adoption of the Declaration of Independence, July 4, 1826.

See Scott Stamp No. 806

2	.60	.08	2c carmine, type III
3	5.50	1.65	3c violet, type I
4	2.35	.35	3c violet, type II
5	2.00	1.60	4c orange brown
6	.55	.35	5c blue
7	4.00	3.25	10c orange yellow Franklin, sia 414

Issues of 1917-19, Perf. 11
Nos. 498-507: Washington, sia 333

8	.20	.04	1c green
8e	.50	.35	Booklet pane of six
8f	110.00		Booklet pane of 30
9	.10	.03	2c rose, type I
9e	.60	.50	Booklet pane of six
9f	1300.00		Booklet pane of 30
0	70.00	25.00	2c deep rose, type Ia
1	1.10	.08	3c light violet, type I
1b	9.00	6.00	Booklet pane of six
2	1.60	.15	3c dark violet, type II
2b	3.00	2.25	Booklet pane of six
3	1.90	.10	4c brown
4	.85	.08	5c blue
5	120.00	100.00	5c rose (error in plate of 2c)
6	1.10	.12	6c red orange
7	4.50	.50	7c black

Nos. 508-518: Franklin, sia 414

8	2.65	.35	8c olive bistre
9	3.35	1.00	9c salmon red
0	1.65	.05	10c orange yellow
1	2.20	1.25	11c light green
2	1.20	.18	12c claret brown
3	2.75	2.25	13c apple green
4	7.50	.35	15c gray
5	4.50	.12	20c light ultramarine
6	5.25	.30	30c orange red
7	6.50	.25	50c red violet
8	12.50	.50	$1 violet brown

Issue of 1917, Perf. 11

Wmkd. (191)

9	30.00	30.00	2c carmine Washington, sia 332 Oct. 10

Privately perforated copies of No. 344 have been made to resemble No. 519.

Issues of 1918, Unwmkd., Perf. 11

3	125.00	57.50	$2 orange red and black Franklin, sia 547 Aug. 19
4	55.00	9.00	$5 deep green and black Franklin, sia 547 Aug. 19

Issues of 1918-20, Washington, sia 333
Perf. 11

5	.65	.30	1c gray green

526	3.25	2.00	2c carmine, type IV
527	1.85	.60	2c carmine, type V
528	1.25	.15	2c carmine, type Va
528A	3.25	.45	2c carmine, type VI
528B	1.70	.08	2c carmine, type VII
529	.40	.10	3c violet, type III
530	.30	.06	3c purple, type IV

Imperf.

531	3.85	3.85	1c green
532	7.00	7.00	2c carmine rose, type IV
533	20.00	16.00	2c carmine, type V
534	4.00	4.00	2c carmine, type Va
534A	8.50	8.50	2c carmine, type VI
534B	600.00	235.00	2c carmine, type VII
535	3.50	3.50	3c violet, type IV

Issues of 1919
Perf. 12-1/2

536	3.00	2.75	1c gray green Washington, sia 333 Aug. 15

Perf. 11

537	3.50	1.90	3c Allied Victory Mar. 3

The Armistice of Nov. 11, 1918 ended World War I on a note of triumph for the Allies.

Nos. 538-546: Washington, sia 333
1919, Perf. 11x10

538	1.75	1.75	1c green
539	650.00	225.00	2c carmine rose, type II
540	1.75	1.75	2c carmine rose, type III
541	8.00	7.50	3c violet, type II

1920, Perf. 10x11

542	1.10	.30	1c green May 26

1921, Perf. 10

543	.10	.06	1c green

1921, Perf. 11

544	3000.00	675.00	1c grn, 19x22-1/2 mm.
545	23.50	22.50	1c grn., 19-1/2-20mm.x22 mm.
546	15.00	14.00	2c rose carmine, type III

Issues of 1920
Perf. 11

547	40.00	9.00	$2 Franklin

THE PILGRIMS

While Captain John Smith traveled to New England and wrote of it with great enthusiasm, the region was settled accidentally by a small group of English Puritans who planned to land at Jamestown.

These colonists, destined to be remembered as the Pilgrim Fathers, were separatists from the Church of England who had moved to Holland in 1607-08. In 1620, after receiving a charter from the London Company, they sailed to North America aboard the *Mayflower* to seek religious freedom.

On November 11, following a two-month journey, the Pilgrims landed off the coast of Cape Cod, Massachusetts, where leaders of the group drew up the Mayflower Compact, America's first written constitution. The Compact was signed by forty-one male members of the group before the Pilgrims disembarked at Plymouth to build the Plymouth Colony.

After a harsh first winter in which fifty-two settlers died, the colony began to take root. Under the governorship of William Bradford annual elections were instituted and the seeds of democracy were firmly planted in America.

See Scott Stamp Nos. 548-550, 1420

			Pilgrims 300th Anniv. Issue, Dec. 21
548	1.90	1.20	1c Mayflower
549	3.50	.80	2c Pilgrims Landing
550	15.00	8.50	5c Signing of Compact

In 1620 the Pilgrims landed in Massachusetts and drew up the Mayflower Compact.

			Issues of 1922-25, Perf. 11
551	.06	.05	½ c Nathan Hale
552	.40	.07	1c deep green Franklin
552a	.50	.25	Booklet pane of six
553	.90	.10	1½ c Harding
554	.50	.03	2c Washington

554e	.85	.60	Booklet pane of six
555	5.25	.35	3c Lincoln
556	3.25	.08	4c Martha Washington
557	3.35	.06	5c Theodore Roosevelt
558	9.50	.25	6c Garfield
559	1.10	.25	7c McKinley
560	10.50	.25	8c Grant
561	2.50	.55	9c Jefferson
562	3.25	.06	10c Monroe
563	.50	.12	11c Rutherford B. Hayes
564	1.50	.08	12c Grover Cleveland

548 549 550

551 552 553 554

THE FRENCH AND INDIAN WAR

The French and Indian War (1754-1763), or Seven Years War as it was known in Europe, capped a long and bitter struggle between France and England to determine who would win control of Canada and the Ohio-Mississippi Valley. It began with a French victory but ended in a triumph for the British.

In 1755 a British force under Braddock was defeated by the French at Fort Duquesne on the site of Pittsburgh, Pennsylvania. The English, used to fighting in the open, proved an easy match for the French, who had been taught by their Indian allies to hide like shadows behind trees and to take their foes by surprise.

The tide began to turn in England's favor when William Pitt became Prime Minister in 1756. Three French forts soon fell to the British and in July, 1759, General James Wolfe began his siege of Quebec, which contained 15,000 French troops under General Montcalm.

Two months later, in the war's most epic struggle, Wolfe defeated Montcalm on the Plains of Abraham above Quebec. The battle, which claimed the lives of both generals, was instrumental in insuring British victory.

The terms of the Paris Peace Treaty of 1763 forever shattered France's hopes of building up a New World Empire. All of Canada fell to the British as did the Ohio Valley from the Mississippi eastward.

See Scott Stamp Nos. 688 and 1123.

565	1.25	.30	14c American Indian
566	3.50	.06	15c Statue of Liberty
567	4.00	.05	20c Golden Gate
568	3.50	.15	25c Niagara Falls
569	5.00	.15	30c Buffalo
570	8.25	.08	50c Arlington Amphitheater
571	7.50	.25	$1 Lincoln Memorial
572	21.00	3.25	$2 U. S. Capitol
573	37.50	4.75	$5 Head of Freedom, Capitol Dome

For listings of other perforated stamps of issues 551–573 see:

Nos. 578 and 579	Perf. 11x10
Nos. 581 to 591	Perf. 10
Nos. 594 and 595	Perf. 11
Nos. 622 and 623	Perf. 11
Nos. 632 to 642, 653, 692 to 696	Perf. 11x10½
Nos. 697 to 701	Perf. 10½x11

Issues of 1923-25 Imperf.

575	2.00	1.90	1c green Franklin, sia 552
576	.60	.60	1½c yellow brown Harding, sia 553
577	.75	.75	2c carmine Washington, sia 554

Perf. 11x10

578	14.00	14.00	1c green Franklin, sia 552
579	6.00	6.00	2c carmine Washington, sia 554

Issues of 1923-26 Perf. 10

581	1.30	.35	1c green Franklin, sia 552
582	.75	.30	1½c brown Harding, sia 553
583	.50	.05	2c carmine Washington, sia 554
583a	7.00	5.00	Booklet pane of six
584	6.50	.75	3c violet Lincoln, sia 555
585	2.90	.15	4c yellow brown M. Washington, sia 556
586	3.25	.08	5c blue T. Roosevelt, sia 557
587	1.50	.25	6c red orange Garfield, sia 558
588	2.00	1.85	7c blk. McKinley, sia 559
589	5.75	1.10	8c olive green Grant, sia 560
590	1.20	.85	9c rose Jefferson, sia 561
591	8.25	.06	10c org. Monroe, sia 562

Perf. 11

594	*4250.00*	*1250.00*	1c green Franklin, 19-3/4x22-1/4mm, sia 552
595	28.50	27.50	2c carmine Washington, 19-3/4x22-1/4mm, sia 554
596		*7500.00*	1c green Franklin, 19-1/4x22-3/4mm, sia 552

Coil Stamps 1923-29, Perf. 10 Vertically

597	.10	.06	1c green Franklin, sia 552
598	.25	.08	1½c brown Harding, sia 553
599	.18	.04	2c carmine Washington, type I, sia 554
599a	40.00	3.00	2c carmine Washington, type II, sia 554
600	.80	.08	3c violet Lincoln, sia 555
601	.65	.20	4c yellow brown M. Washington, sia 556
602	.35	.10	5c dark blue T. Roosevelt, sia 557
603	.80	.06	10c orange Monroe, sia 562

Coil Stamps 1923-25 Perf. 10 Horizontally

604	.10	.08	1c yellow green Franklin, sia 552
605	.15	.12	1½c yellow brown Harding, sia 553
606	.12	.10	2c carmine Washington, sia 554

Harding Memorial Issue, 1923
Flat Plate Printing

610	.35	.08	2c Harding, Perf. 11	Sep. 1
611	2.00	1.75	2c Harding, Imperf.	Nov. 15

Rotary Press Printing

612	6.00	.50	2c black Perf. 10, sia 610	Sep. 12
613		*5000.00*	2c black Perf. 11, sia 610	Sep. 12

Warren G. Harding (1865-1923) was the 28th President of the United States (1921-23).

Huguenot-Walloon 300th Anniv. Issue
1924, May 1

614	1.85	1.50	1c New Netherland
615	2.50	1.52	2c Landing at Fort Orange
616	13.50	8.50	5c Huguenot Monument, Florida

In the seventeenth century Dutch Walloons and French Huguenots fled to America to escape religious persecution. The Walloons founded Albany, New York.

INDIANS OF NORTH AMERICA

When the first Europeans came to North America about 100,000 Indians were living on the land. The richly diverse culture of these people dated from a prehistoric time when their ancestors had crossed the Bering Strait and peopled the New World.

Around 1000 A. D. an ancient Pueblo tribe evolved the first-known etching process, probably by using acid from fermented cactus juice. Along the Northwest Coast the Haida, Kwaikutl, and other tribes had a highly advanced culture and economy that was based on fishing. By 1575 the powerful Five Nations of the Iroquois had a governmental system that would later serve as a model of confederation for no less a personage than Benjamin Franklin.

Despite these accomplishments the Indians could not successfully defend themselves against the colonists who settled the United States and seized their lands. The different tribes, used to fighting one another, tried too late to unite against a common foe and were driven from their homes by settlers moving west. By the late nineteenth century even the great fighters of the Plains had been subdued and placed on reservations by the government. In the words of one chief, "We first thought he (the white man) came from the Light; but he comes like the dusk of evening now . . ."

See Scott Stamp Nos. 565, 972, 1364, 1389

**Czechoslovakia
Scott No. 1406**

Czechoslovakia Scott No. 1400

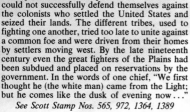

**Czechoslovakia
Scott No. 1404**

614 615 616

617 618 619

THE THIRTEEN COLONIES REVOLT

The Revolution was effected before the war commenced. The Revolution was in the minds and hearts of the people...John Adams

The American War for Independence began on April 19, 1775 in Lexington and Concord, Massachusetts when British troops clashed with armed and angry Minutemen over weapons held by the Americans. On that day the "shots heard round the world" were fired and the military phase of the Revolution finally began.

One says finally because the Revolution had begun long before the Massachusetts skirmish. It began after the French and Indian War, when England barred her growing colonies from settling lands be-

yond the Allegheny Mountains. It began when Britain levied heavy taxes on her colonies but failed to seat their representatives in Parliament. It began when the Americans were forced to "quarter" English troops in their homes; when intellectuals like Franklin, Jefferson, and Adams became convinced that Britain had usurped many of their rights.

This mood — this rebellious spirit — was abetted by the Boston Massacre of 1770. by the Tea Act and the Boston Tea Party, and by the so-called Intolerable Acts, which were designed to punish radicals in Massachusetts but served in effect to unite the colonies against a common enemy.

Following the meeting of the First Continental Congress in Philadelphia on September 24, 1774 and the drafting of a strongly-worded resolution of their rights to rule themselves, the colonies were set on a collision course with England that resulted in the "shots heard round the world." *See Scott Stamp Nos. 617-619*

Monaco Scott No. 354

France Scott No. 814

THE DECLARATION OF INDEPENDENCE

When, in the course of human events, it becomes necessary for one people to dissolve the political bands which have connected them with another...The Declaration of Independence

The United States of America was born on July 4, 1776 when the Second Continental Congress ratified the Declaration of Independence. With this document the colonies renounced all ties with the British Crown and pledged their lives, their fortunes, and their sacred honor to the cause of building a new nation.

The Declaration was, however, far more than a formal statement of rebellion against the government of England and a list of grievances against King George III. It was also an affirmation of the right of every man to "Life, Liberty and the pursuit of Happiness."

Written with great eloquence and force by Thomas Jefferson, it affirmed the hopes and dreams of the founders of the United States and held forth the promise of a just and democratic government for all.

See Scott Stamp Nos. 120,627

631   633   643   644

645   646   648   649

International Philatelic Exhibition Issue, Oct. 18			
		Souvenir Sheet	
630	125.00	110.00	2c car. rose, sheet of 25 with selvage inscription, sia 629
		Imperf.	
631	.90	.90	1½c Harding Aug. 27
		Issues of 1926-34, Perf. 11x10-1/2	
632	.08	.03	1c green Franklin, sia 552
632 a	.35	.25	Booklet pane of 6
633	.30	.08	1½c Harding
634	.10	.03	2c carmine Washington, type I, sia 554
634A	110.00	3.50	2c carmine Washington, type II, sia 554
635	.25	.04	3c violet Lincoln, sia 555

636	.60	.08	4c yellow brown M. Washington, sia 556
637	.60	.03	5c dark blue T. Roosevelt, sia 557
638	.60	.03	6c red org. Garfield, sia 558
639	.65	.08	7c black McKinley, sia 559 ·
640	.65	.05	8c olive grn. Grant, sia 560
641	.70	.05	9c org. red Jefferson, sia 561
642	1.00	.03	10c orange Monroe, sia 562
		Issues of 1927, Perf. 11	
643	.60	.55	2c Vermont 150th Anniversary Aug. 3

Issued for the 150th anniversary of the Battle of Bennington.

644	1.50	1.40	2c Burgoyne Campaign Aug. 3

THE WAR FOR INDEPENDENCE — FROM BUNKER'S HILL...

When John Adams wrote, "We shall have a long, obstinate, and bloody war to go through," few people believed him. At the time (1776) both sides thought the war would be a short-lived thing; both were wrong.

The Battle of Bunker's Hill, fought at Breed's Hill, Massachusetts, was prophetic of the true course that the war would follow. In June, 1775 the British suffered heavy losses (1,054 killed or wounded) while capturing the famous hill from the Americans. As a result the Continentals claimed a "moral victory" and confidently thought that other victories would follow. Yet the war dragged on, through the Battle of White Plains (1776), and through Washington's retreat across New Jersey (1777). As these later conflicts proved, it took more than raw determination to defeat the British.

See Scott Stamp Nos. 629, 1034, 1361

650

654

656 (Coil Pair)

651

657

680

681

...TO SARATOGA

The Battle of Saratoga, fought two years after Bunker's Hill, set in motion a chain of events which gave the Continental Army badly-needed help in its fight for independence.

In 1777 when General Burgoyne proposed to take New York and New England by way of the Hudson River and Lake Champlain, he failed to take Vermont's militia, the Green Mountain Boys, into account. This was a costly oversight, for when diversionary troops went to Vermont in search of food, they were soundly routed by the Green Mountain Boys at Bennington.

From Bennington Americans under Gates followed Burgoyne to New York, where they defeated him again, this time at Saratoga. The general's surrender of October 17 ended British hopes of conquering the North and helped persuade the French to ally themselves with the Americans.

See Scott Stamp Nos. 643, 644

682   683   684   685   688

Electric Light Jubilee Issue
Perf. 11

654	.45	.40	2c Edison's First Lamp

Perf. 11x10-1/2

655	.35	.15	2c carmine rose, sia 654

Coil Stamp, Perf. 10 Vertically

656	8.00	.60	2c Edison's First Lamp

Thomas A. Edison invented the first practical incandescent electric light bulb on Oct. 21, 1879.

Perf. 11

657	.35	.30	2c Sullivan Expedition Jun. 17

In 1779, General Sullivan led a daring Revolutionary War raid against the Iroquois in New York State.

Regular Issue of 1926-27

Overprinted **Kans.**
Perf. 11x10-1/2

658	.70	.70	1c green Franklin, sia 552
659	1.00	1.00	1½c brown Harding, sia 553
660	.90	.25	2c carmine Washington, sia 554
661	5.50	5.50	3c violet Lincoln. sia 555
662	4.50	3.00	4c yellow brown M. Washington, sia 556
663	4.25	3.75	5c dp. bl. T. Roosevelt, sia 557
664	8.50	6.50	6c red orange Garfield, sia 558
665	9.25	8.75	7c black McKinley, sia 559
666	25.00	23.00	8c olive green Grant, sia 560
667	3.85	3.75	9c light rose Jefferson, sia 561
668	7.50	3.50	10c org. yel. Monroe, sia 562

Overprinted **Nebr.**

669	.65	.65	1c green Franklin, sia 552
670	.85	.80	1½c brown Harding, sia 553
671	.75	.30	2c carmine Washington, sia 554
672	4.00	3.50	3c violet Lincoln, sia 555

673	5.25	3.75	4c yellow brown M. Washington, sia 556
674	4.25	4.00	5c dp. bl. T. Roosevelt, sia 557
675	8.00	7.00	6c red orange Garfield, sia 558
676	6.50	6.00	7c black McKinley, sia 559
677	10.00	9.00	8c olive green Grant, sia 560
678	10.50	9.50	9c light rose Jefferson, sia 561
679	23.50	8.50	10c org. yel. Monroe, sia 562
680	.65	.60	2c Battle of Fallen Timbers Sep. 14

A memorial to General "Mad" Anthony Wayne (1745-1796), who fought in the Revolution.

681	.45	.40	2c Ohio River Canal Oct. 19

Issued to commemorate the completion of the Ohio River Canalization Project between Cairo, Illinois, and Pittsburgh, Pennsylvania.

Issues of 1930

682	.30	.25	2c Mass. Bay Colony Apr. 8

In 1630, English Puritans founded the Massachusetts Bay Colony. Stamp shows the seal of the colony.

683	.65	.60	2c Carolina-Charleston Apr. 10

Issued for the 260th anniversary of the Carolina Province and the 250th anniversary of the city of Charleston, South Carolina.

Perf. 11x10-1/2

684	.12	.03	1½c Warren G. Harding
685	.20	.04	4c William H. Taft

Coil Stamps, Perf. 10 Vertically

686	.25	.05	1½c brown Harding, sia 684
687	.35	.12	4c brown W. H. Taft, sia 685

Perf. 11

688	.55	.50	2c Braddock's Field Jul. 9

The Battle of Braddock's Field, fought near Ft. Duquesne, Pennsylvania in the French and Indian War, was a crushing defeat for the English.

ADOPTED PATRIOTS

The inexperienced Americans who faced the veteran British in the Revolutionary War found themselves at a severe disadvantage until Baron von Steuben (1730-94) arrived to aid them. Often called the "Drillmaster of the Continental Army," the Prussian officer joined the Continental Army at Valley Forge, Pennsylvania, where he disciplined and drilled the troops from a rabble to a fighting force. Along with von Steuben, two Polish soldiers also helped the Americans. One of these, Count Casimir Pulaski (c. 1748-79) was killed at the siege of Savannah; the other, Tadeusz (Thaddeus) Kosciuszko (1746-1817), served throughout the war as a colonel of engineers and designed the fortifications of West Point.

See Scott Stamp Nos. 689, 690, 734

Poland Scott No. 267

42

689
690
702
703

689	.35	.30	2c Von Steuben	Sep. 17

Issued for the 200th anniversary of the birth of the Prussian General (1730-1794), who helped train the Continental Army.

Issues of 1931

690	.20	.18	2c Pulaski	Jan. 16

Issued on the 150th anniversary of the death of Casimir Pulaski (1748-1779), a Polish commander who was killed while fighting in our Revolution.

Perf. 11x10-1/2

692	1.00	.08	11c light blue Hayes, sia 563
693	1.50	.06	12c brown violet Cleveland, sia 564
694	.75	.10	13c yellow green Harrison, sia 622
695	1.00	.20	14c dark blue Indian, sia 565
696	2.75	.04	15c gray Statue of Liberty, sia 566

Perf. 10-1/2x11

697	1.20	.12	17c black Wilson, sia 623
698	3.85	.03	20c car. rose Golden Gate, sia 567
699	2.35	.08	25c blue green Niagara Falls, sia 568
700	4.00	.07	30c brown Buffalo, sia 569
701	6.25	.07	50c lilac Amphitheater, sia 570

Perf. 11

702	.15	.12	2c Red Cross	May 21

The American Red Cross was founded by Clara Barton in 1881.

703	.25	.20	2c Yorktown	Oct. 19

The American Revolution ended at Yorktown, Virginia in 1781 when Washington, DeGrasse and Rochambeau defeated Cornwallis.

THE BATTLE OF YORKTOWN

When General Cornwallis surrendered his entire British force to the Americans at Yorktown, Virginia on October 19, 1781, a military band played "The World Turned Upside Down" and Lafayette solemnly remarked, "The play is over; the fifth act has come to an end."

For all intents and purposes the great French patriot and friend of the Americans was right; Yorktown was the last decisive battle of the Revolutionary War. That it ended on a note of triumph for the United States was, in large part, due to the aid given the Continental Army by Lafayette's fellow Frenchmen, De Grasse and Rochambeau.

The Yorktown campaign began when a French fleet of thirty-six ships under De Grasse converged on Yorktown where Cornwallis and 8,000 British troops were encamped. De Grasse successfully blockaded the Chesapeake Bay and cut off British supplies, reinforcements, communications, and escape. On land, Washington and Rochambeau encircled Yorktown with a combined force of 16,000 men, and by September Cornwallis was surrounded by the Allies. The siege itself began on September 28 and continued until October 17 when Cornwallis sent out a white flag of truce.

See Scott Stamp No. 703

France Scott No. 622

Issues of 1932, Perf. 11x10-1/2
Washington Bicentennial Issue, Jan. 1
Various Portraits

704	.06	.05	½c Portrait by Charles W. Peale
705	.08	.04	1c Bust by Jean Antoine Houdon
706	.18	.06	1½c Portrait by Charles W. Peale
707	.07	.03	2c Portrait by Gilbert Stuart
708	.25	.06	3c Portrait by Charles W. Peale
709	.20	.06	4c Portrait by Charles P. Polk
710	.85	.08	5c Portrait by Charles W. Peale
711	2.00	.06	6c Portrait by John Trumbull
712	.35	.12	7c Portrait by John Trumbull
713	2.00	.60	8c Portrait by Charles B. J. F. Saint Memin
714	1.50	.20	9c Portrait by W. Williams
715	5.25	.06	10c Portrait by Gilbert Stuart

Issued for the 200th anniversary of the birth of George Washington.

Perf. 11

716	.18	.15	2c Olympic Games	Jan. 25

The Olympic Winter Games of 1932 were held at Lake Placid in New York.

Perf. 11x10-1/2

717	.15	.08	2c Arbor Day	Apr. 22

In Nebraska trees are planted every year on Arbor Day. Nebraskan Julius Sterling Morton created Arbor Day.

10th Olympic Games Issue, June 15

718	.30	.06	3c Runner at Starting Mark	
719	.45	.20	5c Myron's Discobolus	

In 1932 the Olympic Summer Games were held in Los Angeles, California.

720	.15	.03	3c Washington	Jun. 16
720b	3.50	1.50	Booklet pane of 6	

Coil Stamps
Perf. 10 Vertically

721	.50	.05	3c Washington	Jun. 24

THE OLYMPIC GAMES

Every four years athletes from over 100 countries meet in Olympic competition. A runner with a flaming torch symbolic of the continuity and unity of life enters the arena, and the oldest games in history begin anew.

The first Olympic Games were held in ancient Greece in 776 B. C. to honor Zeus. Then, as now, only amateurs were allowed to compete. Halted by the Romans in 373 A. D., the games were revived in 1896 at Athens. The modern Olympics have done much to foster understanding among competing nations. The United States has hosted three Olympic competitions and will host the winter games in 1976.

See Scott Stamp Nos. 716, 718-719, 1146

<table>
<tr><td colspan="3">Perf. 10 Horizontally</td></tr>
<tr><td>.35</td><td>.12</td><td>3c Washington</td><td>Oct. 12</td></tr>
</table>

Perf. 10 Vertically

1.45 .12 6c Garfield Aug. 18

Perf. 11

.20 .10 3c William Penn Oct. 24
English Quaker William Penn (1644-1718) founded Pennsylvania; laid out Philadelphia in 1682.

.25 .12 3c Daniel Webster Oct. 24
Issued for the 150th anniversary of the birth of the Massachusetts orator and statesman (1782-1852), who was twice Secretary of State, a Congressman, and Senator.

Issues of 1933

.25 .10 3c Georgia 200th Anniv. Feb. 12
Englishman James Oglethorpe (1696-1785) established Georgia as a refuge for imprisoned debtors in 1733.

Perf. 10-1/2x11

.14 .08 3c Peace of 1783 Apr. 19
In 1783, Washington issued a peace proclamation with the British.

Century of Progress Issue, May 25

.10 .06 1c Restoration of Ft. Dearborn
.12 .04 3c Fed. Building at Chicago 1933
The Century of Progress Exposition, held in Chicago, Ill. in 1933, marked the "Windy City's" 100th anniversary.

American Philatelic Society Issue
Souvenir Sheets, Aug. 25
Without Gum, Imperf.

730 14.00 10.00 1c deep yellow green sheet of 25, sia 728
730a .35 .15 Single stamp
731 10.50 8.00 3c dp. vio. sheet of 25, sia 729
731a .30 .20 Single stamp
Issued in sheets of 25 with marginal inscriptions commemorating the 1933 convention of the American Philatelic Society, held in Chicago.

Perf. 10-1/2x11

732 .14 .03 3c National Recovery Act Aug. 15
Issued to publicize the National Recovery Act, F.D.R.'s program of aid for the depression-stricken country.

Perf. 11

733 .65 .60 3c Byrd's Antarctic Expedition, May 9
Issued in connection with Rear Admiral Richard E. Byrd's second South Pole expedition.

734 .55 .20 5c Tadeusz Kosciuszko Oct. 13
Polish patriot Tadeusz Kosciuszko (1746-1817) fought in our Revolution and was awarded American citizenship in 1783.

THE SMITHSONIAN INSTITUTION

An Englishman who never saw the United States contributed greatly to its research activities and to the preservation of its heritage. That man was scientist John Smithson (1765-1829) who willed $500,000 to the United States for the "increase and diffusion of knowledge among men."

Established by an Act of Congress in 1846, the Smithsonian Institution now consists of several galleries, museums, and laboratories, with exhibitions ranging over every area of science and Americana.

The Smithsonian also is the home of the national stamp collection. Many of the stamps displayed at the Institution on Scott Album pages have a fascinating tale to tell about the history of the United States; other stamps in the collection are rare treasures in themselves.

See Scott Stamp No. 943

Issues of 1934
National Stamp Exhibition Issue
Souvenir Sheet, Feb. 10
Without Gum, Imperf.

735	8.50	7.00	3c dk. blue sheet of 6, sia 73.
735a	1.20	1.00	Single stamp

Issued in sheets of six with marginal inscription commemorating the National Stamp Exhibition of 19 held in New York City.

Perf. 11

736	.20	.15	3c Maryland 300th Anniversa Mar.

Lord Baltimore founded Maryland in 1634.

Mothers of America Issue, May 2
Perf. 11x10-1/2

737	.12	.06	3c Whistler's Mother

Perf. 11

738	.20	.18	3c Whistler's Mother

Issued in honor of Mothers Day. Stamp shows adapti of the well-known painting of Whistler's Mothe

739	.20	.12	3c Wisconsin 300th Anniversa Jul.

French explorer Jean Nicolet arrived at Green Ba in present-day Wisconsin in 1634.

National Parks Issue

740	.06	.06	1c El Capitan, Yosemite, Calif.

NATIONAL PARKS AND MONUMENTS

The land was ours before we were the land's. Robert Frost

Long after the government of the United States acquired the land in which we live, Americans were struggling to adapt to the land and tame its wilderness, to cross its deserts and build cities in the midst of mountains.

The story of this struggle is today kept alive in the nation's parks and monuments, which preserve the country's most historic sites and scenic wonders.

The policy of setting land aside for the public dates from 1872 when the Yellowstone Act forbade the destruction of that wilderness. In 1906 President

1	.10	.06	2c Grand Canyon, Ariz.
2	.15	.06	3c Mt. Ranier and Mirror Lake, Wash.
3	.35	.30	4c Mesa Verde, Colo.
4	.35	.30	5c Old Faithful, Yellowstone, Wyoming
5	.70	.50	6c Crater Lake, Ore.
6	.40	.35	7c Great Head, Acadia Park, Me.
7	1.00	.90	8c Great White Throne, Zion Park, Utah
8	.80	.40	9c Mt. Rockwell and Two Medicine Lake, Glacier Nat'l. Park, Mont.
9	1.90	.50	10c Great Smoky Mountains, N. C.

This series was issued in honor of National Parks Year

American Philatelic Society Issue
Souvenir Sheet
Imperf.

50	16.50	12.00	3c deep violet sheet of six, sla 742 Aug. 28
50a	2.00	1.50	Single stamp

Issued in sheets of six with marginal inscription commemorating the 1934 convention of the American Philatelic Society held in Atlantic City, N. J.

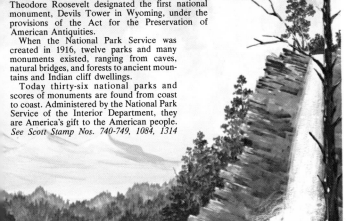

Theodore Roosevelt designated the first national monument, Devils Tower in Wyoming, under the provisions of the Act for the Preservation of American Antiquities.

When the National Park Service was created in 1916, twelve parks and many monuments existed, ranging from caves, natural bridges, and forests to ancient mountains and Indian cliff dwellings.

Today thirty-six national parks and scores of monuments are found from coast to coast. Administered by the National Park Service of the Interior Department, they are America's gift to the American people.
See Scott Stamp Nos. 740-749, 1084, 1314

772

773

774

777

Trans-Mississippi Philatelic Exposition Issue

| 751 | 6.50 | 5.00 | 1c green sheet of 6, sia 740 Oct. |

| 751a | .80 | .60 | single stamp |

Issued in inscribed sheets of six to commemorate t
1934 convention of the Trans-Mississippi Philate
Society, held in Omaha, Nebraska.

**Special Printing (Nos. 752 to 771 inclusive)
Issued March 15, 1935
Without Gum**

In 1940, the Post Office Department offered to an
did gum full sheets of Nos. 754 to 771 sent in by owner

Issues of 1935, Perf. 10-1/2x11

| 752 | .14 | .08 | 3c violet, Peace of 1783, sia 727 Mar. |

Issued in sheets of 400

Perf. 11

| 753 | .50 | .50 | 3c dk. blue Byrd's Antarctic Expedition, sia 733 |

Imperf.

754	.30	.30	3c dp. vio. Whistler's Mother sia 737
755	.30	.30	3c dp. vio. Wisconsin 300th Anniv., sia 739
756	.15	.12	1c green Yosemite, sia 740
757	.20	.20	2c red Grand Canyon, sia 74
758	.40	.40	3c dp. vio. Mt. Ranier, sia 742
759	.50	.50	4c brown Mesa Verde, sia 743
760	.55	.50	5c blue Yellowstone, sia 744
761	.75	.70	6c dk. blue Crater Lake, sia 745
762	.65	.60	7c black Acadia, sia 746
763	.75	.70	8c sage green Zion, sia 747
764	.80	.75	9c red orange Glacier Nat'l., sia 748
765	1.50	1.40	10c gray black Smoky Mts., sia 749

Nos. 753-765 were issued in sheets of 200.

Imperf.

Note: Positive identification of these issues is by block
or pairs showing wide gutters between stamps.

RICHARD E. BYRD (1888-1957)

One of the great modern explorers was American naval officer
Richard E. Byrd. In 1926 he made the first flight over the North Pole;
three years later he was the first to fly over the South Pole.

Byrd, whose South Pole flight earned him the rank of rear
admiral, traveled to Antarctica several times. In 1928 he helped
set up Little America, an exploration base manned by forty-two
men on Ross Shelf Ice, south of the Bay of Whales. Five years
later he returned to Little America and explored the more remote areas of Antarctica, this time moving some 123 miles closer
to the Pole.

Byrd headed scientific expeditions to the South Pole
in 1946 and 1947, and was involved in the International
Geophysical Year. The author of five books about his
explorations, he died in 1957.

See Scott Stamp No. 733

British Antarctic Territory Scott No. 23

13.50	9.50	1c	yellow green, sia 728
			Pane of 25 from sheet of 225 (9 panes)
5a	.30	.20	Single stamp
7	10.00	8.00	3c violet, sia 729
			Pane of 25 from sheet of 225 (9 panes)
7a	.30	.25	Single stamp
8	7.50	7.00	3c dark blue, sia 733
			Pane of 6 from sheet of 150 (25 panes)
8a	1.00	1.00	Single stamp
9	5.00	5.00	1c green, sia 740
			Pane of 6 from sheet of 120 (20 panes)
9a	.60	.60	Single stamp
0	12.00	12.00	3c deep violet, sia 742
			Pane of 6 from sheet of 120 (20 panes)
0a	1.50	1.50	Single stamp
1	1.75	1.75	16c dark blue Seal of U.S., sia CE1, issued in sheets of 200

Perf. 11x10-1/2

2	.10	.06	3c Connecticut 300th Anniv., Apr. 26

Connecticut was settled in 1635. The Founders hid their charter in the Charter Oak (shown).

3	.10	.06	3c Cal.-Pacific Exposition, May 29

The 1935 Exposition was held in San Diego.

Perf. 11

4	.10	.06	3c Boulder Dam Sep. 30

Boulder Dam, now Hoover Dam, was dedicated on September 30, 1935.

Perf. 11x10-1/2

5	.10	.06	3c Mich. 100th Anniv. Nov. 1

Michigan became a state in 1835.

Issues of 1936

6	.10	.06	3c Texas 100th Anniv. Mar. 2

Texas became a Republic in 1836

Perf. 10-1/2x11

7	.12	.06	3c Rhode Island 300th Anniv. May 4

Rhode Island was founded by dissenters from the Massachusetts Bay Colony led by Roger Williams, in 1636.

775

776

782

784   783

THE TEXAS STORY

The story of the Lone Star State is a long and stormy saga filled with famous people and events — from Coronado, who explored it; to Stephen Austin, who settled it.

In 1821 when Stephen Austin led a band of Americans into Texas, the region was part of Mexico. Most of the colonists became Mexican, but others, including Sam Houston, wanted Texas to be independent. By 1835 the colonies were ripe for revolt and when General Santa Ana seized control of Mexico, the Texans pitted their small fighting force against his army.

For Colonel William B. Travis, Davy Crockett, Jim Bowie, and 184 other patriots, the fight for independence ended at the Alamo on March 6, 1836, when all were killed by Santa Ana's army. One month later, however, at the Battle of San Jacinto, Sam Houston rallied the remaining Texans with the cry "Remember the Alamo," defeated the Mexicans, and captured Santa Ana.

In 1836 the Republic of Texas was born and war hero Sam Houston became its first president. For nine years the Lone Star State stood by itself, but in 1845 it joined the Union, and the Americans who fought for Texas once again became United States citizens.

See Scott Stamp Nos. 776, 938, 1242

785

786

787

788

789

THE UNITED STATES ARMY

To be prepared for war is one of the most effectual means of preserving peace. George Washington

The United States Army began before there was a United States. In 1775, the Continental Congress created a Continental Army to win freedom from the British.

Led by the brilliant Washington, Nathanael Greene, and other generals, the Continental Army survived freezing winters and a lack of food and clothing to win the Revolutionary War. Men like Andrew Jackson ("Old Hickory") in the War of 1812 and fiery Winfield Scott in the Mexican War helped perpetuate military excellence.

In 1802 Congress authorized the creation of a military academy at West Point, New York, to train army officers. Distinguished West Point graduates include the opposing heroes of the Civil War: Generals Sherman, Grant, and Sheridan of the North; Lee and "Stonewall" Jackson of the South.

Led by heroes such as Generals Pershing, Patton, Eisenhower, and MacArthur, the twentieth century army has led the United States to victory in two World Wars.

*See Scott Stamp Nos.
785-789, 934*

Grenada Scott No. 377

.08	.06	2c	Andrew Jackson and Winfield Scott
.12	.06	3c	Generals Sherman, Grant and Sheridan
.15	.12	4c	Generals Robert E. Lee and "Stonewall" Jackson
.20	.12	5c	U. S. Military Academy, West Point

Issued to honor the United States Army.

Navy Issue

.06	.06	1c	John Paul Jones and John Barry
.08	.06	2c	Stephen Decatur and Thomas MacDonough
.12	.08	3c	Admirals David G. Farragut and David D. Porter
.15	.12	4c	Admirals William T. Sampson, George Dewey and Winfield S. Schley
.20	.12	5c	Seal of U.S. Naval Academy and Naval Cadets

Issued to honor the United States Navy.

790

791

792

793

794

THE UNITED STATES NAVY

I have not yet begun to fight!
John Paul Jones

The story of the navy is a log of famous battles, ships, and men. In the Revolutionary War, John Paul Jones and John Barry fathered the United States Navy. In the 1801-05 war against the Barbary pirates, Stephen Decatur distinguished himself in a daring raid on Tripoli harbor. In the War of 1812, Thomas MacDonough defeated the British on Lake Champlain.

During the Civil War David D. Porter and his adopted brother David Farragut, the first U. S. Admirals, successfully blockaded the South for the Union.

The Spanish-American War of 1898 was a further demonstration of the navy's might. Admirals Dewey, Schley, and Sampson distinguished themselves in conflicts from Santiago, Cuba to the Philippines.

Ships of the modern navy are stationed around the world. Twentieth century naval heroes include Admirals Mayo, Halsey, King, and Nimitz.

See Scott Stamp Nos.
790-794, 935

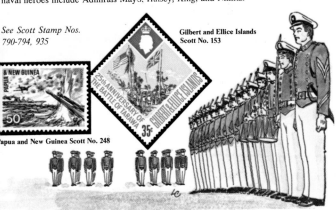

Gilbert and Ellice Islands
Scott No. 153

Papua and New Guinea Scott No. 248

795

796

798

800

801

799

802

THE FRAMING OF THE CONSTITUTION

We the People of the United States, in order to form a more perfect Union... The Constitution

On May 14, 1787, fifty-five delegates from all the states (except Rhode Island) met in historic Philadelphia to revise the inadequate Articles of Confederation. George Washington was elected president of the convention. Other delegates were the patriots Benjamin Franklin, James Madison, and Alexander Hamilton. Deliberating in secrecy, these distinguished men drew on their experience in self-government and on their knowledge of the British common law to form a strong, yet flexible framework of government. Their four month effort produced the Constitution of the United States, "the most wonderful work ever struck off at a given time by the brain and purpose of man" (William Gladstone).

This remarkable document, which became the law of the land in March of 1789, is the solid bedrock upon which the American democratic system is built. Its first three Articles establish and enumerate the divisions of the Federal government — the legislative, executive, and judicial branches. Under its unique system of "checks and balances" a unified nation has grown, liberty flourished, and the dream of its framers become reality.

See Scott Stamp Nos. 798, 835

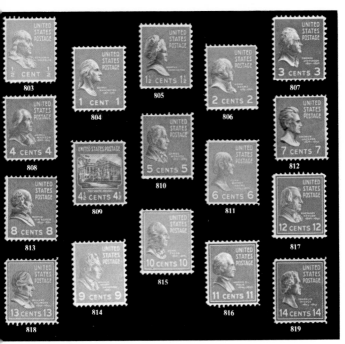

Issues of 1937

5	.12	.06	3c Northwest Ordinance 150th Anniversary Jul. 13

The Northwest Territory was created in 1/87. It included the present states of Ohio, Ind., Ill., Mich., Wisc., and part of Minn.

Perf. 11

6	.35	.20	5c Virginia Dare Aug. 18

Marks the 350th anniversary of the birth of the first child born in America of English parents, at Roanoke Island.

Society of Philatelic Americans
Imperf. Souvenir Sheet

7	.55	.30	10c blue green, sia 749 Aug. 26

Issued in sheets of one stamp with marginal inscription commemorating the 43rd Annual Convention of the Society of Philatelic Americans held in Asheville, North Carolina.

Perf. 11x10-1/2

8	.15	.07	3c Constitution 150th Anniv. Sep. 17

Issued on the 150th anniversary of the signing of the Constitution, Sep. 17, 1787.

Territorial Issues
Perf. 10-1/2x11

9	.15	.07	3c Hawaii Oct. 18

Perf. 11x10-1/2

0	.15	.07	3c Alaska	Nov. 12
1	.12	.07	3c Puerto Rico	Nov. 25
2	.12	.07	3c Virgin Islands	Dec. 15

These stamps show a statue of King Kamehameha I (Hawaii), Mt. McKinley (Alaska), Fortaleza Castle (Puerto Rico), and Charlotte Amalie (Virgin Islands).

Presidential Issue, 1938-54

3	.03	.03	½c Benjamin Franklin
4	.04	.03	1c George Washington

804b	.25	.20	Booklet pane of six
805	.05	.03	1½c Martha Washington
806	.06	.03	2c John Adams
806b	.50	.25	Booklet pane of six
807	.08	.03	3c Thomas Jefferson
807a	.65	.25	Booklet pane of six
808	.15	.04	4c James Madison
809	.15	.06	4½c White House
810	.18	.03	5c James Monroe
811	.20	.03	6c John Q. Adams
812	.25	.05	7c Andrew Jackson
813	.25	.04	8c Martin Van Buren
814	.25	.04	9c William H. Harrison
815	.25	.03	10c John Tyler
816	.30	.08	11c James K. Polk
817	.35	.06	12c Zachary Taylor
818	.40	.08	13c Millard Fillmore
819	.45	.10	14c Franklin Pierce

The U. S. Constitution is commemorated on Honduras Scott No. C84

820	.40	.03	15c James Buchanan	826	.70	.10	21c Chester A. Arthur
821	.55	.25	16c Abraham Lincoln	827	.75	.35	22c Grover Cleveland
822	.55	.12	17c Andrew Johnson	828	.85	.25	24c Benjamin Harrison
823	.60	.08	18c Ulysses S. Grant	829	.70	.03	25c William McKinley
824	.65	.30	19c Rutherford B. Hayes	830	1.40	.05	30c Theodore Roosevelt
825	.55	.03	20c James A. Garfield	831	2.25	.06	50c William Howard Taft

WORLD WAR I

The "Great War" began in 1914 with Russia, France, and Great Britain pitted against Germany and Austria-Hungary. During the war's initial stages the United States, under President Woodrow Wilson, hoped to remain neutral. But when German U-Boats attacked U. S. ships and when 128 American lives were lost in the sinking of the unarmed liner *Lusitania*, U. S. sympathies were irrevocably drawn to France and Britain.

In 1916 Wilson, still hoping to avoid a war, was elected to a second term. But in 1917 Germany again sank U. S. merchant vessels without warning, and in April Congress declared war. U. S. troops under Pershing served in Europe until 1918, when the Armistice of November 11 ended the war with an Allied victory.

Following the war, Wilson, a scholarly and idealistic president, went to Paris to insure the incorporation of a League of Nations into the peace settlement. The League, a forerunner of the United Nations, came into being on June 28, 1919, largely through Wilson's efforts. To the president's great sorrow, however, the United States refused to join. Awarded a Nobel Prize for Peace in 1920, Wilson died in 1924.

See Scott Stamp Nos. 537, 832, 1042A

853	.12	.06	3c New York World's Fair Apr. 1

Issued for the opening of the New York World's Fair of 1939.

Perf. 11

| **854** | .25 | .10 | 3c Washington Inauguration Apr. 30 |

In 1789 George Washington (1732-1799) became the first president of the United States.

Perf. 11x10-1/2

| **855** | .22 | .08 | 3c Baseball 100th Anniv. Jun. 12 |

Baseball was 100 years old in 1939. The sport originated in New York at Cooperstown.

Perf. 11

| **856** | .22 | .08 | 3c Panama Canal Aug. 15 |

Issued for the 25th anniversary of the opening of the Panama Canal.

Perf. 10-1/2x11

| **857** | .12 | .08 | 3c Printing 300th Anniv. Sep. 25 |

The first book printed in America came from the press of Stephen Daye (shown). It was *The Bay Psalm Book.*

Perf. 11x10-1/2

| **858** | .12 | .08 | 3c 50th Anniv. of Statehood Nov. |

North Dakota, South Dakota, Montana and Washington became states in 1889.

Famous Americans Issue, 1940, Perf. 10-1/2x11
Authors

859	.06	.06	1c Washington Irving
860	.10	.08	2c James Fenimore Cooper
861	.12	.06	3c Ralph Waldo Emerson
862	.22	.22	5c Louisa May Alcott
863	1.25	1.10	10c Samuel L. Clemens (Mark Twain)

Poets

864	.12	.08	1c Henry W. Longfellow
865	.10	.08	2c John Greenleaf Whittier
866	.18	.06	3c James Russell Lowell
867	.22	.20	5c Walt Whitman
868	2.00	1.30	10c James Whitcomb Riley

MARK TWAIN (1835-1910)

Tom appeared on the sidewalk with a bucket of whitewash and a long-handled brush. He surveyed the fence, and all gladness left him... Thirty yards of board fence ... Life to him seemed hollow... Tom Sawyer

Known to millions as the author of *Huckleberry Finn* and *The Adventures of Tom Sawyer,* Mark Twain was one of the world's great humorists and satirists. Born Samuel Langhorne Clemens, he took his pen name from the sailor's cry "mark twain" (meaning two fathoms sounded).

Twain spent his youth along the Mississippi River in Missouri, but it was in Connecticut that he created "Tom Sawyer", "Huck Finn", *A Connecticut Yankee in King Arthur's Court,* and other works.

See Scott Stamp No. 863

U.S.S.R. Scott No. 2403

869

870

871

872

873

			Educators					Scientists
9	.09	.08	1c Horace Mann	874	.06	.06	1c John James Audubon
0	.10	.06	2c Mark Hopkins	875	.08	.06	2c Dr. Crawford W. Long
1	.30	.06	3c Charles W. Eliot	876	.10	.06	3c Luther Burbank
2	.35	.22	5c Frances E. Willard	877	.20	.18	5c Dr. Walter Reed
3	1.10	.85	10c Booker T. Washington	878	.95	.75	10c Jane Addams

WALT WHITMAN (1819-92)

I hear America singing, the varied carols I hear. Leaves of Grass

Walt Whitman, a native of Long Island and one of nine children, is the great poetic voice of the democratic ideal, as he proclaimed himself in his longest poem, "Song of Myself." His classic *Leaves of Grass* (1855) is his poetic celebration of America.

During the Civil War Whitman served as a war correspondent and unofficial nurse. This turbulent experience produced *Drum-Taps* (1865), followed by *Sequel to Drum-Taps* (1866), which contains Whitman's elegies of Lincoln—"O Captain! My Captain!" and "When Lilacs Last in the Dooryard Bloom'd." His prose works are *Democratic Vistas* and *Specimen Days and Collect.*

See Scott Stamp No. 867

Czechoslovakia
Scott No. 726

1187

FREDERIC REMINGTON
(1861-1909)

Rarely has the action, mystery, and beauty of the Old West been portrayed as realistically as in the art of Frederic Remington.

Born in Canton, New York, Remington moved to the West while still a youth to seek a remedy for his poor health. The rugged life of the frontier intrigued the young artist and became the subject-matter for his sculpture, paintings, and his writings.

From honest colorful depictions of pioneers to bronze statues such as "Wounded Bunkie" and the "Bronco Buster", Remington created in his art a living record of the winning of the West.

See Scott Stamp Nos. 888 and 1187

874

875

876

877

878

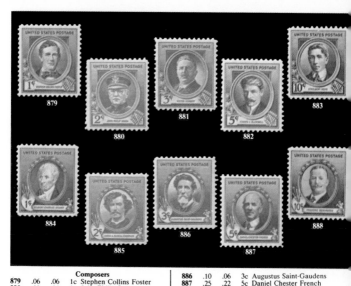

			Composers				
879	.06	.06	1c Stephen Collins Foster	886	.10	.06	3c Augustus Saint-Gaudens
880	.08	.06	2c John Philip Sousa	887	.25	.22	5c Daniel Chester French
881	.15	.06	3c Victor Herbert	888	1.25	1.10	10c Frederic Remington
882	.20	.20	5c Edward MacDowell				**Inventors**
883	2.10	1.00	10c Ethelbert Nevin	889	.12	.08	1c Eli Whitney
			Artists	890	.08	.06	2c Samuel F. B. Morse
884	.06	.06	1c Gilbert Charles Stuart	891	.15	.06	3c Cyrus Hall McCormick
885	.08	.06	2c James A. McNeill Whistler	892	.90	.30	5c Elias Howe
				893	4.75	1.25	10c Alexander Graham Bell

STEPHEN COLLINS FOSTER (1826-64)

All up and down the whole creation, sadly I roam
Still longing for the old plantation, and for the old folks at home.

Stephen Foster began his career as a professional bookkeeper and amateur songwriter. He had no formal musical training; genius was his schooling. Known to have written about two hundred ballads, such as "Swanee River" and "My Old Kentucky Home", Foster translated his environment into memorable lyrical expression. A Negro minstrel group called Christy's Minstrels caught his eye, and he began writing what he termed "Ethiopian" songs for their shows.

With the onslaught of the Gold Rush, his ever-popular "Oh Susanna" became the theme song of the Forty-Niners and carried Foster's reputation across the nation.

See Scott Stamp No. 879

889 1¢

890 2¢

891 3¢

894

895

890

892 5¢

893 10¢

896

898

897

Issues of 1940
Perf. 11x10-1/2

4 .50 .20 3c Pony Express Apr. 3
The famed Pony Express began to carry mail across the continent in 1860.

Perf. 10-1/2x11

5 .45 .15 3c Pan American Union Apr. 14
The Pan American Union was established in 1890. The stamp shows the "Three Graces" from Botticelli's "Spring".

Perf. 11x10-1/2

6 .20 .08 3c Idaho Statehood 50th Anniv. Jul. 3
Idaho became a state in 1890.

Perf. 10-1/2x11

897 .20 .08 3c Wyoming Statehood 50th Anniv. Jul. 10
Wyoming became a state in 1890.

Perf. 11x10-1/2

898 .20 .08 3c Coronado Expedition Sep. 7
In 1540, Coronado, the discoverer of Grand Canyon, led a Spanish expedition through the Southwest. The explorer hoped to find the golden "Cities of Cibola".

ALEXANDER GRAHAM BELL (1847-1922)

"Mr. Watson, come here; I want you," the first telephone transmission, ushered in a new era in communication. But for Alexander Graham Bell, the inventor of the telephone, it meant the end of a long struggle to perfect the revolutionary instrument.

Bell's lifelong interest in sound stimulated his invention of the telephone. A native of Scotland, he came to the United States by way of Canada. After settling in Boston he set up a training school for teachers of the deaf, and in 1873 he joined the faculty of Boston University as professor of vocal physiology.

By 1875 Bell and his assistant, Thomas Watson, had developed a machine that would become the modern telephone. This machine used electricity to transmit vocal sounds. On February 4, 1876 Bell applied for a patent on his revolutionary apparatus and on March 10, 1876 he spoke the first complete sentence over the telephone.

See Scott Stamp No. 893

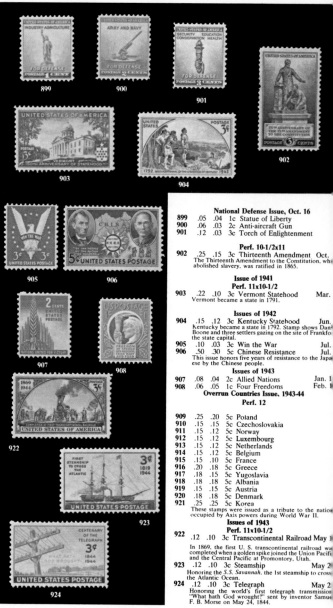

National Defense Issue, Oct. 16

899	.05	.04	1c Statue of Liberty
900	.06	.03	2c Anti-aircraft Gun
901	.12	.03	3c Torch of Enlightenment

Perf. 10-1/2x11

902   .25   .15   3c Thirteenth Amendment Oct.
The Thirteenth Amendment to the Constitution, whi
abolished slavery, was ratified in 1865.

Issue of 1941
Perf. 11x10-1/2

903   .22   .10   3c Vermont Statehood   Mar.
Vermont became a state in 1791.

Issues of 1942

904   .15   .12   3c Kentucky Statehood   Jun.
Kentucky became a state in 1792. Stamp shows Dan
Boone and three settlers gazing on the site of Frankfo
the state capital.

905	.10	.03	3c Win the War Jul.
906	.50	.30	5c Chinese Resistance Jul.

This issue honors five years of resistance to the Japa
ese by the Chinese people.

Issues of 1943

907	.08	.04	2c Allied Nations Jan. 1
908	.06	.05	1c Four Freedoms Feb.

Overrun Countries Issue, 1943-44
Perf. 12

909	.25	.20	5c Poland
910	.15	.15	5c Czechoslovakia
911	.15	.12	5c Norway
912	.15	.12	5c Luxembourg
913	.15	.12	5c Netherlands
914	.15	.12	5c Belgium
915	.15	.10	5c France
916	.20	.18	5c Greece
917	.18	.15	5c Yugoslavia
918	.18	.18	5c Albania
919	.15	.15	5c Austria
920	.18	.18	5c Denmark
921	.25	.25	5c Korea

These stamps were issued as a tribute to the natio
occupied by Axis powers during World War II.

Issues of 1943
Perf. 11x10-1/2

922   .12   .10   3c Transcontinental Railroad May

In 1869, the first U. S. transcontinental railroad wa
completed when a golden spike joined the Union Pacifi
and the Central Pacific at Promontory, Utah.

923   .12   .10   3c Steamship   May 2
Honoring the *S.S. Savannah*, the 1st steamship to cross
the Atlantic Ocean.

924   .12   .10   3c Telegraph   May 2
Honoring the world's first telegraph transmission
"What hath God wrought?" sent by inventor Samue
F. B. Morse on May 24, 1844.

909

910

911

912

913

914

915

916

917

918

919

920

921

SAMUEL F. B. MORSE (1791-1872)

Samuel F. B. Morse, the inventor of the telegraph, began his career not as a scientist, but as an artist. In 1829, the young Yale graduate began a three year art tour of Europe. His return voyage proved to be the turning point in his career. While at sea his idea for a telegraph began to germinate.

For three years Morse worked on the idea, and on Sept. 21, 1837, he exhibited the successful instrument. He petitioned Congress for funds to build a practical working telegraph, but the lawmakers were not interested. More discouraging, neither England, nor Russia, nor France bought his patent. Finally in 1843, after a six year delay, Congress granted funds, and in 1844 Morse's telegraph linked Baltimore and Washington. On May 24th of that year, he tapped out his famous first message, "What hath God wrought?"

See Scott Stamp Nos. 890, 924

925

926

927

928

929

| 925 | .12 | .10 | 3c Philippines | Sep. 27 |

A tribute to the U.S.-Philippine resistance to the Japanese at Corregidor, Jan.-May 1942.

| 926 | .12 | .10 | 3c Motion Picture 50th Anniv. | Oct. 31 |

In 1892, Edison's "Kinetescope," the first motion picture, had its first public showing.

Issues of 1945

| 927 | .10 | .08 | 3c Florida Statehood | Mar. 3 |

Florida became a U.S. territory in 1822; a state in 1845.

| 928 | .10 | .08 | 5c United Nations Conference | Apr. 25 |

The United Nations Conference of April 25, 1945 was a 46 nation effort to establish the U.N. and to draft a charter for it.

DOUGLAS A. MacARTHUR (1880-1964)

On December 8, 1941, one day after the surprise attack on Pearl Harbor, the United States declared war on Japan. In that dark hour the difficult task of defending Allied interests in the Pacific fell to General of the Army Douglas A. MacArthur. The general, who had been first in his 1903 West Point graduating class, proved equal to the task. Though ordered to evacuate the Philippines by President Roosevelt on December 27, his gallant defense of the Bataan Peninsula and Corregidor earned him a Medal of Honor.

When MacArthur assumed control of the Allied Forces in the Southwest Pacific on March 17, 1942, Japan was firmly in control of East Asia. Even so he began to move against the Japanese and by July 1945 the Philippines were once again in his control. He made good his famous promise of 1942, "I shall return."

On September 2, 1945 General MacArthur accepted the Japanese surrender aboard the U. S. S. *Missouri*. Appointed to the post of supreme commander of Allied occupation forces in Japan, MacArthur supervised the reconstruction and democratization of Japan and was greatly loved and respected by his former enemies.

In 1950 MacArthur took charge of the U. N. defending forces in South Korea but was relieved of his command when he openly opposed the president and urged the United States to bomb Communist bases in Manchuria. In 1951 he retired to private life.

See Scott Stamp Nos. 925, 1424

930	931	932	933
	934	935	936

DWIGHT D. EISENHOWER (1890-1969)

The personal history of Dwight D. Eisenhower, General of the Army and 34th President of the United States, parallels the great war which made him a national hero. In 1941, following the Japanese attack on Pearl Harbor, Eisenhower became chief of staff of the war plans division of the Army General Staff in Washington. His superior, General George Marshall, recognized Eisenhower's genius and promoted him to commander general of the European Theater of World War II.

After liberating North Africa from the Axis powers, Eisenhower was named Supreme Commander of Allied Expeditionary Forces (in December, 1943). On June 6, 1944, he directed the landings at Normandy. This decision, he later confessed, was one of the hardest he ever made. In May of 1945 he received Germany's unconditional surrender and returned to Washington as Army Chief of Staff, a post he resigned in 1948 to become president of Columbia University.

Always a popular figure with the American people, Eisenhower was twice elected president, in 1952 and 1956. His administration saw the end of the conflict in Korea, the establishment of the International Atomic Energy Agency, and the creation of a new cabinet post for health, education, and welfare.

See Scott Stamp Nos. 1383, 934

937 | 938

939

941

942

943

944

940 | 945

946

GEORGE S. PATTON (1885-1945)

General George S. Patton, Jr., World War II commander of the Third Army, was one of the most colorful American soldiers of all time. Nicknamed "Old Blood and Guts", Patton was a controversial figure due to his demanding discipline in battle.

The most brilliant phase of his career began at Normandy on D-Day, June 6, 1944. Spearheading the final thrusts of the American forces, he routed the Germans at St. Lô. Moving on toward Germany, Patton's army was the savior of the Allied forces at the Battle of the Bulge. On March 22, 1945 the general and his troops crossed the Rhine into the German heartland, and Allied victory was assured.

See Scott Stamp No. 1026

Belgium Scott No. B610

Belgium
Scott No. B608

937   .10   .04   3c Alfred E. Smith   Nov. 26
Alfred E. Smith (1873-1944) was governor of N. Y.
(1919-20, 1923-28). He was the Democratic Presidential
candidate in 1928.

938   .10   .05   3c Texas Statehood   Dec. 29
Texas became a state in 1845. It had been independent
for nine years.

Issues of 1946

939   .10   .05   3c Merchant Marines   Feb. 26
A tribute to Merchant Mariners who served in World
War II.

940   .10   .04   3c Veterans of World War II   May 9
Issued to honor the Veterans of World War II.

941   .10   .05   3c Tennessee Statehood   Jun. 1
Tennessee became a state in 1796. Stamp shows two
state heroes, Andrew Jackson and John Sevier, first
governor of Tennessee.

942   .10   .05   3c Iowa Statehood   Aug. 3
Iowa became a state in 1846.

943   .10   .05   3c Smithsonian Institution Aug. 10
The Smithsonian Institution in Washington, D. C. was
funded by the will of English scientist John Smithson.
Established in 1846, it houses the national stamp collection and has exhibitions in all areas of science.

944   .10   .05   3c Kearny Expedition   Oct. 16
General Stephen Watts Kearny (1794-1848) captured
Los Angeles and Santa Fe in 1846, thereby bringing
to an end our war with Mexico.

Issues of 1947
Perf. 10-1/2x11

945   .10   .05   3c Thomas A. Edison   Feb. 11
Issued for the 100th anniversary of the birth of Thomas
A. Edison (1847-1931), inventor of the phonograph
and sound movies.

Perf. 11x10-1/2

946   .10   .05   3c Joseph Pulitzer   Apr. 10
Issued for the 100th anniversary of the birth of journalist Joseph Pulitzer (1847-1911). The first Pulitzer Prize
was awarded in 1917.

Monaco Scott No. 355

France No. B400

Germany Scott No. B201

Tunisia Scott No. B132

Mexico Scott No. 826

Monaco Scott No. C16

Monaco Scott No. 202

FRANKLIN DELANO ROOSEVELT
(1882-1945)

Franklin D. Roosevelt, the 32nd president of the United States, guided Americans through the worst economic depression and the worst war in the country's history.

In 1932 when he was first elected to the office he would hold for twelve years, the country was caught in a critical economic crisis. During the historic first "Hundred Days" of his administration, he pushed thirteen emergency measures into law and the country was on its way to recovery. Early legislation included passage of the Social Security Act.

Roosevelt, the World War II leader, knew the horrors of war and dreamed of peace. In 1944, when he was elected president for the fourth and final time, he began to plan for the establishment of a United Nations. By 1945 his dream appeared to be coming true. World War II was coming to an end and delegates from countries all around the globe were about to meet in San Francisco to draw up the United Nations Charter. On April 12, however, shortly before this gathering took place, Roosevelt died of a cerebral hemorrhage while writing at his desk.

Throughout his life Roosevelt was an avid stamp collector. He once had this to say about his hobby: *"The best thing about stamp collecting is that the enthusiasm which it arouses in youth increases as the years pass. It dispels boredom, enlarges the vision, broadens our knowledge, and in innumerable ways enriches our life. I also commend stamp collecting because I really believe it makes one a better citizen."*

See Scott Stamp Nos. 930-933

Philippines Scott No. 544

France Scott No. 1078

Germany Scott No. 9NB6

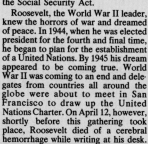

Hungary Scott No. 1261a

Indonesia Scott No. 642

THE U. S. S. CONSTITUTION

They nicknamed her "Old Ironsides." She was the greatest ship of her age—a 44-gun frigate of the United States Navy launched in 1797. An impenetrable hulk in battle, the 204-ft. *Constitution* sailed through conflicts with the Barbary pirates in 1802 and 1804. In the War of 1812 she was under Isaac Hull's command when, she won a brilliant victory against H. M. S. *Guerrière* on August 19, 1812. On that day she razed the British ship in two and one-half hours. In 1830 "Old Ironsides" was declared unseaworthy, but Americans everywhere protested her condemnation. Due to their efforts the ship was pre-served and now rests in the Boston harbor.

See Scott Stamp No. 951

947   .10   .05   3c Postage Stamp 100th Anniv.   May 17

The first United States postage stamps were issued in 1847. This stamp shows Washington and Franklin, who appeared on the first issues, plus different methods used to deliver mail.

Imperf.

948   .60   .40   Souvenir sheet of two   May 19
948a   .25   .15   5c blue, single stamp, sia 1
948b   .35   .20   10c brn. org., single stamp, sia 2

Issued in sheets of two with marginal inscription commemorating the 100th anniversary of U.S. postage stamps and the Centenary International Philatelic Exhibition, held in New York in 1947.

Perf. 11x10-1/2

949   .10   .05   3c Doctors Issue   Jun. 9

This issue honors the American Medical Association on its 100th anniversary; shows "The Doctor" by Sir Luke Fildes.

950   .10   .05   3c Utah Issue   Jul. 24

The settlement of Utah began in 1847. The stamp shows Mormon pioneers entering the state.

951   .10   .05   3c U.S. Frigate Constitution   Oct. 21

Issued for the 150th anniversary of the launching of the U. S. Frigate *Constitution* ("Old Ironsides").

947

949

950

948 (includes 948a and 948b)

Perf. 10-1/2x11			

952   .10   .05   3c Everglades Nat'l. Park Dec. 5

The Everglades National Park in Florida was dedicated on Dec. 6, 1947.

Issues of 1948

953   .10   .05   3c Dr. George Washington
                           Carver   Jan. 5

George Washington Carver (1864-1943), noted agricultural chemist. died five years before the stamp was issued.

Perf. 11x10-1/2

954   .10   .05   3c Calif. Gold 100th Anniv.
                                         Jan. 24

In 1848. gold was found in Sutter's Mill in California.

955   .10   .05   3c Mississippi Territory Apr. 7

The Mississippi Territory was established in 1798. It comprised the present states of Mississippi and Alabama.

956   .10   .05   3c Four Chaplains   May 28

George L. Fox, Clark V. Poling, John P. Washington and Alexander D. Goode sacrificed their lives in the sinking of the *S. S. Dorchester*. Feb. 3, 1943, when they gave their life preservers to their fellow passengers.

957   .10   .05   3c Wis. Statehood   May 29

Wisconsin became a state in 1848.

958   .10   .15   5c Swedish Pioneer   Jun. 4

In the nineteenth century. 1-1/2 million Swedish Pioneers helped to settle thirteen states in the Midwest.

THE GOLD AND SILVER RUSHES

In the sixteenth century the thirst for gold lured the Spanish conquistadores to America. In 1848, gold fever struck a second time when a workman named Marshall found gold at Sutter's sawmill in California.

Scrambling around Cape Horn, across the Isthmus of Panama, or over the Great Plains, thousands of "forty-niners" streamed into California. In a few months San Francisco became a city of nearly 25,000 people where eggs sold for $10 a dozen.

Few prospectors became rich, however; more was made by speculations in both goods and land.

The discovery of silver at the Comstock Lode, Nevada in 1859 unleashed the Silver Rush. Virginia City soon became the most famous mining town in the West and by 1873 the Lode had produced its annual maximum of $36 million in silver ore.

See Scott Stamp Nos. 954, 1130

959   .10   .05   3c Progress of Women Jul. 1█
Issued for the first Women's Rights Convention, hel█ in 1848 at Seneca Falls, N.Y. The stamp shows three important leaders of the movement, Lucretia Mot█ Carrie Catt, and Elizabeth Stanton.

Perf. 10-1/2x11

960   .10   .06   3c William Allen White Jul. 3█
Issued to honor William Allen White (1868-1944) American editor and author.

Perf. 11x10-1/2

961   .10   .05 3c U.S.-Canada Friendship Aug. 2█
Issue notes a century of friendship between the United States and Canada.

962   .10   .05   3c Francis Scott Key Aug. 9█
Lawyer Francis Scott Key (1779-1843) composed the "Star-Spangled Banner".

963   .10   .06   3c Salute to Youth   Aug. 1█
Honoring the Youth of America, the nation's "Leaders of Tomorrow."

964   .12   .10   3c Oregon Territory Aug. 14█
The Oregon Territory was established in 1848. The stamp shows pioneers Jason Lee and John McLoughlin.

Perf. 10-1/2x11

965   .12   .08   3c Harlan Fiske Stone Aug. 25█
Issued to honor U.S. Chief Justice Harlan Fiske Stone (1872-1942).

966   .12   .10   3c Palomar Mt. Obs. Aug. 30
Issued for the dedication of Palomar Mountain Observatory, California, home of the 200-inch Hale reflecting telescope, largest in the world.

THE NATIONAL ANTHEM

And the rocket's red glare, the bombs bursting in air...

The stirring battle scene immortalized by Francis Scott Key in the national anthem took place in the War of 1812. In 1814 Key, a young lawyer, went aboard a British ship to plead for the release of a friend held captive there. By a quirk of fate he himself was imprisoned while the ship bombarded Fort McHenry, Maryland. All through the night of September 14 Key watched and prayed that the Americans could withstand the British onslaught. When the morning mist had cleared and he saw the U. S. flag above the fort, Key jotted down the prayer of thanks that became the "Star-Spangled Banner." In 1931 the song became the national anthem.

See Scott Stamp Nos. 962, 1142, 1346

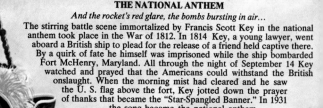

967

968

970

966

969

971

972

MOUNT PALOMAR OBSERVATORY

Ever since Galileo first surveyed the heavens with a telescope, man has tried to learn more about the universe in which he lives.

A giant step in this learning process was the opening in 1948 of the Mount Palomar Observatory in California. Administered by the Carnegie Institute and the California Institute of Technology, Mount Palomar is the home of the Hale reflecting telescope, which boasts a 200 inch mirror (lens). This huge instrument, named for an eminent astronomer, weighs more than 500 tons. The Observatory uses it to look into remote areas of space; astronomers have also used it to photograph distant and faint celestial bodies. The telescope has the light-gathering power of 360,000 times that of the naked eye and is capable of looking two billion light years into space. *See Scott Stamp No. 966*

Italy Scott No. 888

THOMAS A. EDISON (1847-1931)

"Genius is 1% inspiration and 99% perspiration," remarked Thomas Alva Edison, the inventor of the light bulb, the phonograph, and the motion picture machine. Edison's life was the American dream made reality. His formal education lasted three months. At the age of twelve he became a railroad newsboy, then a telegraph operator, experimenting and studying in his spare time. In 1868, at the age of twenty-one, he took out his first patent.

In 1877 Edison became interested in the possibility of an incandescent light bulb. 1,200 experiments later, on October 21, 1879, he produced a bulb which burned steadily for two days. For the next twenty years he worked on methods for the practical use of his invention and eventually developed a bulb with a life of 600 hours.

Edison, the "electrical genius", was an immensely popular hero in his lifetime. His laboratories at Menlo Park, New Jersey, and later at Orange, New Jersey, were flooded with visitors each year. In 1927, he was admitted to the prestigious National Academy of Sciences. A tremendously prolific inventor, Edison was the holder of 1,033 patents.

*See Scott Stamp
Nos. 654-656, 926, 945*

70

983

984

985

986

987

988

		Perf. 10-1/2x11		
975	.10	.08	3c Will Rogers	Nov. 4

Issued in honor of Will Rogers (1879-1935), humorist, philosopher, author, and actor.

| 976 | .15 | .08 | 3c Fort Bliss 100th Anniv. | Nov. 5 |

Fort Bliss, Texas, now a major missile center, was established in 1848.

Perf. 11x10-1/2

| 977 | .10 | .08 | 3c Moina Michael | Nov. 9 |

Moina Michael created the Memorial poppy. Countless numbers of these artificial flowers have been sold to aid disabled veterans.

| 978 | .10 | .08 | 3c Gettysburg Address | Nov. 19 |

Lincoln's famous speech was given in 1863 as a dedication for the military cemetery at Gettysburg, Pennsylvania.

Perf. 10-1/2x11

| 979 | .10 | .08 | 3c American Turners | Nov. 20 |

Issued for the centennial of the American Turners Society, which promotes athletics.

| 980 | .10 | .05 | 3c Joel Chandler Harris | Dec. 9 |

Joel Chandler Harris (1848-1908) created the "Uncle Remus" stories.

Issues of 1949
Perf. 11x10-1/2

| 981 | .10 | .05 | 3c Minnesota Territory | Mar. 3 |

The Minnesota Territory was established in 1849.

| 982 | .10 | .05 | 3c Washington & Lee Univ. | Apr. 12 |

Virginia's Washington and Lee University was established in 1749.

| 983 | .10 | .05 | 3c Puerto Rico Election | Apr. 27 |

In 1949 Luis Muñoz-Marin became Puerto Rico's first elected governor.

| 984 | .10 | .05 | 3c Annapolis 300th Anniv. | May 23 |

Established in 1694, Annapolis, the capital of Maryland, was named for Queen Anne of England.

| 985 | .10 | .05 | 3c Grand Army of the Republic | Aug. 29 |

The final encampment of the Grand Army of the Republic (Civil War Union Veterans) took place in 1949.

Perf. 10-1/2x11

| 986 | .10 | .05 | 3c Edgar Allen Poe | Oct. 7 |

Issued on the 100th anniversary of the death of Edgar Allen Poe (1809-1849), poet and short story author.

Issues of 1950
Perf. 11x10-1/2

| 987 | .10 | .05 | 3c American Bankers Association | Jan. 3 |

Issued for the 75th anniversary of the American Bankers Association.

Perf. 10-1/2x11

| 988 | .10 | .05 | 3c Samuel Gompers | Jan. 27 |

The American labor leader (1850-1924) served as president of the A.F.L. (American Federation of Labor).

GIRL SCOUTS OF AMERICA

On my honour, I will try: to do my duty to God and my country; to help other people at all times...

Girl Scout Promise

The Girl Scouts of America is part of a larger organization called the World Association of Girl Guides and Girl Scouts.

Juliette Gordon Low founded the Girl Scouts in 1912. The group, patterned after the British Guides headed by Lady Baden-Powell, was first called the U. S. Girl Guides, but this name was soon changed.

Including girls from seven to seventeen, today's Scouts have fun while they learn the high ideals of citizenship and morality. Working together for badges that teach valuable skills, Girl Scouts help others while advancing from Brownie and Jr. Scout to Cadette and Senior Scout.

See Scott Stamp Nos. 974, 1199

Montserrat
Scott No. 252

989

990

991

992

993

994

National Capital 150th Anniv. Issue				
Perf. 10-1/2x11, 11x10-1/2				
989	.10	.05	3c Statue of Freedom	
990	.10	.05	3c Executive Mansion	
991	.10	.05	3c Supreme Court Building	
992	.10	.05	3c U. S. Capitol Bldg.	

Washington, D.C., the nation's capital, was 150 years old in 1950. It was built on a site chosen by Washington.

Perf. 11x10-1/2

993	.10	.05	3c Railroad Engineers Apr. 2

Issued to honor the railroad engineers of Americ Stamp shows Casey Jones. who ran the crack "Cannon ball Express."

994	.10	.05	3c Kansas City, Mo.	Jun.

Incorporated in 1850, Kansas City is a leading midwe city known for commerce, industry, and transportatio

THE NATION'S CAPITAL

For the young United States, 1800 meant more than the start of a brand-new century; it also meant the inauguration of a brand-new capital. In that year the Federal Government moved from Philadelphia to Washington, D. C.; from older, finished buildings into partially completed structures made of rough stone and boards.

The new capital city, named for the first President and built on a site chosen by him, was designed by Pierre L'Enfant. Being a far-sighted planner, L'Enfant laid out a design which allowed for growth over the years.

Not so organized, however, were the men who built the Capitol building. They began construction without any detailed architectural plans. When the Capitol, with the White House, was burned by the British in 1814 it had seen only three administrations.

The Capitol we see today was designed and built in 1863 by Charles Bullfinch. The White House, or Executive Mansion, was designed by James Hoban.

A far cry from the boardwalks and mud roads of 1800, Washington is now a lovely city filled with parks and avenues. Its people are constantly in touch with the past as they work for the future.

See Scott Stamp Nos. 989-992, C64

BOY SCOUTS OF AMERICA

A scout is trustworthy, loyal, helpful, friendly…The Scout law.

Sir Robert Baden-Powell, a great lover of outdoor living, is known to countless American boys as the founder of the Boy Scouts. It was he who originated the Scout motto "Be Prepared" and the custom of doing a daily good deed. American William Boyce introduced scouting to America (1910) after being inspired by a British Boy Scout who refused pay for helping him.

The Boy Scouts of America, six-million strong, are organized by age into Cub Scouts (8-10), Boy Scouts (11-13), and Explorer Scouts (14 and older). The Scout, from Tenderfoot to Eagle, is advanced in rank on basis of merit, citizenship, and outstanding adherence to the high Scout ideal.

See Scott Stamp Nos. 995, 1145

995   .10   .05   3c Boy Scouts   Jun. 30
Issued to honor the Boy Scouts of America, whose Second National Jamboree was held in 1950 at Valley Forge, Pennsylvania.

996   .10   .05   3c Indiana Territory   Jul. 4
The Indiana Territory was created in 1800. William Henry Harrison, shown on stamp, was governor of the territory before becoming president of the United States.

997   .10   .05   3c California Statehood Sep. 9
In 1850, California joined the Union.

Issues of 1951

998   .10   .05   3c United Confederate Veterans Final Reunion May 30
The last reunion of the United Confederate Veterans took place in 1951 at Norfolk, Virginia.

999   .10   .05   3c Nevada 100th Anniv. Jul. 14
Nevada was settled in 1851. Stamp shows Carson Valley, named for frontiersman Kit Carson.

1000   .10   .05   3c Landing of Cadillac Jul. 24
Detroit, the "Motor City," was founded by Cadillac in 1701.

1001   .10   .05   3c Colorado Statehood Aug. 1
Colorado became a state in 1876.

1002   .10   .05   3c American Chem. Soc. Sep. 4
One of the world's largest scientific societies the American Chemical Society was established in 1876.

MOUNT RUSHMORE

In the Black Hills of South Dakota, likenesses of four great Americans survey the countryside from the granite cliffs of Mount Rushmore. The sixty-feet high busts of Washington, Jefferson, Theodore Roosevelt, and Lincoln are the work of sculptor Gutzon Borglum (1867-1941).

Borglum died before the awesome effigies were finished, but his son, Lincoln, and a team of dedicated helpers completed his work. The colossal faces, designed to a scale of men 465 feet tall, were blasted from rock with dynamite, then drilled to perfection.

Mount Rushmore, located near Rapid City, South Dakota, rises more than a mile above sea level and juts over 500 feet above the narrow valley at its base. The monument, one of the country's most famous landmarks, attracts thousands of visitors each year.

See Scott Stamp No. 1011

1003 .10 .05 3c Battle of Brooklyn Dec. 10
In 1776 Washington saved his troops at Brooklyn in the Battle of Long Island.

1004 .10 .05 3c Betsy Ross Jan. 2
Issued for the 200th anniversary of the birth of Betsy Ross. According to legend, she made the first official U. S. Flag in 1777.

1005 .10 .05 3c 4-H Club Jan. 15
The 4-H Club movement works to improve the head, heart, hands and health of the nation's youth.

Issues of 1952

1006 .10 .05 3c B&O Railroad Feb.
Chartered in 1827, the B&O used horse-drawn cars carry its first passengers. Stamp also shows the lin first steam engine, the "Tom Thumb", and a mode diesel.

1007 .10 .05 3c American Auto. Assn. Ma
Issued to promote highway safety on the 50th a versary of the American Automobile Association.

1008 .10 .03 3c NATO Ap
The North Atlantic Treaty Organization is a mu defense pact for the Western European natio Canada and the United States. It was created in 19

1003   1004   1005

1006   1008   1007

74

1009

1010

1011

1013

1012

1014

009	.10	.05	3c Grand Coulee Dam May 15	

Issued on the 50th anniversary of the U.S. Bureau of Reclamation, this stamp shows Grand Coulee Dam, one of the largest in the world.

010	.10	.05	3c General Lafayette	Jun. 13

Lafayette came to America in 1777 to help the fledgling Continental Army in its fight for independence from Great Britain.

Perf. 10-1/2x11

011	.10	.05	3c Mt. Rushmore Mem.	Aug. 11

Mount Rushmore, in South Dakota, is famous for its giant busts of Lincoln, Washington, Jefferson and Theodore Roosevelt.

Perf. 11x10-1/2

1012	.10	.05	3c Engineering Anniversary	Sep. 6

The two bridges illustrated on this stamp symbolize 100 years of civil engineering progress in America. One is an early covered wooden bridge; the other, the modern George Washington Bridge between New Jersey and New York.

1013	.10	.05	3c Service Women	Sep. 11

Issued as a tribute to the women members of the Army, Navy, Air Force and Marines.

1014	.10	.05	3c Gutenberg Bible	Sep. 30

Johann Gutenberg (c. 1397-1468) printed the first book from movable type in 1456. This was the Holy Bible.

MARQUIS DE LAFAYETTE (1757-1834)

In 1777 the Marquis de Lafayette, a French nobleman, equipped a ship at his own expense and sailed to the United States to help the Americans win the Revolutionary War.

A young and wealthy idealist in the cause of liberty, Lafayette volunteered his services to General Washington. One month before his 20th birthday Congress made him a major general in Washington's army.

Although Lafayette was an able soldier, his most valuable service to the Continental Army was political. In 1779 he returned to France and persuaded King Louis XVI to send a naval force under Rochambeau to the United States. Rochambeau's aid was crucial to the American victory at Yorktown.

Following Cornwallis' surrender in 1781, Lafayette returned to France, where he later became involved in the French Revolution. A moderate who wished to retain the monarchy, Lafayette was imprisoned from 1792-97. In 1824 he returned to the United States for a one year triumphal tour — a renewal of his friendship with a grateful American people.

See Scott Stamp Nos. 1010, 1097

| 1015 | .10 | .05 | 3c Newspaper Boys | Oc |

Issued "In recognition of the important service rendered their communities and their nation by Amer
newspaper boys."

| 1016 | .10 | .05 | 3c Red Cross | Nov |

The International Red Cross was created in 1864
Geneva Convention at the urging of Jean Dunant,
first Nobel Peace Prize Winner.

Issues of 1953

| 1017 | .10 | .05 | 3c National Guard | Feb. |

A tribute to the National Guard which serves
United States in peace and war.

| 1018 | .10 | .05 | 3c Ohio Statehood | Ma |

Ohio joined the Union as the seventeenth state in 18

| 1019 | .10 | .05 | 3c Washington Territory | |
| | | | | Ma |

Organized on March 2, 1853 the Washington Te
tory was carved from the Pacific Northwest by co
geous pioneers who went there to settle and b
homes.

| 1020 | .10 | .05 | 3c Louisiana Purchase | Apr. |

Issued for the 150th anniversary of the Louisia
Purchase.

| 1021 | .15 | .10 | 5c Opening of Japan 100th | |
| | | | Anniversary | Jul. |

In 1853, Commodore Matthew Perry negotiated
first U.S.-Japanese trade agreement.

NEW YORK CITY

Give my regards to Broadway..
George M. Cohan

Broadway, Wall Street, the Empire
State Building, and Lincoln Center!
All the sights and sounds of America's
largest city typify the twentieth century. But even a giant has humble
beginnings.

In 1626 Peter Minuet, an enterprising
Dutchman, bought Manhattan Island
for $24. The island, named New
Amsterdam by the Dutch, became
New York when it was granted to the
English Duke of York in 1664.

The scene of Washington's inauguration and the nation's capital from
1785 to 1790, New York City is now a
huge metropolis. Each of its five
boroughs — Manhattan, Brooklyn, the
Bronx, Queens, and Staten Island — is
large enough to be a city in itself.
Representing almost every culture in
the world, its eight million residents
look upon their home as the cultural
and commercial capital of the country.

See Scott Stamp Nos.
614, 1027, C38

.10 .05 3c American Bar Assn. Aug. 24
Issued for the American Bar Association's 75th anniversary, this stamp depicts four symbolic figures representing "Wisdom," "Justice," "Truth," and "Divine Inspiration."

.10 .05 3c Sagamore Hill Sep. 14
Sagamore Hill, Theodore Roosevelt's home in Oyster Bay, N. Y. was opened as a national shrine in 1953.

.10 .05 3c Future Farmers Oct. 13
Issued on the 25th anniversary of the Future Farmers of America.

.10 .05 3c Trucking Industry Oct. 27
The American Trucking Association was created in 1903.

.10 .05 3c General Patton Nov. 11
General George S. Patton, Jr. (1885-1945) commanded the Third Army in the Second World War.

.10 .05 3c New York City 300th
Anniversary Nov. 20
Settled by the Dutch in the 17th century, New York City is the nation's largest city.

.10 .05 3c Gadsden Purchase Dec. 30
The 1853 Gadsden Purchase adjusted the boundary between Mexico and the United States.

Issues of 1954

.08 .05 3c Columbia U. 200th
Anniversary Jan. 4
Columbia University was founded in 1754 as Kings College. Stamp depicts the school's Low Memorial Library.

THE FFA AND 4-H CLUBS

Two of the largest rural youth service organizations in the United States are the Future Farmers of America (FFA) and the 4-H Clubs, which offer fun and learning to the leaders of tomorrow.

FFA members gain experience in public speaking, in judging farm products, and in buying and selling cooperatively. The FFA motto is "Learning to do, Doing to learn, Earning to live, Living to serve."

4-H Clubs train boys and girls in agriculture or in homemaking. At present about half the members live on farms; the rest are non-farm rural and urban residents. The four H's stand for "Head, Heart, Hand, and Health."

See Scott Stamp Nos. 1005, 1024

1023

1024

1025

1026

1027

1028

1029

1030

1031

1031A

1032

1033

1034

1035

1036

1037

1038

1039

THE STATUE OF LIBERTY

Give me your tired, your poor,
Your huddled masses yearning to breathe free,
The wretched refuse of your teeming shore,
Send these, the homeless, tempest-tossed, to me;
I lift my lamp beside the golden door... Emma Lazarus

So reads the inscription on the base of the Statue of Liberty; the proud woman who stands at the entrance to the New York harbor.

The Statue of Liberty was presented to the people of the United States by the people of France on July 4, 1884. Since then she has welcomed millions of visitors and immigrants to the United States. In the early part of this century especially, she served as a beacon for the countless Europeans who came to the United States to seek a better life and, in turn, helped make the United States a better country.

The creation of Frederic Auguste Bartholdi, the Statue of Liberty is the largest statue ever made. She stands 151 feet high and weighs 450,000 pounds. Her right arm holds a great torch and her left arm grasps a tablet bearing the date of the adoption of the Declaration of Independence.

See Scott Stamp Nos. 1041, 1042, 1044A

France
Scott No. B44

			Liberty Issue, 1954-68
			Perf. 11x10-1/2, 10-1/2x11
30	.03	.03	½c Benjamin Franklin
31	.04	.03	1c George Washington
31A	.05	.05	1¼c Palace of the Governors, Santa Fe
32	.05	.04	1½c Mount Vernon
33	.05	.03	2c Thomas Jefferson
34	.06	.05	2½c Bunker Hill Monument and Massachusetts flag
35	.08	.03	3c Statue of Liberty
35a	.50	.30	Booklet pane of six
36	.10	.03	4c Abraham Lincoln
36a	.30	.15	Booklet pane of six
37	.12	.08	4½c The Hermitage
38	.12	.03	5c James Monroe
39	.15	.03	6c Theodore Roosevelt
40	.16	.03	7c Woodrow Wilson

Perf. 11

41	.25	.06	8c Statue of Liberty
42	.20	.03	8c Statue of Liberty redrawn

Perf. 11x10-1/2, 10-1/2x11

42A	.20	.03	8c John J. Pershing
43	.20	.04	9c The Alamo
44	.22	.03	10c Independence Hall

Perf. 11

44A	.30	.06	11c Statue of Liberty

Perf. 11x10-1/2, 10-1/2x11

45	.24	.05	12c Benjamin Harrison
46	.35	.03	15c John Jay

1047	.45	.03	20c Monticello
1048	.55	.03	25c Paul Revere
1049	.65	.08	30c Robert E. Lee
1050	.85	.09	40c John Marshall
1051	1.10	.03	50c Susan B. Anthony
1052	2.25	.06	$1 Patrick Henry

Perf. 11

1053	17.00	2.00	$5 Alexander Hamilton

Coil Stamps
Perf. 10 Vertically

1054	.05	.03	1c dark green Washington, sia 1033

Perf. 10 Horizontally

1054A	.10	.06	1¼c turquoise, Palace of the Governors, Santa Fe, sia 1031A

Perf. 10 Vertically

1055	.06	.03	2c rose carmine Jefferson, sia 1033
1056	.12	.07	2½c gray blue, Bunker Hill Monument and Massachusetts flag, sia 1034
1057	.12	.03	3c deep violet Statue of Liberty, sia 1035
1058	.15	.04	4c red vio. Lincoln, sia 1036

Perf. 10 Horizontally

1059	.20	.10	4½c blue green Hermitage, sia 1037

Perf. 10 Vertically

1059A	.60	.20	25c grn. P. Revere, sia 1048

			Issues of 1954, Perf. 11x10-1/2	
1060	.08	.05	3c Nebraska Territory	May

The Nebraska Territory was created in 1854 under terms of the Kansas-Nebraska Act, which gave settlers free choice in the slavery issue.

| **1061** | .08 | .05 | 3c Kansas Territory | May |

The Kansas Territory was established in 1854.

Perf. 10-1/2x11

| **1062** | .08 | .05 | 3c George Eastman | Jul. |

Inventor and philanthropist, George Eastman was born in 1854.

Perf. 11x10-1/2

| **1063** | .08 | .05 | 3c Lewis and Clark Expedition | |
| | | | | Jul. |

The 1804-06 Lewis and Clark Expedition charted much of the Louisiana Territory, purchased by the U.S. in 1803.

Issues of 1955, Perf. 10-1/2x11

| **1064** | | .05 | 3c Pa. Academy of Fine Arts | |
| | | | | Jan. |

The Pennsylvania Academy of Fine Arts was founded in 1805 by artist Charles Willson Peale, whose self-portrait is depicted on the stamp.

Perf. 11x10-1/2

| **1065** | .08 | .05 | 3c Land Grant Colleges | Feb. |

The first two U.S. land grant colleges, Michigan State University and Pennsylvania State University, were established in 1855.

| **1066** | .20 | .10 | 8c Rotary International | Feb. |

Issued to honor the 50th anniversary of Rotary International.

| **1067** | .08 | .04 | 3c Armed Forces Res. | May |

A tribute to the Armed Forces Reserve.

Perf. 10-1/2x11

| **1068** | .08 | .04 | 3c New Hampshire | Jun. |

Immortalized by Hawthorne as "The Great Stone Face," the "Old Man of the Mountains," shown on the stamp, is New Hampshire's best-known scenic wonder.

GEORGE EASTMAN (1854-1932)

George Eastman was an American industrialist and philanthropist who made photography possible as an everyday hobby. While a basic camera had taken pictures as early as 1826, it was Eastman who improved the dryplate process and invented flexible film which could be wound in a camera. It was also Eastman who brought forth the famous Kodak in 1888. This simple box camera sold for $25 and revolutionized photography.

A business pioneer throughout his life, Eastman invested in large-scale advertising, industrial research, and other projects. Throughout the years he donated over $100 million to leading colleges and universities, including the Massachusetts Institute of Technology, the University of Rochester, and the Eastman School of Music.

See Scott Stamp No. 1062

1069

1072

1068

1073

Perf. 11x10-1/2

69 .08 .04 3c Soo Locks Jun. 28
The Soo Locks of the Sault Ste. Marie Canal link Lake Huron and Lake Superior. They were opened in 1855.

70 .08 .04 3c Atoms for Peace Jul. 28
Issued to promote Eisenhower's Atoms for Peace policy, this stamp quotes a speech he made to the U.N. on the peaceful uses of atomic energy.

1070

71 .08 .04 3c Fort Ticonderoga Sep. 18
Fort Ticonderoga was the scene of many battles in the Revolution and the French and Indian War. In one of the most famous of these, Ethan Allen, shown on stamp, stormed the Fort and won it from the British in 1775.

Perf. 10-1/2x11

72 .08 .04 3c Andrew W. Mellon Dec. 20
Born in 1855, Andrew Mellon was a noted financier, industrialist and philanthropist.

Issues of 1956

73 .08 .04 3c Benjamin Franklin Jan. 17
Issued on the 250th anniversary of the birth of Benjamin Franklin.

1071

Perf. 11x10-1/2

74 .08 .04 3c Booker T. Washington Apr. 5
Black educator Booker T. Washington was born in 1856. Stamp shows cabin similar to his birthplace.

Fifth International Philatelic Exhibition
Souvenir Sheet, Imperf.

75 3.50 2.50 Sheet of two Apr. 28
75a 1.25 .80 3c dp. vio., sia 1035
75b 1.65 1.10 8c dk. vio. bl. & car., sia 1041
Issued in sheets of two with marginal inscription commemorating the Fifth International Philatelic Exhibition held in New York City.

Perf. 11x10-1/2

76 .08 .04 3c New York Coliseum and
Columbus Monument Apr. 30
Stamp honors the opening of the New York Coliseum and the Fifth International Philatelic Exhibition held there in 1956.

1074

1075

1076

1077

1078

1079

1080

1082

1081

1083

Wildlife Conservation Issue

1077	.08	.04	3c Wild Turkey	May
1078	.08	.04	3c Pronghorn Antelope	Jun.
1079	.08	.04	3c King Salmon	Nov.

The Wildlife Conservation Series calls attention to t need to save our wildlife from extinction. King Salmo pronghorn antelope and the wild turkey have bee helped by conservationists.

Perf. 10-1/2x11
1080	.08	.04	3c Pure Food and Drug Laws	Jun.

Chemist Harvey W. Wiley, shown on stamp, helpe enact the first Pure Food and Drug Act in 1906.

Perf. 11x10-1/2
1081	.08	.04	3c Wheatland	Aug.

Wheatland was the home of President James Buchana (1791-1868). It is located in Lancaster, Pa.

Perf. 10-1/2x11
1082	.08	.04	3c Labor Day	Sep.

Labor Day has been a U.S. legal holiday since 189

Perf. 11x10-1/2
1083	.08	.04	3c Nassau Hall	Sep. 2

Constructed in 1756. Nassau Hall is Princeton Un versity's most famous building.

Perf. 10-1/2x11
1084	.08	.04	3c Devils Tower	Sep. 2

In 1906 Devils Tower in Wyoming became the firs U.S. national monument.

Perf. 11x10-1/2
1085	.08	.04	3c Children's Issue	Dec. 1

Designed by a high school student, this stamp pro motes friendship as the key to peace throughout th world.

Issues of 1957
1086	.08	.04	3c Alexander Hamilton	Jan. 1

Issued for the 200th anniversary of the birth o Alexander Hamilton.

Perf. 10-1/2x11
1087	.08	.04	3c Polio Issue	Jan. 1

A tribute to the March of Dimes and the Nationa Foundation for Infantile Paralysis.

WILDLIFE CONSERVATION

To waste, to destroy, our natural resources, to skin and exhaust the land...will result in undermining (it) in the days of our children... Theodore Roosevelt

Today forty-four species of U. S. wildlife, victims of man's thoughtlessness, are in danger of extinction. Once the private cause of a few dedicated conservationists, the preservation of our wildlife has become the public will. Stringent measures are being taken to protect world wildlife. Laws now protect the fur seal whose numbers were decimated in the 19th century. In 1969 President Nixon signed the Endangered Species Conservation Act, which prohibits the import into the U. S. of skins (or trophies) of any wildlife threatened with extinction. Integral to the conservation of wildlife is the preservation of its sanctuaries. During the 1960's sixty-four new additions were made to the national parks and forests.

See Scott Stamp Nos. 1077-1079, 1098, 1306, 1362, 1427-1430

1085

1086

1084

1087

1090

Perf. 11x10-1/2

.08 .04 3c Coast and Geodetic Survey
Feb. 11

The Coast and Geodetic Survey, established in 1807, charts coasts and navigation routes; records tides.

.08 .04 3c Architects Feb. 23

The American Institute of Architects was created in 1857.

Perf. 10-1/2x11

.08 .04 3c Steel Industry May 22

The U. S. is one of the world's leading steel producers. The industry is 100 years old in 1957.

Perf. 11x10-1/2

.08 .04 3c Int'l. Naval Review Jun. 10

The International Naval Review was held in 1957 in connection with the 250th anniversary of Jamestown, Virginia.

.08 .04 3c Oklahoma Statehood Jun. 14

From 1828 to 1846, Oklahoma was an Indian Reservation. In 1907 it became a state.

.08 .04 3c School Teachers Jul. 1

A tribute to the school teachers of America.

Perf. 11

.12 .08 4c Flag Issue Jul. 4

This stamp which depicts the 48-star flag was the first U.S. issue printed by Giori Press. The press can print three colors simultaneously.

Perf. 10-1/2x11

.08 .04 3c Shipbuilding Aug. 15

The "Virginia of Saeadahock," the first U.S. international trading vessel, was constructed in 1607.

Perf. 11

.18 .15 8c Champion of Liberty Aug. 31

Ramon Magsaysay, honored here, was president of the Philippines from 1953 to 1957.

Perf. 10-1/2x11

.08 .04 3c Lafavette Sep. 6

Issued for the 200th anniversary of the birth of the Marquis de Lafayette.

1088

1089

1091

1092

1093

1094

1095

1096

1097

ABRAHAM LINCOLN (1809-65)

With malice toward none; with charity for all...let us strive to finish the work we are in; to bind up the nation's wounds...Second Inaugural Address

On the eve of the Civil War Abraham Lincoln became the sixteenth president of the United States. On a bleak March day the new President took his oath "to preserve, protect and defend" the Union. Six weeks later the guns of Fort Sumter challenged the existence of that Union.

Despite dissension in the Cabinet and Congress, Lincoln's wise and just leadership carried the nation through the war. He claimed special powers which he felt were necessary in this unique crisis. "The moment came," he said, "when I felt that slavery must die that the nation might live." So, not waiting for congressional action, Lincoln freed all slaves by the Emancipation Proclamation on January 1, 1863.

Lincoln's attitude toward the defeated South typified his great humanity. At the war's end he urged charity and reconciliation between the North and South. The assassin's bullet fired by John Wilkes Booth on April 14, 1865, however, was to change the course of Reconstruction.

See Scott Stamp Nos. 367-369, 906, 978, 1113-1116, C59

Perf. 11

098 | .08 | .04 | 3c Wildlife Conservation Nov. 22
The almost extinct whooping crane points up urgent need for wildlife conservation.

Perf. 10-1/2x11

099 | .08 | .04 | 3c Religious Freedom Dec. 27
The Flushing Remonstrance of 1657 helped create religious freedom in America.

Issues of 1958

100 | .08 | .04 | 3c Gardening-Horticulture Mar. 15
Horticulture issue honors birth in 1858 of botanist Liberty Hyde Bailey.

Perf. 11x10-1/2

104 | .08 | .04 | 3c Brussels Fair Apr. 17
Issued for the opening of the Brussels World's Fair, this stamp shows the United States Pavilion at the Fair.

105 | .08 | .04 | 3c James Monroe Apr. 28
Issued for the 200th anniversary of the birth of James Monroe (1758-1831), fifth president of the United States.

106 | .08 | .04 | 3c Minnesota Statehood May 11
Minnesota became a state in 1858.

Perf. 11

107 | .08 | .04 | 3c Geophysical Year May 31
The International Geophysical Year of 1957-58 was a team effort by world scientists for research and discovery. The stamp shows part of Michelangelo's famous fresco, "The Creation of Adam."

Perf. 11x10-1/2

108 | .08 | .04 | 3c Gunston Hall Jun. 12
Gunston Hall was the Virginia home of George Mason (1725-92), author of Virginia's constitution.

Perf. 10-1/2x11

109 | .08 | .04 | 3c Mackinac Bridge Jun. 25
Dedicated in 1958, the Mackinac Bridge connects the two peninsulas of Michigan.

110 | .08 | .04 | 4c Champion of Liberty Jul. 24

Perf. 11

111 | .20 | .15 | 8c Champion of Liberty
Simon Bolivar (1783-1830) liberated much of South America from Spanish domination.

Perf. 11x10-1/2

1112 | .08 | .04 | 4c Atlantic Cable 100th Anniversary Aug. 15
The first Atlantic cable, between London and New York was finished in 1858.

Lincoln 150th Anniv. Issue, 1958-59
Perf. 10-1/2x11, 11x10-1/2

1113 | .05 | .05 | 1c Portrait by George Healy
1114 | .10 | .06 | 3c Sculptured Head by Gutzon Borglum
1115 | .10 | .05 | 4c Lincoln and Stephen Douglas Debating
1116 | .10 | .05 | 4c Statue in Lincoln Memorial by Daniel Chester French
Issued for the 150th anniversary of the birth of Abraham Lincoln.

Issues of 1958
Perf. 10-1/2x11

1117 | .08 | .04 | 4c Champion of Liberty Sep. 19

Perf. 11

1118 | .20 | .12 | 8c Champion of Liberty
Lajos Kossuth (1802-1892), patriot of Hungary, was a leading figure in that nation's revolution.

Perf. 10-1/2x11

1119 | .08 | .04 | 4c Freedom of Press Sep. 22
The world's first journalism school was established in 1908 at the University of Missouri.

Perf. 11x10-1/2

1120 | .08 | .04 | 4c Overland Mail Oct. 10
The first overland mail coach arrived in San Francisco, California in 1858. It began its journey in Tipton, Missouri.

Perf. 10-1/2x11

1121 | .08 | .04 | 4c Noah Webster Oct. 16
Noah Webster (1758-1843) was a noted scholar and a lexicographer.

Perf. 11

1122 | .08 | .04 | 4c Forest Conservation Oct. 27
Issued on the 100th anniversary of the birth of Theodore Roosevelt, an ardent conservationist.

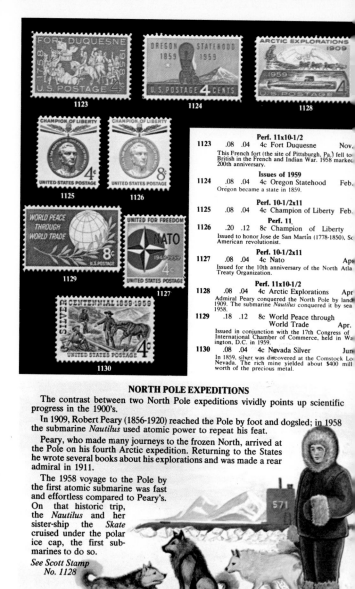

		Perf. 11x10-1/2		
1123	.08	.04	4c Fort Duquesne	Nov.

This French fort (the site of Pittsburgh, Pa.) fell to British in the French and Indian War. 1958 marked 200th anniversary.

Issues of 1959

1124	.08	.04	4c Oregon Statehood	Feb.

Oregon became a state in 1859.

Perf. 10-1/2x11

1125	.08	.04	4c Champion of Liberty	Feb.

Perf. 11

1126	.20	.12	8c Champion of Liberty	

Issued to honor Jose de San Martín (1778-1850), So American revolutionist.

Perf. 10-1/2x11

1127	.08	.04	4c Nato	Apr

Issued for the 10th anniversary of the North Atla Treaty Organization.

Perf. 11x10-1/2

1128	.08	.04	4c Arctic Explorations	Apr

Admiral Peary conquered the North Pole by land 1909. The submarine *Nautilus* conquered it by sea 1958.

1129	.18	.12	8c World Peace through	
			World Trade	Apr.

Issued in conjunction with the 17th Congress of International Chamber of Commerce, held in Wa ington, D.C. in 1959.

1130	.08	.04	4c Nevada Silver	Jun

In 1859, silver was discovered at the Comstock Lo Nevada. The rich mine yielded about $400 mill worth of the precious metal.

NORTH POLE EXPEDITIONS

The contrast between two North Pole expeditions vividly points up scientific progress in the 1900's.

In 1909, Robert Peary (1856-1920) reached the Pole by foot and dogsled; in 1958 the submarine *Nautilus* used atomic power to repeat his feat.

Peary, who made many journeys to the frozen North, arrived at the Pole on his fourth Arctic expedition. Returning to the States he wrote several books about his explorations and was made a rear admiral in 1911.

The 1958 voyage to the Pole by the first atomic submarine was fast and effortless compared to Peary's. On that historic trip, the *Nautilus* and her sister-ship the *Skate* cruised under the polar ice cap, the first submarines to do so.

See Scott Stamp No. 1128

THE ST. LAWRENCE SEAWAY

When French explorers discovered the St. Lawrence River in 1535, they hoped it might be a new route to China. Later pioneers realized its value as a shipping route from the Atlantic Ocean to the Great Lakes. As early as 1895 a Canadian-U. S. commission urged that a deep-sea channel be dredged in the St. Lawrence. The U. S. Congress delayed action for almost sixty years. Finally Canada announced it would proceed alone. Congress, faced with the Canadian challenge, approved the St. Lawrence Seaway Development Corporation in 1954.

The Seaway, 2,300 miles of canals and locks, stretches from the mouth of the St. Lawrence to the western tip of Lake Superior. During construction peaks, the power and navigation works, costing an estimated $1 billion, employed as many as 20,000 men. By July 1, 1958, Ontario and upper New York State received power from the hydroelectric plant at International Rapids. On June 26, 1959, Queen Elizabeth II and President Dwight D. Eisenhower dedicated the completed Seaway, a great river highway to the middle of a continent.

See Scott Stamp No. 1131

Perf. 11

.08 .04 4c St. Lawrence Seaway Jun. 26
This stamp was issued jointly by both Canada and the United States for the opening of the St. Lawrence Seaway.

.08 .05 4c 49-Star Flag Jul. 4
The 49-star flag of 1959 marked Alaska's entry to the Union.

.08 .04 4c Soil Conservation Aug. 26
Contour plowing, shown on stamp, is an effective means of conserving soil.

Perf. 10-1/2x11

.08 .04 4c Petroleum Industry Aug. 27
Oil was found at Titusville, Pa. in 1859 when Col. Drake hit "black gold" at 69-1/2 feet.

Perf. 11x10-1/2

.08 .04 4c Dental Health Sep. 14
The American Dental Association was established in 1859.

Perf. 10-1/2x11

.08 .04 4c Champion of Liberty Sep. 29

Perf. 11

.20 .12 8c Champion of Liberty
Ernst Reuter, honored here, was mayor of Berlin during the blockade of 1948-1949.

Perf. 10-1/2x11

.08 .04 4c Dr. Ephraim McDowell
Dec. 3
Dr. Ephraim McDowell (1771-1830) performed the first operation in ovarian surgery.

1131

1132

1133

1135

1138

1136

1137

1134

Issues of 1960-61, Perf. 11
American Credo Issue

1139	.08	.04	4c Quotation from Washington's Farewell Address
1140	.08	.04	4c B. Franklin Quotation
1141	.08	.04	4c T. Jefferson Quotation
1142	.08	.04	4c Francis Scott Key Quotation
1143	.08	.04	4c Lincoln Quotation
1144	.08	.04	4c Patrick Henry Quotation

Issued to perpetuate and emphasize American ideals.

1145	.08	.04	4c Boy Scout Jubilee Feb. 8

Issued for the 50th anniversary of the founding of the Boy Scouts of America.

Perf. 10-1/2x11

1146	.08	.04	4c Olympic Winter Games Feb. 18

The Olympic Winter Games of 1960 were held in Squaw Valley, California.

Perf.11

1147	.08	.04	4c Champion of Liberty Mar. 7
1148	.20	.12	8c Champion of Liberty

Thomas Masaryk (1850-1937) was the founder and first president of the Czechoslovakian Republic.

Perf. 11x10-1/2

1149	.08	.04	4c World Refugee Year Apr. 7

World Refugee Year lasted from July 1, 1959 until June 30, 1960.

Perf. 11

1150	.08	.04	4c Water Conservation Apr. 18

Water Conservation Issue depicts the ecological water cycle: rain runoff to watershed to reservoir to city use.

Perf. 10-1/2x11

1151	.08	.64	4c Seato May 3

The South-East Asia Treaty Organization is a mutu defense pact for some Asian nations and the U. S.

Perf. 11x10-1/2

1152	.08	.04	4c American Woman Jun.

A tribute to the women of America.

Perf. 11

1153	.10	.06	4c 50-Star Flag Jul.

When Hawaii joined the Union (in 1959) the fiftie star was added to the flag.

Perf. 11x10-1/2

1154	.08	.04	4c Pony Express 100th Anniv. Jul.

The Pony Express was founded in 1860.

Perf. 10-1/2x11

1155	.08	.04	4c Employ the Handicapped Aug. 2

"Employ the Handicapped" was the theme of th Eighth World Congress of the International Societ for the welfare of crippled persons.

	.08	.04	4c World Forestry Congress Aug. 2

The Fifth World Forestry Congress was held i Seattle, Washington in 1960.

Perf. 11

1157	.08	.04	4c Mexican Independence Sep. 1

Issued for the 150th anniversary of Mexica independence.

1158	.08	.04	4c U.S.-Japan Treaty Sep. 2

The U.S. Japan Treaty of Amity and Commerce wa ratified in 1860.

THE PONY EXPRESS
The mail must go through.

In 1861 a Pony Express rider crossed the country in record-breaking time: seven days and seventeen hours. The urgent news he carried was the text of President Abraham Lincoln's first inaugural address. The usual schedule for the mail trip from St. Joseph, Missouri to Placerville, California was eight days, about 24 days faster than the journey of a mail coach traveling by the southern route.

The Pony Express began on the eve of the Civil War as a means of rapid communication between California and the East — a necessity during this time of crisis. Operated by the Overland Mail Company, this legendary mail service had operated for a mere eighteen months when it was replaced by a telegraph line. Even so, it has enjoyed an enduring fame due to the heroism and stamina of the anonymous Pony Express rider. Passing through the hostile Indian country of the Great Plains, this lone horseman braved the snow of the Rockies and the heat of the desert to accomplish his duty: the delivery of the United States Mail.

See Scott Stamp Nos. 894, 1120, 1154

San Marino Scott No. 271 shows the first U.S. postage stamps.

Perf. 11x10-1/2

| 1159 | .08 | .04 | 4c Champion of Liberty | Oct. 8 |

Perf. 11

| 1160 | .20 | .12 | 8c Champion of Liberty |

Issued to honor I. J. Paderewski (1860-1941), Polish pianist and statesman.

Perf. 10-1/2x11

| 1161 | .08 | .04 | 4c Sen. Taft Memorial | Oct. 10 |

Robert A. Taft (1889-1953) was a U. S. Senator from 1939-1953.

| 1162 | .08 | .04 | 4c Wheels of Freedom | Oct. 15 |

Issued in connection with the National Automobile Show, held in Detroit in 1960.

Perf. 11

| 1163 | .08 | .04 | 4c Boys' Clubs of America | Oct. 18 |

The Boys' Clubs of America movement was organized in 1860.

| 1164 | .08 | .04 | 4c Automated P.O. | Oct. 20 |

The first U.S. automated post office opened on October 20, 1960, in Providence, Rhode Island.

Perf. 10-1/2x11

| 1165 | .08 | .04 | 4c Champion of Liberty | Oct. 26 |

Perf. 11

| 1166 | .20 | .12 | 8c Champion of Liberty |

Baron Gustaf Mannerheim (1867-1951) was president of Finland from 1944 to 1946.

| 1167 | .08 | .04 | 4c Camp Fire Girls | Nov. 1 |

The Camp Fire Girls was organized in 1910.

Perf. 10-1/2x11

| 1168 | .08 | .04 | 4c Champion of Liberty | Nov. 2 |

Giuseppe Garibaldi (1807-1882) was a leader in the fight to unify all Italy.

BOYS' CLUBS OF AMERICA

Building boys is better than mending men. The Boys' Clubs motto.

The Boys' Clubs of America is a national organization with a membership of 850,000 urban youth. For minimal dues it offers boys a recreational meeting place which is open after school hours and six days a week. Larger clubs have swimming pools, libraries, gymnasiums, workshops, and clubrooms. When possible Boys' Clubs sponsor summer camps and provide medical examinations to promote good health.

The first Boys' Club was organized in 1860 for the sons of Hartford, Connecticut millworkers. Boys' Clubs now exist throughout the nation. In cities or small towns they serve boys of all backgrounds and ages (from eight years up) and perpetuate high ideals through word, example, and fun.

See Scott Stamp No. 1163

CAMP FIRE GIRLS

Worship God, seek beauty, give service, pursue knowledge, be trustworthy, hold on to health, glorify work, be happy.

The Camp Fire Girl Law.

The Camp Fire Girls were established in 1910 by Luther and Charlotte Gulick of New York City, whose summer camp in Maine was one of the first girls' camps in the country. The group has always emphasized camping, learning by doing, and the giving of service. Since 1910 over four million girls have learned the value and joy of community service through their Camp Fire Girl experience.

The Girls are organized into three age brackets: the Blue Birds (7-10), Camp Fire Girls (10-15), and Horizon Club Girls (15-18). The fun and learning activities are based on the seven crafts: home, creative arts, outdoors, frontiers, business, sports and games, and citizenship. As she progresses from Trail Seeker to Torch Bearer, this wide range of activity helps the Campfire Girl to develop into a good homemaker and citizen, the Camp Fire ideal.

See Scott Stamp No. 1167

Perf. 11

1169   .20   .12   8c Champion of Liberty

Perf. 10-1/2x11

1170   .08   .04   4c Sen. George Memorial Nov. 5

Walter F. George (1878-1957) was Ambassador to NATO and a U.S. Senator.

1171   .08   .04   4c Andrew Carnegie   Nov. 25
Steel magnate Andrew Carnegie (1835-1919) gave $350 million to various educational institutions.

1172   .08   .04   4c John Foster Dulles Memorial Dec. 6

John Foster Dulles (1888-1959) served as Secretary of State under Eisenhower.

Perf. 11x10-1/2

1173   .20   .05   4c Echo 1—Communications for Peace   Dec. 15
The world's first communications satellite, Echo 1, was placed in orbit on August 12, 1960.

Issues of 1961
Perf. 10-1/2x11

1174   .08   .04   4c Champion of Liberty   Jan. 26

Perf. 11

1175   .20   .12   8c Champion of Liberty
Pacifist Mahatma Gandhi (1869-1948) led India to freedom from the British in 1947.

1176   .08   .04   4c Range Conservation   Feb. 2
Issue dramatizes the development of range conservation from the age of the pioneers to the age of modern science.

Perf. 10-1/2x11

1177   .08   .04   4c Horace Greeley   Feb. 3
Journalist Horace Greeley (1811-1872) was editor and publisher of the *N. Y. Tribune*.

1170   1171

1176

1172   1173   1174

1175   1177

Civil War 100th Anniv. Issue, 1961-1965			
		Perf. 11x10-1/2	
1178	.10	.04	4c Fort Sumter Centenary, 196
1179	.10	.04	4c Shiloh Centenary, 1962
		Perf. 11	
1180	.12	.04	5c Gettysburg Centenary, 1963
1181	.12	.04	5c Wilderness Centenary, 1964
1182	.12	.04	5c Appomattox Centenary, 196
Issued for the Civil War Centennial.			

Issues of 1961

1183	.08	.04	4c Kansas Statehood	May
Kansas became a state in 1861.				

Perf. 11x10-1/2

1184	.08	.04	4c Sen. George W. Norris	Jul.
U.S. Senator George Norris (1861-1944) helped fath the Tennessee Valley Authority in 1933.				

THE CIVIL WAR

A house divided against itself cannot stand. Abraham Lincoln

The Civil War (1861-65) was the most costly struggle in the nation's history. Arising out of years of controversy over slavery and states' rights, it tested the right of the South to withdraw from the Union to preserve a way of life.

The cotton culture of the South, made possible by the invention of the cotton gin, was sustained by slavery. As the United States grew and expanded, the question soon arose whether new states entering the Union would be "slave" or "free". Compromise after compromise failed to solve the problem and tempers flared. Wrangling over the status of fugitive slaves, the activities of Northern abolitionists and the repeal of the Missouri Compromise (a "half-slave", "half-free" solution) added fuel to the fire. Southerners began to talk about secession, while a man from Illinois, Abraham Lincoln, argued to preserve the Union.

When Lincoln was elected president in 1860, South Carolina left the Union, followed by Georgia, Alabama, Mississippi, Louisiana, Florida, and Texas. When the Confederates bombarded Charleston's federal Fort Sumter in 1861, Lincoln called for a militia of 75,000 troops to put down the rebellion. This appeal to arms decided the issue for Virginia, Arkansas, North Carolina, and Tennessee, who joined the Confederate States of America.

1183

1184

1187

1188

1189

1185

1185 .08 .04 4c Naval Aviation **Aug. 20**
Issued for the 50th anniversary of Naval aviation.

Perf. 10-1/2x11

1186 .08 .04 4c Workmen's Comp. **Sep. 4**
Issued for the 50th anniversary of the passage of the first successful Workmen's Compensation Law.

Perf. 11

1187 .08 .04 4c Frederic Remington **Oct. 4**
Artist Frederic Remington (1861-1909) captured the "Old West" in sculpture and on canvas. Stamp shows his work "The Smoke Signal."

Perf. 10-1/2x11

1188 .08 .04 4c Republic of China **Oct. 10**
Issued for the 50th anniversary of the Republic of China. Stamp shows Sun Yat-sen (1866-1925), first president of China.

1189 .08 .04 4c Naismith-Basketball **Nov. 6**
James Naismith invented basketball in 1891.

The armed struggle between North and South lasted over four long years, despite the North's superiority in numbers, wealth, industry, and sea power.

Early in the war Lincoln formed a three-fold plan for Union victory. He hoped to capture the Confederate capital at Richmond, take control of the Mississippi River, and blockade all Southern ports. Eventually this strategy was successful; initially it was thwarted by Robert E. Lee.

In 1862 the great Southern general started the campaign that led to Southern victories at Bull Run, Fredericksburg, and Chancellorsville. But when Lee moved north to Pennsylvania he was met by Meade at Gettysburg. The bloody battle fought there in July, 1863 ended in a Union victory and marked the turning point of the war on land.

The turning point of the naval phase of the war took place in March, 1862 when the first ironclad ships, the Northern *Monitor* and the Southern *Merrimac*, clashed at Hampton Roads. While neither ship emerged victorious, the battle was a defeat for the South because it failed to break the North's blockade of the Atlantic coast. This blockade, which cut off valuable supplies and tools, slowly starved the South into submission.

The final phase of the war began in 1864. William Sherman's march to the sea crushed the South's ability and will to fight. General Grant's Wilderness campaign started his relentless thrust to Richmond. Lee's army, decimated by Grant, retreated from Petersburg to Richmond. On April 9, 1865, in Virginia's Appomattox Courthouse, Lee accepted Grant's surrender terms.

See Scott Stamp Nos. 1178-1182

			Perf. 11	
1190	.08	.04	4c Nursing	Dec. 28

A tribute to the nursing profession.

Issues of 1962

| 1191 | .08 | .04 | 4c New Mexico Statehood | Jan. 6 |

This 50th anniversary issue depicts Shiprock, sacred mountain of the Navajos, in New Mexico.

| 1192 | .08 | .04 | 4c Arizona Statehood | Feb. 14 |

In 1912 Arizona joined the Union. Stamp depicts the Arizona desert.

| 1193 | .20 | .10 | 4c Project Mercury | Feb. 20 |

Issued for the first orbital flight of a U.S. astronaut. Flight made by Colonel John Glenn Feb. 20, 1962.

| 1194 | .08 | .04 | 4c Malaria Eradication | Mar. 30 |

Many nations of the world, including the United States, joined the U.N.'s World Health Organization in its fight against malaria.

Perf. 10-1/2x11

| 1195 | .08 | .04 | 4c Charles Evans Hughes | Apr. 11 |

Chief Justice Charles Evans Hughes (1862-1948) also governed the state of New York.

Perf. 11

| 1196 | .08 | .04 | 4c Seattle World's Fair | Apr. 25 |

The "Century 21" International Exposition was held at Seattle in 1962.

| 1197 | .08 | .04 | 4c Louisiana Statehood | Apr. 30 |

In 1812, Louisiana joined the Union.

Perf. 11x10-1/2

| 1198 | .08 | .04 | 4c Homestead Act | May 20 |

The Homestead Act, signed into law by Lincoln in 1862, played a major role in settling the West.

| 1199 | .08 | .04 | 4c Girl Scout Jubilee | Jul. 24 |

Issued for the 50th anniversary of the founding of the Girl Scouts of America.

| 1200 | .08 | .04 | 4c Sen. Brien McMahon | Jul 28 |

Senator Brien McMahon of Connecticut authored the McMahon Act for the peaceful uses of atomic energy.

| 1201 | .08 | .04 | 4c Apprenticeship | Aug. 31 |

Enacted under the New Deal, the National Apprenticeship Act trained people in industry.

Perf. 11

| 1202 | .08 | .04 | 4c Sam Rayburn | Sep. 16 |

Sam Rayburn of Texas (1882-1961) was Speaker of the House of Representatives for 17 years.

| 1203 | .08 | .04 | 4c Dag Hammarskjold | Oct. 23 |

Swedish diplomat Dag Hammarskjold was Secretary General of the United Nations from 1953 until his death in 1961.

| 1204 | .15 | .08 | 4c Hammarskjold Special Printing; black, brown & yellow (yellow inverted) | |

| 1205 | .08 | .03 | 4c Christmas Issue | Nov. 1 |
| 1206 | .08 | .04 | 4c Higher Education | Nov. 14 |

Issued as a tribute to U.S. colleges and universities.

| 1207 | .08 | .04 | 4c Winslow Homer | Dec. 15 |

Artist Winslow Homer (1836-1910) was best-known for seascapes such as "Breezing Up," shown on stamp.

Flag Issue of 1963-66

| 1208 | .12 | .03 | 5c Flag over White House | |

Regular Issue of 1962-66

Perf. 11x10-1/2

| 1209 | .03 | .03 | 1c Andrew Jackson | |

THE HOMESTEAD ACT

Go west, young man. Attributed to Horace Greeley

The Homestead Act of 1862 opened the West to small farmers. The law provided that for ten dollars a settler could file a claim on 160 acres of land in the public domain. After having "resided upon or cultivated" the land for five years, he could then receive a deed. Within forty years of the passage of the Act, half a million families had found new homes in the West. When the Cherokee Strip in Oklahoma was opened to settlement on April 22, 1889, about 20,000 people entered the race for land.

Despite its advantages, homesteading was a risky adventure. Unscrupulous promoters paid drifters to stake claims on the best land to control timber, minerals, and water rights. Between 1862 and 1890 only one farmer in three kept his property.

See Scott Stamp No. 1198

ELEANOR ROOSEVELT (1884-1962)

Anna Eleanor Roosevelt, humanitarian and diplomat, was the wife of Franklin D. Roosevelt. As First Lady she defied tradition by writing a syndicated column, "My Day", and by touring prisons, coal mines, and military bases all over the world. As a delegate to the United Nations, she headed its Commission on Human Rights (1945-51). Her work for world peace and human rights earned her the title "First Lady of the World".

See Scott Stamp No. 1236

Jamaica Scott No. 239.

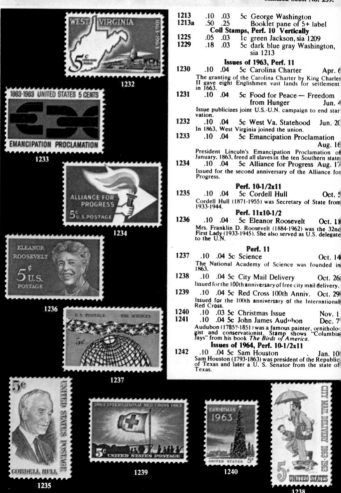

1213	.10	.03	5c George Washington		
1213a	.50	.25	Booklet pane of 5+ label		
Coil Stamps, Perf. 10 Vertically					
1225	.05	.03	1c green Jackson, sia 1209		
1229	.18	.03	5c dark blue gray Washington, sia 1213		

Issues of 1963, Perf. 11

1230	.10	.04	5c Carolina Charter	Apr. 6

The granting of the Carolina Charter by King Charles II gave eight Englishmen vast lands for settlement in 1663.

1231	.10	.04	5c Food for Peace — Freedom from Hunger	Jun. 4

Issue publicizes joint U.S.-U.N. campaign to end starvation.

1232	.10	.04	5c West Va. Statehood	Jun. 20

In 1863, West Virginia joined the union.

1233	.10	.04	5c Emancipation Proclamation	Aug. 16

President Lincoln's Emancipation Proclamation of January, 1863, freed all slaves in the ten Southern states.

1234	.10	.04	5c Alliance for Progress	Aug. 17

Issued for the second anniversary of the Alliance for Progress.

Perf. 10-1/2x11

1235	.10	.04	5c Cordell Hull	Oct. 5

Cordell Hull (1871-1955) was Secretary of State from 1933-1944.

Perf. 11x10-1/2

1236	.10	.04	5c Eleanor Roosevelt	Oct. 11

Mrs. Franklin D. Roosevelt (1884-1962) was the 32nd First Lady (1933-1945). She also served as U.S. delegate to the U.N.

Perf. 11

1237	.10	.04	5c Science	Oct. 14

The National Academy of Science was founded in 1863.

1238	.10	.04	5c City Mail Delivery	Oct. 26

Issued for the 100th anniversary of free city mail delivery.

1239	.10	.04	5c Red Cross 100th Anniv.	Oct. 29

Issued for the 100th anniversary of the International Red Cross.

1240	.10	.03	5c Christmas Issue	Nov. 1
1241	.10	.04	5c John James Audubon	Dec. 7

Audubon (1785?-1851) was a famous painter, ornithologist and conservationist. Stamp shows "Columbia Jays" from his book *The Birds of America*.

Issues of 1964, Perf. 10-1/2x11

1242	.10	.04	5c Sam Houston	Jan. 10

Sam Houston (1793-1863) was president of the Republic of Texas and later a U. S. Senator from the state of Texas.

Togo Scott No. 601

Ghana Scott No. 191

Haiti Scott No. C313

Montserrat Scott No. 207

Liberia Scott No. 397

Dominican Republic Scott No. 475

Burundi Scott No. C92

THE BLACK AMERICAN

Whether the first Black man came to the United States in 1526 as a Spanish slave or in 1619 on a Dutch Man-of-War has yet to be determined. What is clear is that the Black American has risen from the bonds of slavery to contribute to the growth of the United States in many spheres.

In all fields — from science to sports — he has left his mark. The scientist George Washington Carver revolutionized agriculture in the South, adding the peanut, sweet potato, and soybean to its one-crop cotton economy. Dr. Daniel Hale Williams performed one of the first two open-heart operations in 1893. Dr. Charles Richard Drew pioneered in the development of blood banks. In 1959 Lorraine Hansberry won the New York Drama Critics Circle award for "Raisin in the Sun", an ever-popular American drama . In the 1936 Olympics Jesse Owens won four gold medals. Twice, in less than forty years, the Nobel Peace Prize has been awarded to Black Americans — Dr. Ralph Bunche and Dr. Martin Luther King, Jr.

Paralleling the Black American's contribution in peace has been his service in war: about 5,000 served in the Continental Army, some 200,000 in the Union Army, 367,000 in World War I, and more than a million in World War II.

See Scott Stamp Nos. 873, 953, 1074, 1233, 1290, 1372

1241

1242

1243

1244

1245

Jordan
Scott No. 506

Ajman Scott No. 24

CORREOS DE EL SALVADOR

El Salvador Scott No. 749

Ajman Scott No. 22

DUBAI AIR MAIL 1 R
Dubai
Scott No. C26

Nigeria Scott No. 160

JOHN F. KENNEDY (1917-1963)

Those who make peaceful revolution impossible will make violent revolution inevitable. John F. Kennedy

John F. Kennedy, who became the 35th president of the United States in 1961 at the age of 43, was the youngest man to be elected chief executive. During his brief term in office his quick wit, magnetic personality, and style injected new and hopeful vigor into politics.

He put young men, most in their 30's and 40's, in the chief posts of his administration, which he called the "New Frontier". He established the Peace Corps, which was enthusiastically received. He proposed comprehensive legislation in the field of civil rights, a continuation of the movement of the Eisenhower era.

Internationally his short administration was beset by crises, including the Bay of Pigs invasion of Cuba, the erection of the Berlin Wall, and the Cuban missile crisis, when the United States and the Soviet Union stood on the brink of war.

Late in 1962 the United States learned that the Soviet Union had fortified Cuba with offensive missiles. In response the young president imposed a naval quarantine on all shipments of arms from the U.S.S.R. to Cuba. Two weeks of negotiations followed, after which Premier Khrushchev agreed to dismantle the bases.

The Kennedy era came to a tragic end on November 22, 1963, when the president was assassinated by Lee Harvey Oswald in Dallas, Texas.

See Scott Stamp No. 1246

REPUBLIQUE RWANDAISE 8F
Rwanda Scott No. 134

L.130 SAN MARINO
San Marino
Scott No. 608

REPUBLIQUE DE CÔTE D'IVOIRE 100F
Ivory Coast
Scott No. C29

1'6 Malta
Malta Scott No. 354

VENEZUELA
Venezuela Scott No. 884

UBLIQUE GABONAISE 100F
Gabon Scott No. C27

| 1246 | 1247 | 1248 | 1249 |
| 1250 | 1252 | 1251 | 1253 |

Perf. 11		
243	.10 .04 5c Charles M. Russell	Mar. 19

This stamp honors frontier artist Charles M. Russell (1864-1926). It depicts his painting, "Jerked Down."

Perf. 11x10-1/2

244   .10   .04 5c New York's World's Fair   Apr. 22

Issued for the opening of the New York World's Fair of 1964-65.

Perf. 11

245   .10   .04 5c John Muir   Apr. 29

Conservationist John Muir (1838-1914) worked to save California's redwood trees.

Perf. 11x10-1/2

246   .10   .04 5c Kennedy Memorial   May 29

A memorial to John F. Kennedy, president of the United States from 1961 until his death in 1963.

Perf. 10-1/2x11

247   .10   .04 5c New Jersey 300th Anniv.   Jun. 15

In 1664, the English colonized New Jersey.

Perf. 11

1248   .10   .04 5c Nevada Statehood   Jul. 22

Nevada became a state in 1864.

1249   .10   .04 5c Register and Vote   Aug. 1

Issued for the 1964 presidential elections.

Perf. 10-1/2x11

1250   .10   .04 5c Shakespeare   Aug. 14

English dramatist William Shakespeare was born in 1564, 400 years before this stamp was issued.

1251   .10   .04 5c Doctors Mayo   Sep. 11

A tribute to the Mayo brothers, surgeons who established the Mayo Foundation. The heads on the stamp are from a sculpture by James E. Fraser.

Perf. 11

1252   .10   .04 5c American Music   Oct. 15

Issued for the 50th anniversary of the founding of the American Society of Composers, Authors and Publishers (ASCAP).

1253   .10   .04 5c Homemakers   Oct. 26

Designed in the style of an early sampler, this stamp honors U.S. homemakers.

THE MAYO BROTHERS

William James Mayo (1861-1939) and Charles Horace Mayo (1865-1939) were Minnesota surgeons whose dedication to their work resulted in new hope for millions. With their father, William Worrall Mayo, they founded the Mayo Clinic in Rochester, Minnesota, in 1889.

The number of successful operations performed at the new clinic made it a mecca for the sick. The two brothers quickly gained an international reputation for their diagnostic ability and surgical technique.

In 1915 the Doctors Mayo contributed $2.8 million to establish the Mayo Foundation for Education and Research, which became a part of the University of Minnesota Graduate School. During World War I the two brothers served the army as chief consultants for all surgical services. One of the founders of the American College of Surgeons, William Mayo was president of numerous medical societies, including the American Medical Association (1905-06).

See Scott Stamp No. 1251

THE WAR OF 1812

A lasting peace with England was the positive result of the War of 1812, which began over the issue of freedom of the seas and ended with the emergence of a new national hero.

In 1806 England, then at war with France, began to blockade U. S. ships that carried war supplies to France. This blockade, coupled with the British practice of "conscripting" U. S. sailors from their ships, led Congress to delcare war on June 18, 1812 at the urging of President James Madison.

The ensuing conflict proved a series of frustrating stalemates. Early U. S. naval triumphs, such as Commodore Oliver Perry's Lake Erie victory of 1812, were almost nullified by the burning of the Capitol by 4,000 British troops in 1814.

The Ghent Peace Treaty brought the war to an end in December, 1814, but before news of the Treaty reached America, the war's most famous battle took place. This was the Battle of New Orleans, a U. S. victory from which Andrew Jackson emerged a great hero.

See Scott Stamp No. 1261

Christmas Issue, Nov. 9

.10	.03	5c	Holly
.10	.03	5c	Mistletoe
.10	.03	5c	Poinsettia
.10	.03	5c	Sprig of Conifer
.40	.12		Block of four

Perf. 10-1/2x11

.10	.04	5c	Verrazano-Narrows Bridge	Nov. 21

The world's longest suspension bridge was opened on November 21, 1964. It connects Staten Island and Brooklyn, N. Y.

Perf. 11

.10	.04	5c	Fine Arts	Dec. 2

Stamp depicts "Abstract Design" by Stuart Davis.

Perf. 10-1/2x11

.10	.04	5c	Amateur Radio	Dec. 15

The American Radio Relay League for "ham operators" was established in 1914.

Issues of 1965, Perf. 11

.10	.04	5c	Battle of New Orleans	Jan. 8

The Battle of New Orleans established 150 years of peace between the United States and Britain.

.10	.04	5c	Physical Fitness-Sokol	Feb. 15

The Sokol Athletic Organization was founded in 1915. Issue also promotes physical fitness.

.10	.04	5c	Crusade Against Cancer	Apr. 1

Issue publicized the fight against cancer; also stressed the importance of an early diagnosis.

Perf. 10-1/2x11

.10	.04	5c	Churchill Memorial	May 13

In memory of the British statesman (1874-1965), Prime Minister and World War II leader.

1264

Perf. 11

.10	.04	5c	Magna Carta	Jun. 15

This famous document, signed by King John in 1215, is the basis of the common law of England and the U.S.

.10	.04	5c	Intl. Cooperation Year	Jun. 26

Issued for International Cooperation Year and the 20th anniversary of the United Nations.

.10	.04	5c	Salvation Army	Jul. 2

William Booth founded the Salvation Army in 1865.

1265

Perf. 10-1/2x11

.10	.04	5c	Dante Alighieri	Jul. 17

The Italian poet born in 1265, is best-known for the *Divine Comedy*.

.10	.04	5c	Herbert Hoover	Aug. 10

The 31st president of the United States (1929-1933) was born in 1874. He died in 1964.

Perf. 11

.10	.04	5c	Robert Fulton	Aug. 19

Fulton (1765-1815) invented the first commercial steamboat.

.10	.04	5c	Settlement of Florida	Aug. 28

Established in 1565, St. Augustine, Florida was the first permanent European settlement in the U.S.

.10	.04	5c	Traffic Safety	Sep. 3

Issued to help prevent traffic accidents and to publicize highway safety.

.10	.04	5c	John Singleton Copley	Sep. 17

John Singleton Copley (1738-1815) was an important early U.S. painter. Detail on the stamp is from his oil "The Copley Family" and portrays his daughter.

1266

1267

1268

1269

1271

1270

1273

1272

FRANK LLOYD WRIGHT (1869-1959)

No house should ever be on any hill or on anything. It should be of the hill, belonging to it...Wright's autobiography

Frank Lloyd Wright, pioneer of 20th century architecture, felt that a building should be an organic part of the land. One of his finest works, "Falling Water" House at Bear Run, Pennsylvania, juts out over the rock ledges of a waterfall and stream. The floating cantilever construction which he used in the Imperial Hotel, Tokyo, Japan, was criticized as unsafe until the hotel emerged intact from the earthquake of 1923 that destroyed most of the city. The Solomon R. Guggenheim Museum in New York, completed in 1959, is one of his most revolutionary designs (see illustration). Breaking away from the "room" structure of tradition, Wright set up the galleries and the building on a continuous spiral ramp six-stories high.

See Scott Stamp No. 1280

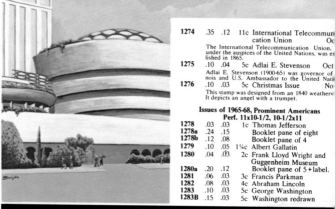

| 1274 | .35 | .12 | 11c | International Telecommunication Union |
| | | | | Oc... |

The International Telecommunication Union, under the auspices of the United Nations, was es... lished in 1865.

| 1275 | .10 | .04 | 5c | Adlai E. Stevenson Oct... |

Adlai E. Stevenson (1900-65) was governor of ... nois and U.S. Ambassador to the United Nati...

| 1276 | .10 | .03 | 5c | Christmas Issue No... |

This stamp was designed from an 1840 weather... It depicts an angel with a trumpet.

Issues of 1965-68, Prominent Americans
Perf. 11x10-1/2, 10-1/2x11

1278	.03	.03	1c	Thomas Jefferson
1278a	.24	.15		Booklet pane of eight
1278b	.12	.08		Booklet pane of 4
1279	.10	.05	1¼c	Albert Gallatin
1280	.04	.03	2c	Frank Lloyd Wright and Guggenheim Museum
1280a	.20	.12		Booklet pane of 5+label.
1281	.06	.03	3c	Francis Parkman
1282	.08	.03	4c	Abraham Lincoln
1283	.10	.03	5c	George Washington
1283B	.15	.03	5c	Washington redrawn

ALBERT EINSTEIN (1879-1955)

*Since I do not foresee that atomic energy is to be a great boon for a long time,
I have to say that for the present it is a menace.* Einstein in 1945

Albert Einstein was one of the greatest, most creative thinkers of the modern
age. In 1915 he published his general theory of relativity, which chartered new
courses in three branches of physics and altered previous concepts of our universe.
His famous equation $E = mc^2$, pointed the way for development in the field of atomic
energy. In 1921 another discovery, the law of photoelectric effect (one basis of
modern electronics) earned him a Nobel Prize.

In 1932 Einstein, a native of Germany and the son of Jewish parents, saw the
inevitability of Hitler's rise to power and sailed to the United States. In 1933
he joined the Institute for Advanced Study in Princeton, New Jersey, where he
continued his research. He became an American citizen in 1940.

See Scott Stamp No. 1285

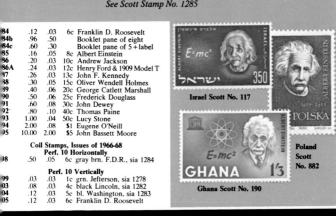

84	.12	.03	6c Franklin D. Roosevelt
84b	.96	.50	Booklet pane of eight
84c	.60	.30	Booklet pane of 5 + label
85	.16	.05	8c Albert Einstein
86	.20	.03	10c Andrew Jackson
86A	.24	.03	12c Henry Ford & 1909 Model T
87	.26	.03	13c John F. Kennedy
88	.30	.05	15c Oliver Wendell Holmes
89	.40	.06	20c George Catlett Marshall
90	.50	.06	25c Frederick Douglass
91	.60	.08	30c John Dewey
92	.80	.10	40c Thomas Paine
93	1.00	.04	50c Lucy Stone
94	2.00	.08	$1 Eugene O'Neill
95	10.00	2.00	$5 John Bassett Moore

Coil Stamps, Issues of 1966-68
Perf. 10 Horizontally

98	.50	.05	6c gray brn. F.D.R., sia 1284

Perf. 10 Vertically

99	.03	.03	1c grn. Jefferson, sia 1278
03	.08	.03	4c black Lincoln, sia 1282
04	.12	.03	5c bl. Washington, sia 1283
05	.12	.03	6c Franklin D. Roosevelt

Israel Scott No. 117

Poland
Scott
No. 882

Ghana Scott No. 190

1285   1286   1286 A   1287

1288   1289   1290   1291

1292   1293   1294   1295   1305

1311

		Issues of 1966, Perf. 11				
1306	.10	.04	5c Migratory Bird Treaty			
					Mar. 16	

In 1916 Canada and the United States ratified this treaty to protect their migratory birds.

| 1307 | .10 | .04 | 5c Humane Treatment of Animals | | | |
| | | | | | Apr. 9 | |

The American Society for the Prevention of Cruelty to Animals was established in 1866.

1308	.10	.04	5c Indiana Statehood	Apr. 16

In 1816, Indiana joined the Union.

1309	.10	.04	5c American Circus	May 2

This tribute to the circus also marked the 100th anniversary of the birth of John Ringling, circus-master.

Sixth International Philatelic Exhibition Issues

1310	.10	.04	5c Stamped Cover	May

Imperf.

1311	.12	.10	5c Souvenir Sheet	

Issued in sheets of one stamp with marginal inscription commemorating the Sixth International Philatelic Exhibition (SIPEX), held in Washington, D.C. May 21-30.

Perf. 11

1312	.10	.04	5c Bill of Rights	Ju

Issued for the 175th anniversary of the Bill of Rig

Perf. 10-1/2x11

1313	.10	.04	5c Polish Millennium	Jul

The people of Poland adopted Christianity 966 A.D.

Perf. 11

1314	.10	.04	5c National Park Service	Aug

Issued for the 50th anniversary of the National Service of the Department of the Interior.

EUGENE GLADSTONE O'NEILL (1888-1953)

During the long career of dramatist Eugene O'Neill, the United States theater came of age.

O'Neill himself grew up in the theater; his father, James O'Neill was an actor. In 1913, while afflicted with a slight case of tuberculosis, he turned his thoughts to writing plays. "Beyond the Horizon", his first full-length effort, was awarded the coveted Pulitzer Prize for drama as were "Anna Christie", "Strange Interlude", and "Long Day's Journey Into Night."

Probably the greatest playwright this country has produced, O'Neill was visionary in his grasp of the problems and frustrations of machine-age life. His tragic and near-tragic plays were prophets of the realistic dramas of today. From "Mourning Becomes Electra" and "The Hairy Ape" to the autobiographically revealing "Long Day's Journey Into Night", the roster of his dramas markedly enriched the culture of the world.

See Scott Stamp No. 1294.

MIGRATORY BIRD TREATY
1916~UNITED STATES·CANADA~1966
U.S. POSTAGE FIVE CENTS

1306

U.S. POSTAGE
5¢
HUMANE TREATMENT of ANIMALS

1307

SESQUICENTENNIAL
INDIANA
1816 1966
5¢
U.S. POSTAGE

1308

CIRCUS
UNITED STATES
5¢

1309

5 CENTS
US POSTAGE
Sixth International
Philatelic Exhibition
Washington D.C. 20008

1310

The UNITED STATES
Bill of Rights
5¢

1312

POLAND'S
MILLENNIUM
966 † 1966
UNITED STATES 5¢

1313

National
Park Service
1916-1966
5 U.S.

1314

THE BILL OF RIGHTS

Congress shall make no law…a-bridging the freedom of speech or of the press; or the right of the people peacefully to assemble…

Revolutions often breed dictatorships. Not so in the United States, where government by the people resulted from the Revolutionary War.

The founding fathers, anxious to preserve the freedoms fought for in the war, acted quickly to set up a democratic form of government at the war's conclusion. The Constitution, written in 1787, was the bulwark of this government.

When the Constitution was presented to the people for approval they demanded — and received — a bill of rights to preserve their civil liberties. Such a bill was not a new idea. Its roots lay deep in English history — in the Magna Carta, which established the right of trial by jury in 1215; and in the English Bill of Rights of 1689.

When the first ten amendments were added to the Constitution in 1791, liberty was truly made the Law of the Land.

See Scott Stamp No. 1312

Religious Freedom IN AMERICA
3¢ UNITED STATES POSTAGE

1099

FREEDOM OF THE PRESS
U.S. POSTAGE 4¢

1119

US POSTAGE

908

UNITED STATES POSTAGE 5¢
MAGNA CARTA 1215

1265

1315

1316

1317

1319

1318

1320

1321

1322

THE RACE TO UTAH

A railroad to the Pacific? Well, I would not buy a ticket on it for my grandchildren! Gen. Wm. T. Sherman.

In 1864 most Americans ridiculed the idea of a transcontinental railroad. Yet President Lincoln insisted—"That road *must* be built,"and two great railroads began an epic race across the continent to their meeting place in Utah. The obstacles they faced were formidable. In the path of the Central Pacific, originating at Sacramento, loomed the Sierra Nevada Mountains. In front of the Union Pacific, which began at Omaha, lay Indian territory and the Rockies. Even so, work on the railroad progressed at a feverish pace. By the end of 1866 the Union Pacific had laid 265 miles of track. The Central Pacific, using as much as 400 kegs of blasting powder a day, was tunneling its way across the Sierras to the Utah desert. In the desert, water had to be imported; mules and horses died from heat. Finally, however, on May 10, 1869, the two thin ribbons of iron met at Promontory. Governor Leland Stanford of California drove the golden spike which connected the railroads and linked the continent.

See Scott Stamp Nos. 922,993

1315	.10	.04	5c Marine Corps Reserve Aug.

The U.S. Marine Corps Reserve was established 1916.

1316	.10	.04	5c General Federation of Women's Clubs Sep.

Issue notes "75 Years of Service for Freedom a Growth" by the General Federation of Wome Clubs.

1317	.10	.04	5c American Folklore Issue Sep.

Issued to honor Johnny Appleseed (John Chapma 1774-1845), who roamed over 100,000 square mi planting apple trees.

1318	.10	.04	5c Beautification of America Oct

This stamp helped encourage interest in the "Be tify America" campaign of President and Mrs. Lync Johnson. It carries the legend "Plant for a me beautiful America."

1324

1325

1323

1326

1328

1327

HENRY DAVID THOREAU (1817-62)

The mass of men lead lives of quiet desperation. Walden

On Independence Day, 1845, Henry David Thoreau began his two-year residence at Walden Pond, a few miles south of Concord, Massachusetts. Insisting that a man need not mortgage his life just to live, he built his house for $28 and lived off the land. In the same year, as a protest against slavery, he personally seceded from the Union, refused to pay the poll tax, and spent a night in the Concord jail. Although *Walden* is Thoreau's most famous work, his most influential has been *Civil Disobedience.* Objecting to the continuance of slavery, the treatment of Indians, and the Mexican War, he delineated his policy of passive resistance to unjust governments. His essay, inspiration to Mahatma Ghandi, has been the basis for many peaceful revolutions throughout the world.

See Scott Stamp No. 1327

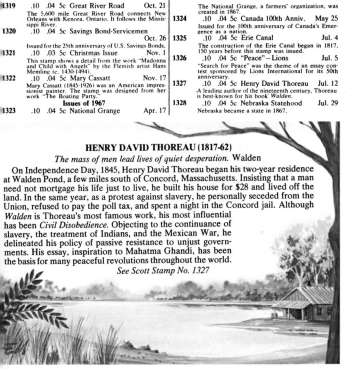

FRONTIERS OF SPACE

Live television coverage of happenings in far-off lands... weather satellites that track down storms while orbiting in outer space... a race to Mars...

These are but a few of the miraculous achievements of the Space Age, which was launched in 1957 by Russia's Sputnik satellite. The United States, which followed Russia with Explorer 1 in 1958, has also landed the first men upon the moon; launched Early Bird, the first communications satellite; and orbited the weather satellites Nimbus and TIROS. Two United States unmanned expeditions, Viking and "Grand Tour" are planned for in the future. "Grand Tour" will go to Jupiter, Uranus, Neptune, Saturn, and Pluto. Viking will orbit Mars. In 1970, the Space Race, long the domain of the United States and the Soviet Union, was joined by the People's Republic of China, which launched a 380-pound earth satellite.

See Scott Stamp Nos. 1331-1332, 1371, C76

U.S.S.R.
Scott No. 3224

Ascension Scott No. 104

Great Britain Scott No. 466

Togo Scott No. 505

| 1329 | .10 | .04 | 5c Voice of America | Aug. 1 |

Issued for the 25th anniversary of the Voice of America, the radio branch of the United States Information Agency.

| 1330 | .10 | .04 | 5c American Folklore Issue | Aug. 17 |

The second stamp in the "Folklore" series honors Davy Crockett (1786-1836), frontiersman and congressman, who died at the Alamo.

Space Accomplishments Issue, Sep. 29

1331	.75	.15	5c Space-Walking Astronaut
1331a	1.50	.30	Pair
1332	.75	.15	5c Gemini 4 Capsule and Earth

Nos. 1331-1332, the first twin stamps in U.S. postal history, note U.S. accomplishments in outer space.

| 1333 | .10 | .04 | 5c Urban Planning | Oct. 2 |

"Plan for better cities" was the theme of this stamp, issued in conjunction with the International Conference of the American Institute of Planners, held in Washington, D.C. from Oct. 1-6.

| 1334 | .10 | .04 | 5c Finnish Independence | Oct. 6 |

Issued for the 50th anniversary of Finnish independence, this stamp reproduces Finland's coat of arms.

Perf. 12

| 1335 | .10 | .04 | 5c Thomas Eakins | Nov. 2 |

Painter Thomas Eakins (1844-1916), is honored on this stamp. Designed from an Eakins oil, "The Biglin Brothers Racing," it was the first U.S. stamp printed by the gravure method.

36	.10	.03	5c Christmas Issue	Nov. 6

This stamp shows "Madonna and Child with Angels," by Hans Memling. The painting, which hangs in the National Gallery of Art, was also shown on the 1966 Christmas Issue.

37	.10	.04	5c Mississippi Statehood	Dec. 11

In 1817, Mississippi joined the Union. Stamp depicts the Mississippi flower, the magnolia.

38	.12	.03	6c Flag and White House	

Perf. 11x10-1/2

38D	.12	.03	6c dk. blue, red & grn., sia 1338	
38F	.16	.03	8c multicolored, sia 1338	

Coil Stamps of 1969-71
Perf. 10 Vertically

1338A	.12	.03	6c dk. blue, red & grn., sia 1338	
1338G	.16	.03	8c multicolored, sia 1338	

Issues of 1968, Perf. 11

1339	.12	.04	6c Illinois Statehood	Feb. 12

Illinois became a state in 1818.

1340	.12	.04	6c Hemis Fair '68	Mar. 30

San Antonio, Texas was the site of the Hemis Fair '68 Exposition.

1341	2.25	1.25	$1 Airlift	Apr. 4

Issued for airposting parcels to servicemen overseas.

1342	.12	.04	6c "Youth"—Elks	May 1

National Youth Week of 1968 was sponsored by the Elks.

FOLK HEROES OF THE OLD FRONTIER

The names and exploits of Daniel Boone and Davy Crockett loom large in the legends of early frontier heroes—rugged, fearless men who, fiercely independent, thrived on a life of lonely danger.

Celebrated as the discoverer and founder of Kentucky, Daniel Boone (1734-1820), more than any other man, molded the frontier tradition. Legend says that he could trap a bear in record time, outrun any Indian, and better any shot. In 1775 he blazed the Wilderness Road into Kentucky and built Boonesboro, the town that bears his name. But when settlers poured into Kentucky, Boone grew restless. "If you can see smoke from your neighbor's chimney, it's time to move on," he said, and so he did, this time blazing a trail to Missouri.

Davy Crockett (1786-1836) acquired his legendary reputation both in Tennessee and at the Alamo. An expert marksman, a fine trapper, and a hunter, he brought the coonskin cap of the woodsman into Washington, D.C. when he became a Congressman in 1827 and again in 1832. Always a conspicuous and eccentric figure in the capital, he moved to Texas after his congressional defeat in 1835. There, he joined the fight for Texas independence, and with 186 other men died at the historic Battle of the Alamo.

See Scott Stamp Nos. 904, 1330, 1357

1343 — 6¢ LAW AND ORDER — UNITED STATES POSTAGE

1344 — REGISTER & VOTE US 6¢

1345 — 6¢ U.S. POSTAGE — LIBERTY — FORT MOULTRIE FLAG 1776

1346 — 6¢ U.S. POSTAGE — U.S. FLAG 1795-1818 (FT. McHENRY FLAG)

1347 — 6¢ U.S. POSTAGE — AN APPEAL TO HEAVEN — WASHINGTON'S CRUISERS FLAG 1775

1348 — 6¢ U.S. POSTAGE — 76 — BENNINGTON FLAG 1777

1349 — 6¢ U.S. POSTAGE — HOPE — RHODE ISLAND FLAG 1775

1350 — 6¢ U.S. POSTAGE — FIRST STARS AND STRIPES 1777

1351 — 6¢ U.S. POSTAGE — GRAND UNION FLAG 1776

1352 — 6¢ U.S. POSTAGE — BUNKER HILL FLAG 1775

1353 — 6¢ U.S. POSTAGE — PHILADELPHIA LIGHT HORSE FLAG 1775

1354 — 6¢ U.S. POSTAGE — DONT TREAD ON ME — FIRST NAVY JACK 1775

WALT DISNEY (1901-1966)

A brilliant fantasyland where Goofy, Donald Duck, Jiminy Cricket, Chip and Dale, Thumper the rabbit, Dumbo the elephant, the fairies Flora, Fauna and Merriweather, and their cartoon relatives cavort is the magic legacy of Walt Disney, film producer and animation pioneer.

Over two dozen Academy Awards attest to the perennial popularity of Disney's films. Yet one of his best-loved characters, Mickey Mouse, did not capture the public imagination until Mickey's third picture, "Steamboat Willie" came around the bend and Walt let him talk. To the World War II effort, Disney contributed animated features for government training programs. Disneyland Park near Los Angeles, a children's fairyland since its birth in 1954, attracts thousands of young, middle-aged, and old "children" each year.

See Scott Stamp No. 1355

1355			
1356			
1357			
1358			
1359			
1360			

43	.12	.04	6c Law and Order	May 17

This stamp reaffirmed the role of the policeman as a friend and a protector of the citizen.

44	.12	.04	6c Register and Vote	Jun. 27

Issued to remind Americans to "Register and Vote" in the 1968 elections.

Historic Flag Series, Jul. 4

45	.15	.10	6c Ft. Moultrie Flag (1776)
46	.15	.10	6c Ft. McHenry Flag (1795-1818)
47	.15	.10	6c Washington's Cruisers Flag (1775)
48	.15	.10	6c Bennington Flag (1777)
49	.15	.10	6c Rhode Island Flag (1775)
50	.15	.10	6c First Stars and Stripes Flag (1777)
51	.15	.10	6c Bunker Hill Flag (1775)
52	.15	.10	6c Grand Union Flag (1776)
53	.15	.10	6c Phila. Light Horse Flag (1775)
54	.15	.10	6c First Navy Jack (1775)
54a	1.50	1.00	Strip of ten

Nine of the flags shown in this series were associated with our Revolution. The remaining flag, that of Fort McHenry, was associated with the War of 1812. It inspired Francis Scott Key to compose the "Star Spangled Banner."

Perf. 12

1355	.12	.04	6c Walt Disney	Sep. 11

A memorial to Walt Disney (1901-1966), film producer and animator.

1356	.12	.04	6c Father Marquette	Sep. 20

Father Jacques Marquette (1637-1675) explored the Mississippi River with fur trapper Louis Jolliet.

1357	.12	.04	6c American Folklore	Sep. 26

Frontiersman and trapper Daniel Boone (1734-1820) founded Boonesboro, Kentucky.

1358	.12	.04	6c Arkansas River Navigation
			Oct. 1

Issued for the opening of the Arkansas River to commercial navigation.

1359	.12	.04	6c Leif Erikson	Oct. 9

Leif Erikson, the 11th century Norse explorer, may have been the first European to set foot on the North American continent. The stamp shows a statue of Erikson in Reykjavik, Iceland.

Perf. 11x10-1/2

1360	.12	.04	6c Cherokee Strip	Oct. 15

Issued for the 75th anniversary of the opening of the Cherokee Strip (in the Oklahoma panhandle) to white settlers.

THE VIKINGS AND LEIF ERIKSON

In the year 1,000 the Vikings — or sons of the fjords as they called themselves — were the undisputed rulers of the sea; master mariners who plundered coastal settlements from Sicily to Normandy and struck terror in the hearts of landsmen throughout Europe. In that year, according to Norse sagas, Leif the Lucky sailed from Norway to take Christianity to Greenland. But as fate would have it he failed to reach his destination. Blown off course by a storm he landed on an unknown shore filled with wild grapes which he named Vinland the Good.

Was Vinland a real place? Yes, say some modern scholars. Most of them believe it was located in North America, probably in Nova Scotia or in Newfoundland. Certain scholars think the Vikings tried to colonize the land but found the task too difficult. It remained for better-known explorers to seek Vinland out in a way that would alter history.

See Scott Stamp Nos. 621, 1359

JOHN TRUMBULL (1756-1843)

There is never anything beautiful about war; only about the heroism men display in times of war.

John Trumbull was an artist sensitive enough to capture the heroic people, places, and events associated with the Revolutionary War and preserve them in his paintings. Renowned for portraits of George Washington, and for classics like "The Signing of the Declaration of Independence" and "The Battle of Bunker's Hill", he was a native of Connecticut, a graduate of Harvard, and a student of another early master, Benjamin West. During his illustrious career, Trumbull maintained studios in both New York and London and served as president of the American Academy of Fine Arts. Examples of his paintings may be seen on many postage stamps of the United States.

See Scott Stamp Nos. 120, 711, 712, 1361

Perf. 11

1361 .12 .04 6c John Trumbull Oct. 18
John Trumbull (1756-1843) was a noted early U.S. painter. Stamp shows a detail from his work "The Battle of Bunker Hill."

1362 .12 .04 6c Waterfowl Conservation Oct. 24
Issued to encourage waterfowl conservation and to honor Ducks Unlimited, an organization which has spent nearly $15 million on conservation.

1363 .12 .04 6c Christmas Issue Nov. 1
This stamp shows the Angel Gabriel, a detail from "The Annunciation" by Flemish painter Jan van Eyck (c. 1390-1441).

1364 .12 .04 6c American Indian Nov. 4
A tribute to the Indian, this stamp shows the great Chief Joseph (c. 1840-1904), leader of the Nez Perce tribe.

Issues of 1969
Beautification of America, Jan. 16

1365 .15 .05 6c Capitol, Azaleas and Tulips

1366 .15 .05 6c Washington Monument, Potomac River and Daffodils

1367 .15 .05 6c Poppies and Lupines along Highway

1369	.15	.05	6c	Blooming Crabapples along Street

368 | .15 | .05 | 6c | Blooming Crabapples along Street

368a | .60 | .20 | | Block of four
Nos. 1365-1368 were issued to promote the "Beautification of America" campaign.

369 | .12 | .04 | 6c | American Legion | Mar. 15
The American Legion was founded in 1919 in Paris.

370 | .12 | .04 | 6c | American Folklore | May 1
Issued to honor Grandma Moses (1860-1961), American primitive painter.

371 | .15 | .04 | 6c | Apollo 8 | May 5
The Apollo 8 mission of Dec. 21-27, 1968 put the first men into orbit around the moon.

372 | .12 | .04 | 6c | W. C. Handy | May 17

William Christopher Handy (1873-1958) was a jazz musician and composer ("The St. Louis Blues"). Stamp also notes the 150th anniversary of Memphis, Tennessee.

1373 | .12 | .04 | 6c | California Settlement | Jul. 16
Issued for the 200th anniversary of the settlement of California by Father Junipero Serra and Gaspar de Portola.

1374 | .12 | .04 | 6c | John Wesley Powell | Aug. 1
Geologist John Wesley Powell (1834-1902) explored the Green and Colorado Rivers.

1375 | .12 | .04 | 6c | Alabama Statehood | Aug. 2
In 1819, Alabama joined the union. Stamp shows the yellowhammer and the camellia, Alabama's bird and flower.

JAZZ

Jazz, America's unique contribution to music, originated during the 19th century when the American Negro took the songs of his new home — folk songs, church hymns and other popular music — and transformed them into a distinctive Afro-American idiom — that is, into work songs, spirituals, and the blues.

In jazz, especially the brass-band variety, emphasis is on the improvisational abilities of the player, usually in "jam" sessions. Great artists in its history include Jelly-Roll Morton, Louis Armstrong, Duke Ellington, and Bix Beiderbecke.

Among the composers of blues, jazz steeped with emotion, W. C. Handy is probably the most famous. During his lifetime (1873-1958), he wrote "Memphis Blues ', "St. Louis Blues", and about sixty other songs.

See Scott Stamp No. 1372

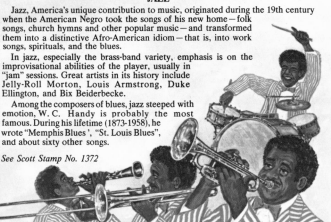

				Botanical Congress Issue
1376	.15	.05	6c	Douglas Fir (Northwest)
1377	.15	.05	6c	Lady's-slipper (Northeast)
1378	.15	.05	6c	Ocotillo (Southwest)
1379	.15	.05	6c	Franklinia (Southeast)
1379a	.60	.20		Block of four

Issued in conjunction with the 11th Internation Botanical Congress, held in Seattle, Washing from Aug. 24-Sep. 2.

Perf. 10-1/2x11

1380	.12	.04	6c	Dartmouth College Case Sep.

The Dartmouth College Case, argued by Dan Webster before the Supreme Court in 1819, guaranteed the sanctity of contracts.

Perf. 11

1381	.12	.04	6c	Professional Baseball Sep.

Issued for the 100th anniversary of professio baseball.

1382	.12	.04	6c	Intercollegiate Football Sep.

Issued for the 100th anniversary of intercollegi football.

1383	.12	.04	6c	Dwight D. Eisenhower Oct.

Issued in memory of Dwight D. Eisenhower (18 1969), General of the Army and 34th president of United States (1953-1961).

FOOTBALL

The first intercollegiate football game was played in 1869 at New Brunswick, New Jersey between Rutgers and Princeton Universities. Since then the game has gained steadily in popularity and prestige. Early players such as Jim Thorpe, "Red" Grange, and Clyde "Bulldog" Turner captured the popular imagination and before long the game became professional. In 1922 the National Football League (NFL) was organized and in 1959 the American Football League (AFL) was founded. In 1970 Alvin "Pete" Rozelle became the first commissoner of Pro Football and the two leagues merged into the National Football League, which now has two conferences, the National and American. Each year the championship Super Bowl pits the top pro teams against one another in one of the country's most exciting sports events.

See Scott Stamp No. 1382

DWIGHT D.
EISENHOWER

1383

WILLIAM M. HARNETT

1386

AMERICAN BALD EAGLE

1387

AFRICAN ELEPHANT HERD

1388

HAIDA CEREMONIAL CANOE

1389

THE AGE OF REPTILES

1390

			Perf. 11x10-1/2	
4	.12	.03	6c Christmas Issue	Nov. 3
4a		.20	Precanceled	

"A Winter Sunday in Norway, Maine," shown on stamp, was painted around 1870 by an unknown artist.

5	.12	.04	6c Hope for Crippled	Nov. 20

Issued for the 50th anniversary of the National Society for crippled children and adults, the sponsor of Easter Seals.

6	.12	.04	6c William M. Harnett	Dec. 3

Artist William M. Harnett (1848-1892) is known for still-life paintings like "Old Models," shown on stamp.

Issues of 1970
Natural History, May 6

7	.12	.04	6c American Bald Eagle	
8	.12	.04	6c African Elephant Herd	
9	.12	.04	6c Tlingit Chief in Haida Ceremonial Canoe	
0	.12	.04	6c Brontosaurus, Stegosaurus and Allosaurus from Jurassic Period	
0a	.48	.16	Block of four	

These stamps honor the American Museum of Natural History in New York City on its 100th anniversary.

BASEBALL

Tradition has it that Abner Doubleday created America's national pastime in 1839 at Cooperstown, New York. Since then, the cry "Play ball!" has started countless season and post-season clashes between members of the two professional leagues: the National (dating from 1876) and the American (dating from 1901).

In 1903 the Boston Red Sox defeated the Pittsburgh Pirates in the first World Series, now a yearly classic. In 1939, on baseball's 100th anniversary, the National Baseball Hall of Fame and Museum was built at Cooperstown. The first five "greats" honored on its roster were Ty Cobb, Babe Ruth, Walter Johnson, Honus Wagner, and Christy Mathewson.
See Scott Stamp Nos. 855, 1381

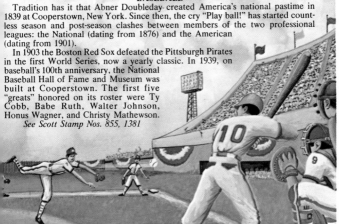

1391	.12	.04	6c Maine Statehood	Jul. 9

Designed from an oil by artist Edward Hopper (1882-1967) this stamp honors Maine on the 150th anniversary of its statehood.

Perf. 10-1/2x11

1392	.12	.04	6c Wildlife Conservation	Jul. 20

This Conservation Issue calls attention to the plight of the American bison, of which about 30,000 now exist.

Issues of 1970-71
Perf. 11x10-1/2

1393	.12	.03	6c Dwight D. Eisenhower	
1393a	.96	.50	Booklet pane of eight	
1393b	.60	.35	Booklet pane of 5 + label	

Perf. 11

1394	.16	.03	8c Eisenhower	

Perf. 11x10-1/2

1395	.16	.03	8c reddish brn.. sia 1393	
1395a	1.28		Booklet pane of eight	
1395b	.96		Booklet pane of six	

Perf. 10-1/2x11

1396	.16	.03	8c U.S. Postal Service	Jul.

Perf. 11x10-1/2

1398	.32	.03	16c Ernie Pyle	

Issued to honor Ernest Taylor Pyle, journalist.

Coil Stamps, Perf. 10 Vertically

1401	.12	.03	6c dk. blue gray Eisenhower,. sia 1393	
1402	.16	.03	8c reddish brn. Eisenhower, 1393	

Issues of 1970, Perf. 11

1405	.12	.04	6c Edgar Lee Masters	Aug.

Edgar Lee Masters (1869-1950), poet, is best known for the *Spoon River Anthology*. This stamp was the first in a series honoring U.S. poets.

1406	.12	.04	6c Woman Suffrage	Aug.

Issued for the 50th anniversary of the passage of the 19th amendment, which allowed women to vote.

VOTES FOR WOMEN

The right of citizens of the United States to vote shall not be denied or abridged by the United States or by any State on account of sex.

The Nineteenth Amendment to the Constitution

Does a democracy have the right to bar half its citizens from voting? Leaders of the women's suffrage movement argued it does not. To prove their point they waged a long and uphill struggle to participate in local, state, and national elections.

The struggle began in 1848 when Lucretia Mott and Elizabeth Cady Stanton, two active abolitionists who had been barred from an anti-slavery meeting, held the first Women's Rights Convention. Led by Susan B. Anthony, Lucy Stone, and Carrie Chapman Catt, the women's suffrage movement culminated in the 1920 passage of the nineteenth amendment to the Constitution.

See Scott Stamp Nos. 784, 959, 1293, 1406

THE MENACE OF POLLUTION

In recent years pollution has become a problem of nation-wide concern, for it threatens to destroy the resources on which life depends. Lakes and streams in parts of the United States are clogged with algae. City air is thick with smog. Chemicals have poisoned once-rich soil, and many forms of wildlife are on the verge of extinction. The situation is now so acute that nation-wide campaigns are being waged to save the country's cities, soil, air, and water. Ecology, a term once known only to scientists, has become a household word as children and adults fight to preserve the balance between man and his environment which sustains and nurtures life.

See Scott Stamp Nos. 1410-1413

1407	.12	.04	6c	South Carolina	Sep. 12

In 1670, South Carolina was settled by the English. Charleston was the state's first permanent settlement.

1408	.12	.04	6c	Stone Mtn. Mem.	Sep. 19

Stone Mountain Memorial, a famous monument to the Confederacy, is carved into the side of Stone Mountain, Georgia.

1409	.12	.04	6c	Fort Snelling	Oct. 17

Established in 1820, Fort Snelling, Minnesota played a major role in the opening of the Northwest.

Perf. 11x10-1/2
Anti-Pollution Issue, Oct. 28

1410	.12	.04	6c	Save our Soil
1411	.12	.04	6c	Save our Cities
1412	.12	.04	6c	Save our Water
1413	.12	.04	6c	Save our Air

1413a	.48	.16	Block of four

Issued to call attention to the mounting problems of pollution.

Christmas Issue, Nov. 5
Perf. 10-1/2x11

1414	.12	.03	6c	Nativity, by Lorenzo Lotto
1414a		.12		Precancelled

Perf. 11x10-1/2

1415	.12	.03	6c	Tin and Cast Iron Locomotive
1415a		.12		Precancelled
1416	.12	.03	6c	Toy Horse on Wheels
1416a		.12		Precancelled
1417	.12	.03	6c	Mechanical Tricycle
1417a		.12		Precancelled
1418	.12	.03	6c	Doll Carriage
1418a		.12		Precancelled
1418b	.48	.12		Block of four

THE TRUMAN ERA

The responsibility of great states is to serve and not dominate the world. Harry S. Truman

Harry S. Truman (1884-), the son of a poor Missouri farmer, rose to become the 33rd president of the United States. On April 12, 1945, when Franklin Roosevelt died, the presidency passed on to then Vice-President Truman. Shortly afterwards the new president made the difficult decision to drop the atomic bomb on Japan. This decision, the first of many made by Truman, hastened Japan's surrender and the end of World War II.

In 1947 General George C. Marshall, Truman's secretary of state, proposed the Marshall Plan of economic aid to war-devastated Europe. The Marshall Plan was an outgrowth of the "Truman Doctrine", a policy of economic and military aid to countries threatened by aggression. In 1949 the North Atlantic Treaty Organization (NATO) was approved.

During Truman's first full term in office, which began in 1948, postwar international problems continued to overshadow domestic affairs. In 1950 armed hostilities erupted in Korea and U. S. troops were sent to the Orient as part of the U. N. forces supporting the government of South Korea. On March 29, 1952, Truman, who was lauded by Winston Churchill for making "great and valiant decisions," announced that he would not seek another term.

See Scott Stamp Nos. 1008, 1127, 1289, 1426

		Perf. 11		
1419	.12	.04	6c United Nations	Nov. 20

Issued for the 25th anniversary of the United Nations.

1420	.12	.04	6c Landing of the Pilgrims	
				Nov. 21

Issued for the 350th anniversary of the landing of the Pilgrims.

Disabled Veterans and Servicemen Issue, Nov. 24

1421	.12	.04	6c Disabled American Veterans Emblem
1421a	.24	.08	Pair, sia 1421-1422
1422	.12	.04	6c U.S. Serviceman

Issued for the 50th anniversary of the Disabled Veterans and as a tribute to our servicemen held prisoner in North Vietnam.

Issues of 1971

1423	.12	.04	6c American Wool Industry	Jan. 19
1424	.12	.04	6c Gen. Douglas MacArthur	
				Jan. 26
1425	.12	.04	6c Blood Donor	Mar. 12
			Perf. 11x10-1/2	
1426	.16	.05	8c Missouri 150th Anniv.	May 8

Stamp depicts a detail from "Independence and the Opening of the West" by Thomas Hart Benton.

THE UNITED STATES
POSTAL SERVICE

*Neither snow, nor rain, nor heat,
nor gloom of night stays these
couriers from the swift completion
of their appointed rounds.*

These words, adapted from the
Greek historian Herodotus (484-425
B. C.) have long been the pledge of
the U. S. government's 740,000 Post
Office Department employees.

With the inauguration of a new
postal service, however, the pledge
was transferred to a brand-new corporation. On July 1, 1971 the old Post
Office became the United States
Postal Service, a quasi-independent
public utility.

The position of postmaster general
is no longer a presidential cabinet post.
He and his deputy will be appointed
by a nine-member Board of Governors,
who will manage the postal service
much as a board of directors manages
a modern corporation. Under the
Postal Reorganization Act it is hoped
that the postal system will become a
modern, efficient operation that can
use new ideas, new methods, and new
machines to handle the great load of
mail that passes through the world's
largest post office. No longer subject
to political patronage, the directors
of the Service plan to serve their 204
million customers on the basis of
sound business practice.

See Scott Stamp No. 1396

Perf. 11
Wildlife Conservation Issue, Jun. 12

1427	.16	.05	8c Trout
1428	.16	.05	8c Alligator
1429	.16	.05	8c Polar Bear and Cubs
1430	.16	.05	8c California Condor
1430a	.64	.20	Block of four

1431	.16	.05	8c Antarctic Treaty Issue Jun. 23

Tenth anniversary of the Antarctic Treaty pledging
peaceful uses of and scientific co-operation in
Antarctica.

Perf. 11x10-1/2

1432	.16	.05	8c American Revolution
			200th Anniv. Jul. 4

Special issue marks start of U.S. Revolution bicenten-
nial celebration: shows official emblem of Bicenten-
nial Commission.

MORE RECENT ISSUES SHOWN IN ADDENDA BEGINNING ON PAGE 202

THE INVERTED "JENNY" (C3a)
The first U. S. airmail stamps show a Curtiss "Jenny" biplane. By a spectacular error a sheet of 100 of the 24c denomination reached the public with inverted centers. Today these stamps are among the most valuable of U. S. rarities. In 1971 a fine single sold for $36,000.

Air Post Stamps
For prepayment of postage on all mailable matter sent by air mail. All unwatermarked.

Issue of 1918, Perf. 11			
C1	22.50	10.00	6c Curtiss "Jenny"
C2	37.50	17.50	16c Curtiss "Jenny"
C3	32.50	17.00	24c Curtiss "Jenny"
C3a	36,000.00		Center inverted
Issue of 1923			
C4	11.00	7.00	8c Wooden Propeller & Engine Nose
C5	30.00	17.00	16c Air Service Emblem
C6	35.00	11.00	24c De Havilland Biplane
Issue of 1926-27			
C7	1.00	.25	10c Map of U.S. and Two Mail Planes
C8	1.50	1.10	15c olive brown, sia C7
C9	2.50	.90	20c yellow green, sia C7
Issue of 1927			
C10	2.15	1.60	10c Lindbergh's "Spirit of St. Louis" Jun.
C10a	32.50	23.50	Booklet pane of three
Nos. C1-C10 inclusive were also available for ordinary postage.			
Issue of 1928			
C11	1.25	.40	5c Beacon on Rocky Mt. Jul.
Issue of 1930, Perf. 11			
C12	5.00	.30	5c Winged Globe Feb.

CHARLES A. LINDBERGH
(1902-   )
In 1927 at the age of twenty-five the "Lone Eagle", Charles A. Lindbergh, captured the world's imagination when he made the first solo non-stop New York to Paris flight in his single-engine *Spirit of St. Louis.*

The historic flight began at Roosevelt Field, New York, on May 20, at 7:53 A. M. and ended in Paris at 10 P. M. French time on May 21. It made Lindbergh a hero overnight. The recipient of medals from Great Britain, France, and the United States, Lindbergh received $250,000 from *The New York Times* for the rights to the story of his flight. His autobiography, *We,* was a national best seller. It was followed in 1953 by *The Spirit of St. Louis.*

See Scott Stamp No. C10

C12

C13

Graf Zeppelin Issue, Apr. 19			
3	125.00	87.50	65c Zeppelin Over Atlantic Ocean
4	200.00	125.00	$1.30 Zeppelin Between Continents
5	325.00	220.00	$2.60 Zeppelin Passing Globe

Issued for use on mail carried on the first Europe-Pan-America round trip flight of Graf Zeppelin, May, 1930.

Issue of 1931-32, Perf. 10-1/2x11			
6	1.75	.30	5c violet, sia C12
7	.65	.18	8c olive bistre, sia C12
Issue of 1933, Perf. 11			
8	50.00	35.00	50c Century of Progress Oct. 2

Issued in connection with the flight of the "Graf Zeppelin" in October, 1933, to Miami, Akron, and Chicago, and from the last city to Europe.

Issue of 1934, Perf. 10-1/2x11			
9	.60	.06	6c dull orange, sia C12 Jul. 1
Issue of 1935, Perf. 11			
20	1.25	1.10	25c Transpacific Nov. 22

Issued to pay postage on mail carried on the Trans-pacific air post service inaugurated Nov. 22, 1935.

Issue of 1937			
21	2.25	1.35	20c The "China Clipper" Over the Pacific Feb. 15
22	4.00	2.35	50c carmine, sia C21

C14

C15

C18

C20

C21

Germany
Scott No. C35

"GRAF ZEPPELIN"

In 1929 the *Graf Zeppelin* became the first airship to fly around the world. Eight hundred feet long and one hundred feet wide, the giant dirigible held fifty passengers and could travel faster than 70 mph. The *Graf Zeppelin* made 590 flights before it was decommissioned in 1937. The developer of the dirigible, Count ("Graf" in German) Ferdinand von Zeppelin (1838-1917), was a retired German army officer.

Germany dominated the manufacture and commerce of airships until May 6, 1937, when the spectacular *Hindenburg* disaster by hydrogen fire ended passenger flights. In 1938, however, a second *Graf Zeppelin* which operated on noninflammable helium was completed. But also in 1938 the United States refused to export helium to Germany, and the new *Zeppelin* made no commercial flights. In April 1940 both *Graf Zeppelins* were dismantled by Nazi directive.

See Scott Stamp Nos. C13-C15, C18

C23   C24   C25

C32   C33   C34

C35   C36   C38

C40   C42   C43

Issue of 1938

C23	45	.06	6c Eagle Holding Shield, Olive Branch, and Arrows May 14

Issue of 1939

C24	4.75	1.00	30c Transatlantic May 16

Issues of 1941-44. Perf. 11x10-1/2

C25	.18	.03	6c Twin-motor Transport Plane
C25a	1.35	.70	8c Booklet pane of three
C26	.25	.05	8c olive green, sia C25
C27	.45	.15	10c violet, sia C25
C28	1.00	.18	15c brown carmine, sia C25
C29	.85	.15	20c bright green, sia C25
C30	1.35	.20	30c blue, sia C25
C31	3.25	1.25	50c orange, sia C25

Singles from No. C25a are imperf. at sides or imperf. at sides and bottom.

Issue of 1946

C32	.15	.04	5c DC-4 Skymaster Sep. 25

Issues of 1947, Perf. 10-1/2x11

C33	.15	.04	5c DC-4 Skymaster Mar. 26

Perf. 11x10-1/2

C34	.25	.06	10c Pan American Union Bldg., Washington, D.C.
C35	.40	.05	15c Statue of Liberty and New York Skyline
C36	.60	.10	25c Plane over San Francisco-Oakland Bay Bridge

Issues of 1948

Coil Stamp, Perf. 10, Horizontally

C37	.55	.25	5c carmine, sia C33 Jan. 15

Perf. 11x10-1/2

C38	.22	.20	5c New York City Jul. 31

Issued for the 50th anniversary of the consolidation of the five boroughs of New York City.

Issues of 1949

Perf. 10-1/2x11

C39	.15	.03	6c carmine, sia C33 Jan. 18
C39a	2.75	1.50	Booklet pane of six

Perf. 11x10-1/2

C40	.16	.10	6c Alexandria 200th Anniv. May 11

Issued for the 200th anniversary of the founding of Alexandria, Virginia.

Coil Stamp, Perf. 10, Horizontally

C41	1.60	.05	6c carmine, sia C33 Aug. 25

Universal Postal Union Issue

Perf. 11x10-1/2

C42	.30	.25	10c Post Office Dept. Bldg.
C43	.25	.25	15c Globe and Doves Carrying Messages
C44	.75	.55	25c Boeing Stratoliner & Globe

The Universal Postal Union was established in 1874.

C45	.16	.10	6c Wright Brothers Dec. 17

Issued for the 46th anniversary of the first flight of the Wright brothers. December 17, 1903.

	Issue of 1952					**Issues of 1958**		
6	4.00	.90	80c Diamond Head, Honolulu, Hawaii	Mar. 26	C50	.18	.08	5c rose red, sia C48
	Issue of 1953					**Perf. 10-1/2x11**		
7	.16	.10	6c Powered Flight	May 29	C51	.18	.03	7c Silhouette of Jet Liner Jul. 31
	Issued for the 50th anniversary of powered flight.				C51a	5.00	4.00	Booklet pane of six
	Issue of 1954					**Coil Stamp, Perf. 10 Horizontally**		
8	.12	.08	4c Eagle in Flight	Sep. 3	C52	3.75	.12	7c blue, sia C51
	Issue of 1957					**Issues of 1959, Perf. 11x10-1/2**		
9	.20	.10	6c Air Force	Aug. 1	C53	.25	.10	7c Alaska Statehood Jan. 3
	Issued for the 50th anniversary of the U.S. Air Force.							

THE WRIGHT BROTHERS AT KITTY HAWK

If you are looking for perfect safety, you will do well to sit on a fence and watch the birds . . . Wilbur Wright

At 10:30 A.M. on December 17, 1903, Orville (1871-1948) and Wilbur Wright (1867-1912) made the first successful airplane flight. The scene was Kitty Hawk, North Carolina, where steady winds and high sand dunes had long been ideal for the gliding hobby of the Wright brothers, two young bicycle repairmen from Dayton, Ohio.

Plane and pilot weighed 750 pounds. The wings were wooden frames strung together with piano wire and spanned forty feet, six inches. The biplane, propelled by a twelve horsepower, four-cylinder gasoline engine, stayed aloft twelve seconds and flew 120 feet. On this first historic journey Orville piloted the brothers' revolutionary vehicle. At noon Wilbur set the record for the day, a flight of 852 feet in 59 seconds.

See Scott Stamp Nos. 649-650, C45

		Perf. 11				Issues of 1959-66		
C54	.25	.10	7c Balloon Jupiter	Aug. 17	C57	.55	.20	10c Liberty Bell	
					C58	.50	.06	15c Statue of Liberty	
					C59	.60	.05	25c Abraham Lincoln	
		Perf. 11x10-1/2					Issue of 1960, Perf. 10-1/2x11		
C55	.25	.10	7c Hawaii Statehood	Aug. 21	C60	.25	.04	7c Jet Airliner	Aug.
					C60a	20.00	7.00	Booklet pane of six	
		Perf. 11					Coil Stamp, Perf. 10 Horizontally		
C56	.30	.15	10c Pan-American Games		C61	4.50	.20	7c carmine, sia C60	Oct.
				Aug. 27			Issue of 1961-67, Perf. 11		
					C62	.35	.10	13c Liberty Bell	
					C63	.35	.08	15c Statue of Liberty	

Issued for the 100th anniversary of the carrying of mail by the balloon Jupiter from Lafayette to Crawfordsville, Ind.

Hawaii became a state in 1959.

Issued for the 3rd Pan-American Games, held at Chicago from Aug. 27-Sept. 7, 1959.

No. C63 has a gutter between the two parts of the design; No. C58 does not.

AMELIA EARHART (1898-1937)

The bravest thing I did was to try to drop a bag of oranges and a note on the head of an ocean liner's captain — and I missed the whole ship!

Thus remarked Amelia Earhart on June 17, 1928, when she became the first woman passenger to fly the Atlantic Ocean. In spite of such protests, her courage and daring made her an international celebrity. In 1932 she soloed the *Friendship* across the Atlantic and in 1935 conquered the Pacific (Hawaii to California). In 1937, she began a 27,000 mile round-the-world flight. With Fred Noonan navigating, Miss Earhart completed the next-to-last leg of her journey in late June. In July radio contact was lost. Their bodies were never found, and their deaths remain shrouded in mystery.

See Scott Stamp No. C68

Surinam Scott No. 346

Issue of 1962-64			
Perf. 10-1/2x11			
•4	.18	.03	8c Jetliner over Capitol Dec. 5
•4b	1.65	.65	Booklet pane of 5 +label
Coil Stamp, Perf. 10 Horizontally			
•5	.45	.08	8c carmine, sia C64 Dec. 5

Nos. C64 and C65 were issued on Dec. 5, 1962.

•6	.80	.30	15c Montgomery Blair May 3

Montgomery Blair (1813-1883), was Postmaster General from 1861-1864. In 1863 he called the first International Postal Conference, which was a forerunner of the Universal Postal Union.

Issues of 1963-67			
Perf. 11x10-1/2			
•7	.15	.08	6c Bald Eagle Jul. 12, 1963
Perf. 11			
•8	.25	.10	8c Amelia Earhart Jul. 24

Amelia Earhart (1898-1937), was the first woman to fly across the Atlantic.

Issue of 1964			
•9	.30	.10	8c Robert H. Goddard Oct. 5

Dr. Robert H. Goddard (1882-1945), was a physicist and a pioneer rocket researcher.

Issues of 1967			
C70	.25	.12	8c Alaska Purchase Mar. 30

Issued for the 100th anniversary of the Alaska Purchase, this stamp shows a Tlingit totem from southern Alaska.

C71	.65	.15	20c "Columbia Jays" by Audubon Apr. 26

See note after 1241.

Issues of 1968, Perf. 11x10-1/2			
C72	.20	.03	10c 50-Star Runway Jan. 5
C72b	1.60	.75	Booklet pane of eight
C72c	1.00	.45	Booklet pane of 5+ label

Coil Stamp, Perf. 10 Vertically			
C73	.20	.04	10c carmine, sia C72

The $1 Air Lift stamp is listed as No. 1341.

Air Mail Service Issue			
Perf. 11			
C74	.35	.10	10c Curtiss Jenny May 15

Issued for the 50th anniversary of regularly scheduled U.S. air mail service.

C75	.40	.06	20c U.S.A. and Jet Nov. 22

ROBERT H. GODDARD (1882-1945)

More than 800 years ago — before Western man had developed gunpowder — the Chinese hit upon the idea of the rocket. Not until the 20th century, however, did the development of the sophisticated liquid fuel rocket usher man into a new age.

Robert H. Goddard began the first serious work with rockets in the United States about 1909. As early as 1920 he suggested it was theoretically possible to send a rocket to the moon. His theories were scorned in the U.S. but were studied in Germany and Russia with great interest. German research on his models led to the development of the V-2 rocket of World War II. On March 16, 1926, after more than fifteen years of research, Goddard fired the first rocket propelled by liquid fuel. In 1935 he launched a rocket to a height of 7,500 feet.
See Scott Stamp No. C69.

C67 C69 C70 C71

C72 C74 C75

C76   C80   C77   C78   C82   CE2

Issue of 1969				
C76	.20	.10	10c Moon Landing	Sep. 9
Issue of 1971, Perf. 11x10-1/2				
C77	.18	.09	9c Plane	May 15
C78	.22	.11	11c Silhouette of Jet	May 7
C78a	.88	.40	Booklet pane of 4 + 2 labels	
Perf. 11				
C80	.34	.15	17c Statue of Liberty	Jul. 13
Perf. 11x10-1/2				
C81	.42	.21	21c red, blue & black, sia C75	May 21

Coil Stamp, Perf. 10 Vertically				
C82	.22	.11	11c Silhouette of Jet	May 7

Air Post Special Delivery Stamps

To provide for the payment of both the postage and the special delivery fee in one stamp.

CE1	.60	.55	16c dark blue, sia CE2
			For imperforate variety, see No. 771.
Issue of 1936			
CE2	.45	.18	16c Great Seal of United States

MEN ON THE MOON

That's one small step for a man, one giant leap for mankind. Neil A. Armstrong

On July 20, 1969 a concept of science fiction became fact when man took his first steps on the moon. Millions of people watched Apollo 11 astronauts Neil Armstrong and Edwin Aldrin Jr. descend to the landing site in the lunar module "Eagle", while Michael Collins continued to orbit the moon in the command module "Columbia". For 21 hours and 37 minutes the astronauts lived on the forbidding lunar surface. During their two-hour moon walk they collected about fifty pounds of moon rocks and soil samples for scientific analysis. Before leaving Armstrong and Aldrin planted a United States flag which, due to the absence of atmosphere, had to be flown on a metal support. An accompanying plaque, signed by President Nixon, states that the people of the United States achieved the moon landing for "peaceful purposes".

Since 1969 four more manned U.S. moon flights have been made. During the Apollo 15 mission of 1971 astronauts David Scott and James Irwin established the first U.S. post office on the moon.

See Scott Stamp No. C76

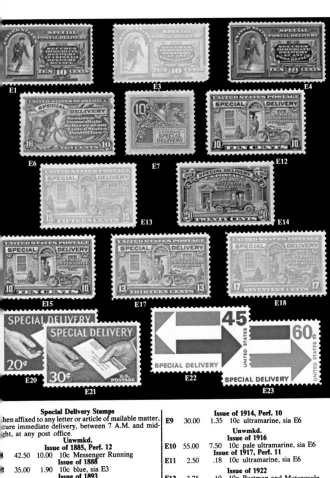

Special Delivery Stamps

...hen affixed to any letter or article of mailable matter, ...cure immediate delivery, between 7 A.M. and mid-...ght, at any post office.

Unwmkd.

Issue of 1885, Perf. 12

	42.50	10.00	10c Messenger Running

Issue of 1888

	35.00	1.90	10c blue, sia E3

Issue of 1893

	11.00	3.50	0c Messenger Running

Issue of 1894, Line under "Ten Cents"

	95.00	5.00	10c Messenger Running

Issue of 1895

Wmkd. USPS (191)

	8.75	.55	10c blue, sia E4

Issue of 1902

	8.50	.80	10c Messenger on Bicycle

Issue of 1908

	8.25	8.00	10c Mercury Helmet and Olive Branch

Issue of 1911

Wmkd. USPS (190)

	11.00	1.00	10c ultramarine, sia E6

Issue of 1914, Perf. 10

E9	30.00	1.35	10c ultramarine, sia E6

Unwmkd.

Issue of 1916

E10	55.00	7.50	10c pale ultramarine, sia E6

Issue of 1917, Perf. 11

E11	2.50	.18	10c ultramarine, sia E6

Issue of 1922

E12	3.75	.10	10c Postman and Motorcycle

Issue of 1925

E13	2.50	.20	15c Postman and Motorcycle
E14	1.00	.60	20c Post Office Truck

Issue of 1927, Perf. 11x10-1/2

E15	.35	.04	10c Postman and Motorcycle

Issue of 1931

E16	.50	.08	15c orange, sia E12

Issue of 1944

E17	.35	.06	13c Postman and Motorcycle
E18	.90	.60	17c Postman and Motorcycle

Issue of 1951

E19	.60	.10	20c black. sia E14

Issue of 1954-57

E20	.55	.08	20c Delivery of Letter
E21	.60	.04	30c Delivery of Letter

Issue of 1969-71, Perf. 11

E22	.90	.08	45c Arrows
E23	1.20	.10	60c Arrows

F1

FA1

Registration Stamp

Issued for the prepayment of registry; not usable for postage. Sales discontinued May 28, 1913.

Issue of 1911, Perf. 12

Wmkd. USPS (190)

F1   12.00   1c Bald Eagle

Certified Mail Stamp

For use on first-class mail for which no indemnity value is claimed, but for which proof of mailing and proof of delivery are available at less cost than registered mail.

Issue of 1955, Perf. 10-1/2x11

FA1   .35   .25   15c Letter Carrier

J2   J25

J19

J33

J69   J78

J88   J98   J101

JQ1

JQ5

128

Postage Due Stamps

For affixing by a postal clerk to any mail to de amount to be collected from addressee becaus insufficient prepayment of postage.

Printed by American Banknote Company
Issue of 1879, Design of J2, Perf. 12 Unwmk.

J1	2.50	1.25	1c brown
J2	18.00	1.50	2c Figure of Value
J3	.95	.60	3c brown
J4	16.00	5.00	5c brown
J5	42.50	2.85	10c brown
J6	8.50	5.25	30c brown
J7	21.50	8.00	50c brown

Special Printing

J8	1100.00	1c deep brown
J9	600.00	2c deep brown
J10	600.00	3c deep brown
J11	475.00	5c deep brown
J12	475.00	30c deep brown
J13	350.00	30c deep brown
J14	350.00	50c deep brown

Regular Issue of 1884-89 Design of J19, Perf.

J15	1.60	.55	1c red brown
J16	1.00	.45	2c red brown
J17	36.00	15.00	3c red brown
J18	8.50	2.25	5c red brown
J19	9.00	1.10	10c Figure of Value
J20	8.00	6.00	30c red brown
J21	100.00	35.00	50c red brown

Issue of 1891-93 Design of J25, Perf. 12

J22	.30	.15	1c bright claret
J23	.45	.10	2c bright claret
J24	1.00	.85	3c bright claret
J25	1.40	.95	5c Figure of Value
J26	3.50	1.45	10c bright claret
J27	18.50	14.00	30c bright claret
J28	21.00	16.00	50c bright claret

Printed by the Bureau of Engraving and Printing
Issue of 1894 Design of J33, Perf. 12

J29	38.50	14.00	1c vermilion
J30	12.50	7.00	2c vermilion
J31	.85	.75	1c deep claret
J32	.55	.45	2c deep claret
J33	4.75	4.00	3c Figure of Value
J34	7.00	5.00	5c deep claret
J35	4.00	2.50	10c deep rose
J36	18.00	13.50	30c deep claret
J37	35.00	27.00	50c deep claret

Issue of 1895 Design of J33, Perf. 12

Wmkd. USPS (191)

J38	.18	.12	1c deep claret
J39	.18	.08	2c deep claret
J40	1.20	.45	3c deep claret
J41	1.20	.35	5c deep claret
J42	1.40	.55	10c deep claret
J43	21.00	4.00	30c deep claret
J44	7.25	5.00	50c deep claret

Issue of 1910-12 Design of J33, Perf. 12

Wmkd. USPS (190)

J45	.85	.75	1c deep claret
J46	.50	.08	2c deep claret
J47	25.00	4.00	3c deep claret
J48	2.50	.65	5c deep claret
J49	2.50	1.45	10c deep claret
J50	57.50	15.00	50c deep claret

Issue of 1914-15, Design of J33, Perf. 10

J52	3.75	2.00	1c carmine lake
J53	.90	.12	2c carmine lake
J54	35.00	2.25	3c carmine lake
J55	1.25	.75	5c carmine lake
J56	1.85	.30	10c carmine lake
J57	6.75	5.50	30c carmine lake
J58	250.00	100.00	50c carmine lake

Issue of 1916, Design of J33, Perf. 10
Unwmkd.

J59	100.00	40.00	1c rose
J60	2.75	.55	2c rose

Issue of 1917, Design of J33 Perf. 11

61	.08	.05	1c carmine rose
62	.15	.04	2c carmine rose
63	.35	.08	3c carmine rose
64	.35	.08	5c carmine rose
65	.55	.20	10c carmine rose
J66	2.00	.20	30c carmine rose
J67	2.65	.08	50c carmine rose

Issue of 1925, Design of J33, Perf. 11

J68	.08	.06	1/2c dull red

Issue of 1930-31, Design of J69, Perf. 11

69	.25	.18	1/2c Figure of Value
70	.20	.10	1c carmine
71	.30	.10	2c carmine
72	1.40	.40	3c carmine
73	1.15	.50	5c carmine
74	1.60	.30	10c carmine
75	4.25	.50	30c carmine
76	4.50	.12	50c carmine

Design of J78

J77	2.75	.12	$1 carmine
J78	10.00	.18	$5 "FIVE" on $

Issue of 1931-56, Design of J69
Perf. 11x10-1/2

J79	.10	.08	1/2c dull carmine
J80	.05	.03	1c dull carmine
J81	.06	.03	2c dull carmine
J82	.10	.03	3c dull carmine
J83	.15	.03	5c dull carmine
J84	.30	.10	10c dull carmine
J85	1.20	.08	30c dull carmine
J86	1.45	.06	50c dull carmine

Perf. 10-1/2x11

J87	3.25	.20	$1 scarlet, same design as J78

Issue of 1959, Perf. 11x10-1/2
Design of J88 and J98

J88	.40	.20	1/2c Figure of Value
J89	.03	.03	1c carmine rose
J90	.04	.03	2c carmine rose
J91	.06	.03	3c carmine rose
J92	.08	.03	4c carmine rose
J93	.10	.03	5c carmine rose
J94	.12	.04	6c carmine rose
J95	.14	.04	7c carmine rose
J96	.16	.04	8c carmine rose
J97	.20	.03	10c carmine rose
J98	.60	.04	30c Figure of Value
J99	1.00	.05	50c carmine rose

Design of J101

J100	2.00	.05	$1 carmine rose
J101	7.50	.15	$5 Outline Figure of Value

Parcel Post Postage Due Stamps

For affixing by a postal clerk, to any parcel post package, to denote the amount to be collected from the addressee because of insufficient prepayment of postage.

Beginning July 1, 1913, these stamps were valid for use as regular postage due stamps.

Issue of 1912

Wmkd. USPS (190)

Design of JQ1 and JQ5
Perf. 12

Q1	1.50	1.00	1c Figure of Value
Q2	8.50	5.00	2c dark green
Q3	1.75	1.50	5c dark green
Q4	18.50	13.00	10c dark green
Q5	10.00	1.20	25c Figure of Value

United States Offices in China

Issued for sale by the postal agency at Shanghai, China, at their surcharged value in local currency. Valid to the amount of their original values for the prepayment of postage on mail dispatched from the United States postal agency at Shanghai to addresses in the United States.

Issue of 1919, Perf. 11
K1-K7: Washington, sia K1

K1	2.75	3.25	2c on 1c
K2	2.75	3.25	4c on 2c rose
K3	3.25	3.75	6c on 3c violet
K4	4.00	4.75	8c on 4c brown
K5	5.00	5.75	10c on 5c blue
K6	5.25	6.00	12c on 6c red orange
K7	5.50	6.50	14c on 7c black

K8-K16: Franklin, sia K8

K8	4.50	5.25	16c on 8c
K9	4.50	5.50	18c on 9c salmon red
K10	4.00	4.75	20c on 10c orange yellow
K11	5.50	6.25	24c on 12c brown carmine
K12	6.25	7.00	30c on 15c gray
K13	6.25	7.25	40c on 20c deep ultramarine
K14	7.00	8.25	60c on 30c orange red
K15	45.00	45.00	$1 on 50c light violet
K16	22.50	22.50	$2 on $1 violet brown

Issue of 1922

K17	10.00	10.00	2c on 1c Washington
K18	11.00	11.00	4c on 2c Washington

U.S. Stamps of 1917-19 Surcharged:

K1   K8

U.S. Stamp Nos. 498 and 528B Surcharged:

K17   K18

Official Stamps
Perf. 12, Unwmkd.

The franking privilege having been abolished, as of July 1, 1873, these stamps were provided for each of the departments of Government for the prepayment of postage on official matter.

These stamps were supplanted on May 1, 1879 by penalty envelopes and on July 5, 1884 were declared obsolete.

Designs are as follows: Post Office officials, figures of value and department name; all other departments, various portraits and department names.

O6   **O7**

Issues of 1873
Printed by the Continental Bank Note Co.
Thin Hard Paper
Dept. of Agriculture: Yellow

O1	11.50	10.00	1c Franklin
O2	4.25	4.25	2c Jackson
O3	2.65	1.10	3c Washington
O4	4.75	4.00	6c Lincoln
O5	15.00	13.00	10c Jefferson
O6	23.00	20.00	12c Clay
O7	15.00	13.00	15c Webster
O8	16.00	15.00	24c Winfield Scott
O9	20.00	18.50	30c Hamilton

Executive Dept.

O10	42.50	40.00	1c carmine, Franklin
O11	30.00	27.50	2c Jackson
O12	28.00	22.50	3c violet rose, Washington
O13	50.00	45.00	6c carmine, Lincoln
O14	45.00	40.00	10c Jefferson

Dept. of the Interior: Vermillion

O15	1.35	1.20	1c Franklin
O16	.80	.80	2c Jackson
O17	3.25	.75	3c Washington
O18	2.00	.80	6c Lincoln

O11   **O14**

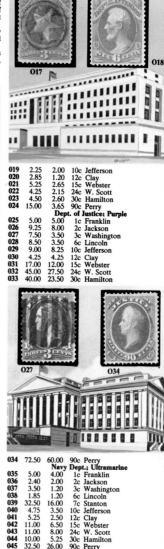

O17   **O18**

O19	2.25	2.00	10c Jefferson
O20	2.85	1.20	12c Clay
O21	5.25	2.65	15c Webster
O22	4.25	2.15	24c W. Scott
O23	4.50	2.60	30c Hamilton
O24	15.00	3.65	90c Perry

Dept. of Justice: Purple

O25	5.00	5.00	1c Franklin
O26	9.25	8.00	2c Jackson
O27	7.50	3.50	3c Washington
O28	8.50	3.50	6c Lincoln
O29	9.00	8.25	10c Jefferson
O30	4.25	4.25	12c Clay
O31	17.00	12.00	15c Webster
O32	45.00	27.50	24c W. Scott
O33	40.00	23.50	30c Hamilton

O27   **O34**

O34	72.50	60.00	90c Perry

Navy Dept.; Ultramarine

O35	5.00	4.00	1c Franklin
O36	2.40	2.00	2c Jackson
O37	3.50	1.20	3c Washington
O38	1.85	1.20	6c Lincoln
O39	32.50	16.00	7c Stanton
O40	4.75	3.50	10c Jefferson
O41	5.25	2.50	12c Clay
O42	11.00	6.50	15c Webster
O43	11.00	8.00	24c W. Scott
O44	10.00	5.25	30c Hamilton
O45	32.50	26.00	90c Perry

Post Office Dept.: Black

O47	1.10	1.10	1c Figure of Value
O48	1.35	1.00	2c Figure of Value
O49	.40	.30	3c Figure of Value
O50	1.10	.85	6c Figure of Value

1	6.75	6.25	10c Figure of Value
2	2.25	2.00	12c Figure of Value
3	2.75	2.65	15c Figure of Value
4	4.00	3.25	24c Figure of Value
5	2.50	2.25	30c Figure of Value
6	4.00	2.65	90c Figure of Value

Dept. of State

7	3.75	3.50	1c dark green Franklin
8	8.50	6.25	2c dark green Jackson
9	2.85	2.65	3c bright green Washington
0	2.65	2.50	6c bright green Lincoln
1	6.00	4.50	7c dark green Stanton

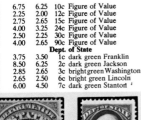

O57

O71

2	3.50	3.25	10c dark green Jefferson
3	9.50	9.00	12c dark green Clay
4	5.75	5.75	15c dark green Webster
5	24.00	18.00	24c dark green W. Scott
6	20.00	16.50	30c Hamilton
7	36.00	31.50	90c dark green Perry
8	90.00	57.50	$2 green and black Seward
9	625.00	425.00	$5 green and black Seward
0	400.00	300.00	$10 green and black Seward
1	350.00	265.00	$20 Seward

Treasury Dept.: Brown

2	1.70	.75	1c Franklin
3	2.10	.70	2c Jackson
4	1.10	.35	3c Washington
5	1.50	.40	6c Lincoln
6	2.90	2.00	7c Stanton
7	3.25	1.10	10c Jefferson
8	3.35	.65	12c Clay

O44

O91

O50

O52

079	3.50	.95	15c Webster
080	19.00	11.50	24c W. Scott
081	6.50	1.35	30c Hamilton
082	7.50	1.10	90c Perry

War Dept.: Rose

083	10.00	1.25	1c Franklin
084	7.75	2.35	2c Jackson
085	7.50	.65	3c Washington
086	25.00	1.10	6c Lincoln
087	7.00	6.00	7c Stanton
088	1.60	1.50	10c Jefferson
089	8.00	1.00	12c Clay
090	.65	.65	15c Webster
091	1.10	1.10	24c W. Scott
092	1.00	.90	30c Hamilton
093	4.00	3.75	90c Perry

O76

O77

Issues of 1879
Printed by the American Banknote Co.
Soft, Porous Paper

Dept. of Agriculture: Yellow

094	300.00		1c Franklin, issued without gum
095	27.50	6.50	3c Washington

Dept. of the Interior: Vermilion

096	17.50	16.00	1c Franklin
097	.55	.55	2c Jackson
098	.45	.35	3c Washington
099	.55	.55	6c Lincoln
0100	5.25	5.25	10c Jefferson
0101	9.00	8.00	12c Clay
0102	20.00	18.50	15c Webster
0103	225.00		24c W. Scott

Dept. of Justice: Bluish Purple

0106	6.50	6.00	3c Washington
0107	17.50	15.00	6c Lincoln

			Post Office Dept.
0108	1.20	.90	3c black, Figure of Value

Treasury Dept: Brown

0109	3.25	1.00	3c Washington
0110	7.00	5.00	6c Lincoln
0111	11.00	3.00	10c Jefferson
0112	115.00	40.00	30c Hamilton
0113	110.00	50.00	90c Perry

War Dept.

0114	.45	.45	1c Franklin
0115	.70	.65	2c rose red, Jackson
0115a	.80	.75	2c dull vermilion, Jackson
0116	.55	.35	3c rose red, Washington
0116a	425.00		3c Imperf. (pair)
0117	.45	.40	6c rose red, Lincoln
0118	2.75	3.00	10c rose red, Jefferson
0119	1.40	1.00	12c rose red, Clay
0120	6.00	6.00	30c rose red, Hamilton

O93   O95

O101   O114

O121   O122   O123

O124   O125   O126

Official Postal Savings Mail
Perf. 12

These stamps were used to prepay postage on official correspondence of the Postal Savings Division of the Post Office Department.
Discontinued Sept. 23, 1914

Issues of 1911

Wmkd. USPS (191)

0121	1.85	.55	2c Official Postal Savings
0122	17.50	8.50	50c Official Postal Savings
0123	10.00	3.25	$1 Official Postal Savings

Wmkd. USPS (190)

0124	1.20	.55	1c Official Postal Savings
0125	4.50	1.20	2c Official Postal Savings
0126	1.85	.50	10c Official Postal Savings

132

NEWSPAPER STAMPS

The spread of popular education and improved production methods in the mid-1800's led to the rise of the mass penny press. Because the mails were used for bulk shipments of newspapers, the U.S. Post Office issued special stamps for them beginning in 1865. Many of these stamps were not used on mail, but were cancelled by postal clerks and kept on file. Because the stamps did not circulate, used copies are quite rare and valuable. Newspaper issues also include the largest U.S. stamps and denominations are quite high—up to $100. When the stamps were discontinued, on July 1, 1898, collectors persuaded the post office to sell the remainders. Sold at $5 a set, this is the only time in history that the post office has sold stamps at a discount.

Newspaper Stamps
Perf. 12
Issues of 1865
Printed by the National Bank Note Co.
Thin, Hard Paper, No Gum, Unwmkd.
Colored Borders

PR1	35.00	5c Washington
PR2	13.50	10c Franklin
PR3	14.00	25c Lincoln

White Border, Yellowish Paper

PR4	9.50	9.50	5c light blue, sia PR1

Reprints of 1875
Printed by the Continental Bank Note Co.
Hard, White Paper, No Gum

PR5	15.00	5c dull blue, sia PR1, white border
PR6	11.00	10c dark bluish green, sia PR2, colored border
PR7	18.00	25c dark carmine, sia PR3, colored border

Issue of 1880
Printed by the American Bank Note Co.
Soft, Porous Paper, White Border

PR8	25.00	5c dark blue, sia PR1

Issues of 1875
Printed by the Continental Bank Note Co.
Thin, Hard Paper
PR9-PR15: "Statue of Freedom", sia PR15

PR9	1.35	1.35	2c black
PR10	2.35	2.25	3c black
PR11	2.25	2.00	4c black
PR12	3.25	3.00	6c black
PR13	4.25	4.00	8c black
PR14	5.75	5.75	9c black
PR15	3.65	2.90	10c Statue of Freedom

PR16-PR23: "Justice", sia PR18

PR16	4.85	4.50	12c rose
PR17	7.50	7.00	24c rose
PR18	9.50	8.50	36c "Justice"
PR19	17.00	10.00	48c rose
PR20	8.25	8.00	60c rose
PR21	23.50	20.00	72c rose
PR22	25.00	21.00	84c rose
PR23	19.50	17.00	96c rose
PR24	14.00	11.00	1.92 Ceres
PR25	20.00	14.50	$3 "Victory"
PR26	50.00	37.50	$6 Clio
PR27	55.00	45.00	$9 Minerva
PR28	55.00	47.50	$12 Vesta
PR29	60.00	50.00	$24 "Peace"
PR30	87.50	75.00	$36 "Commerce"

PR31	140.00	115.00	$48.00 red brown Hebe, sia PR78
PR32	130.00	110.00	$60.00 violet Indian Maiden, sia PR79

Special Printing, Hard, White Paper, Without Gum
PR33-PR39: Statue of Freedom, sia PR15

PR33	10.00	2c gray black
PR34	9.00	3c gray black
PR35	9.00	4c gray black
PR36	10.00	6c gray black
PR37	10.00	8c gray black
PR38	10.00	9c gray black
PR39	17.00	10c gray black

PR40-PR47: "Justice", sia PR18

PR40	30.00	12c pale rose
PR41	47.50	24c pale rose
PR42	55.00	36c pale rose
PR43	67.50	48c pale rose
PR44	90.00	60c pale rose
PR45	120.00	72c pale rose
PR46	130.00	84c pale rose
PR47	150.00	96c pale rose
PR48	*600.00*	1.92 dk. brn. Ceres, sia PR24
PR49	800.00	$3 verm. "Victory", sia PR25

PR1   PR2   PR3

PR15   PR18   PR24   PR25   PR26

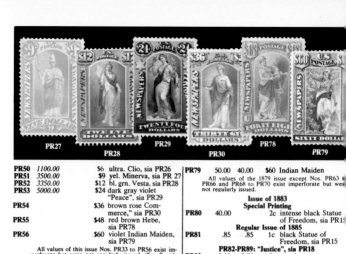

| PR27 | PR28 | PR29 | PR30 | PR78 | PR79 |

PR50	*1100.00*		$6 ultra. Clio, sia PR26
PR51	*3500.00*		$9 yel. Minerva, sia PR 27
PR52	*3350.00*		$12 bl. grn. Vesta. sia PR28
PR53	*5000.00*		$24 dark gray violet "Peace", sia PR29
PR54			$36 brown rose Commerce," sia PR30
PR55			$48 red brown Hebe, sia PR78
PR56			$60 violet Indian Maiden, sia PR79

All values of this issue Nos. PR33 to PR56 exist imperforate but were not regularly issued. (See Scott's U.S. Specialized Catalogue.)

Issue of 1879
Printed by the American Bank Note Co.
Soft, Porous Paper
PR57-PR62: Statue of Freedom, sia PR15

PR57	1.00	1.00	2c black
PR58	1.10	1.10	3c black
PR59	1.40	1.40	4c black
PR60	3.00	3.00	6c black
PR61	3.00	3.00	8c black
PR62	2.50	2.25	10c black

PR63-PR70: "Justice", sia PR18

PR63	7.50	6.50	12c red
PR64	7.00	5.50	24c red
PR65	30.00	22.50	36c red
PR66	20.00	16.50	48c red
PR67	16.50	15.00	60c red
PR68	40.00	38.50	72c red
PR69	30.00	27.50	84c red
PR70	21.50	20.00	96c red
PR71	13.00	12.00	$1.92 purple brown Ceres, sia PR24
PR72	14.50	13.00	$3 red vermilion "Victory", sia PR25
PR73	30.00	25.00	$6 blue Clio, sia PR26
PR74	18.50	16.50	$9 org. Minerva, sia PR27
PR75	22.50	19.00	$12 yellow green Vesta, sia PR28
PR76	35.00	27.50	$24 dark violet "Peace" sia PR29
PR77	45.00	35.00	$36 Indian red, "Commerce," sia PR30
PR78	50.00	40.00	$48 Hebe

PR79	50.00	40.00	$60 Indian Maiden

All values of the 1879 issue except Nos. PR63 & PR66 and PR68 to PR70 exist imperforate but were not regularly issued.

Issue of 1883
Special Printing

PR80	40.00	2c intense black Statue of Freedom, sia PR15

Regular Issue of 1885

PR81	.85	.85	1c black Statue of Freedom, sia PR15

PR82-PR89: "Justice", sia PR18

PR82	3.00	2.75	12c carmine
PR83	4.25	4.00	24c carmine
PR84	5.50	5.00	36c carmine
PR85	6.50	6.50	48c carmine
PR86	10.00	9.50	60c carmine
PR87	12.50	11.50	72c carmine
PR88	25.00	23.50	84c carmine
PR89	16.00	15.00	96c carmine

All values of the 1885 issue exist imperforate but were not regularly issued.

Issue of 1894
Printed by the Bureau of Engraving and Printing
Soft Wove Paper
PR90-PR94: Statue of Freedom, sia PR90

PR90	2.00		1c Statue of Freedom
PR91	2.00		2c intense black
PR92	3.00		4c intense black
PR93	*375.00*		6c intense black
PR94	5.00		10c intense black

PR95-PR99: "Justice", sia PR18

PR95	25.00		12c pink
PR96	15.00		24c pink
PR97	185.00		36c pink
PR98	185.00		60c pink
PR99	250.00		96c pink
PR100	*600.00*		$3 scarlet "Victory", sia PR25
PR101	*1000.00*		$6 pl. blue Clio, sia PR26

Issue of 1895, Unwmkd.
PR102-PR105: Statue of Freedom, sia PR116

PR102	2.00	1.35	1c black
PR103	2.25	1.75	2c black
PR104	2.50	2.25	5c black
PR105	7.00	5.75	10c black

| PR90 | PR116 | PR118 | PR119 | PR120 |

GROWTH OF A FREE PRESS

Were it left to me to decide whether we should have a government without newspapers, or newspapers without a government, I should not hesitate to prefer the latter. Thomas Jefferson

The first newspaper in the American colonies, published in 1690, promptly came under government attack. But by the time of the American Revolution the right to freedom of the press was firmly established and since then journalists have been among our most influential citizens. Most important of the early printers was Benjamin Franklin who in 1729 bought the *Pennsylvania Gazette.* In 1737 Franklin was appointed postmaster of Pennsylvania and began the practice of cheap and fast distribution of the news through the mails. Later editors such as Horace Greeley and Frederick Douglass helped institute social reforms including the abolition of slavery. Such men began the traditions of modern journalism. In addition to dispensing the news, newspapers began to include informational and educational features. Directed at the masses, newspapers spread education and culture, creating an enlightened citizenry to lead the growth and direction of the nation.

See Scott Stamp Nos. 946, 1073, 1119, 1177, 1290

06	8.00	6.50	25c carmine "Justice," sia PR118
07	19.00	15.00	50c carmine "Justice," sia PR119
08	13.50	6.00	$2 scarlet "Victory," sia PR120
09	32.00	21.50	$5 ultra, Clio, sia PR121
10	25.00	19.00	$10 green Vesta, sia PR122
11	55.00	37.50	$20 slate "Peace", sia PR123
12	52.50	25.00	$50 dull rose, "Commerce," sia PR124
13	70.00	47.50	$100 purple Indian Maiden, sia PR125

Issue of 1895-97

Wmkd. USPS (191)

Yellowish Gum

14	.70	.70	1c black, Statue of Freedom, sia PR116
15	.60	.60	2c black, Statue of Freedom, sia PR116

PR116	1.45	1.40	5c Statue of Freedom
PR117	.75	.65	10c black, Statue of Freedom, sia PR116
PR118	1.35	1.20	25c "Justice"
PR119	1.60	1.10	50c "Justice"
PR120	2.00	1.85	$2 "Victory"
PR121	20.00	7.50	$5 Clio
PR122	3.50	3.50	$10 Vesta
PR123	3.25	3.00	$20 "Peace"
PR124	4.75	4.50	$50 "Commerce"
PR125	7.00	5.50	$100 Indian Maiden

In 1899, the Government sold 26,989 sets of these stamps, but as the stock of the high values was not sufficient to make up the required number, the $5.00, $10.00, $20.00, $50.00 and $100.00 were reprinted. The reprints may be distinguished by the gum which is white instead of yellowish and by the shades.

Reprints of 1899

PR126	2.25		$5 dk. blue, sia PR121
PR127	2.25		$10 green, sia PR122
PR128	2.25		$20 slate, sia PR123
PR129	3.25		$50 dull rose, sia PR124
PR130	3.25		$100 purple, sia PR125

PR121   PR122   PR123   PR124   PR125

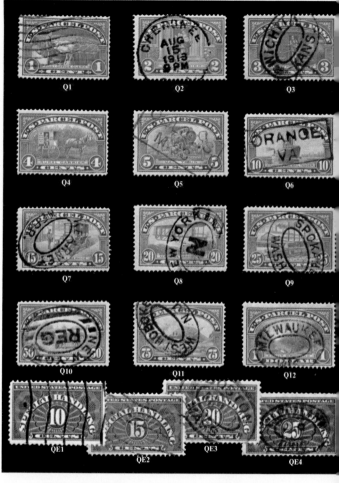

PARCEL POST STAMPS

Issued for the prepayment of postage on parcel post packages only.

Beginning July 1, 1913, these stamps were valid for all postal purposes.

Wmkd. **USPS** (190)

Issue of 1912-13, Perf. 12

Q1	1.10	.55	1c Post Office Clerk
Q2	1.15	.40	2c City Carrier
Q3	2.75	2.00	3c Railway Postal Clerk
Q4	6.50	.95	4c Rural Carrier
Q5	5.00	.50	5c Mail Train
Q6	8.25	.80	10c Steamship and Mail Tender
Q7	13.00	4.50	15c Automobile Service
Q8	16.00	5.50	20c Airplane Carrying Mail
Q9	9.50	1.75	25c Manufacturing
Q10	53.50	18.50	50c Dairying
Q11	10.00	7.25	75c Harvesting
Q12	72.50	7.25	$1 Fruit Growing

SPECIAL HANDLING STAMPS

For use on parcel post packages to secure the same expeditious handling accorded to first class mail matter.

Issue of 1925-29, Design of QE3
Perf. 11

QE1	.45	.25	10c Special Handling
QE2	.60	.35	15c Special Handling
QE3	.75	.60	20c Special Handling
QE4	4.00	2.85	25c Special Handling

136

JEFFERSON DAVIS (1808-89)

While Grant and Lee fought on the bloody battlefields of the Civil War, Jefferson Davis waged an insurmountable war to provide food and guns for his troops. Early in the war Davis, the first and only president of the Confederate States of America, had seen that it would be a long fight and had chosen his military leaders well—such as Robert E. Lee and Stonewall Jackson. But in spite of tactical victories, the agricultural South could not hold out against the industrial North, and Davis was faced with a crumbling economy and a short-sighted congress in Richmond, Virginia. Despite such odds Davis managed to keep the South together for four long years. Following the Confederacy's collapse, he was imprisoned on treason charges for two years but was released after the amnesty proclamation of 1868.

Confederate States
Postmasters' Provisionals

On June 1, 1861, the Confederate States of America stopped using U. S. stamps. Between that date and the first issue of Confederate Government stamps on October 16, 1861, postmasters in different cities issued provisional stamps for use on Southern mail.

1X2	350.00	150.00	5c Baton Rouge, La.
47X2	1000.00	450.00	5c Knoxville, Tenn.
56X1	20.00	300.00	2c Memphis, Tenn.
58X2	95.00	35.00	5c Mobile, Ala.
62X1	22.50	60.00	2c New Orleans, La.
62X2	27.50	200.00	2c New Orleans, La.
62X3	35.00	22.50	5c New Orleans, La.

General Issues, All Imperf.
Issue of 1861: Lithographed Unwatermarked

	25.00	14.00	5c Jefferson Davis
	25.00	21.00	10c Thomas Jefferson

Issues of 1862

3	82.50	130.00	2c Andrew Jackson
4	13.00	13.00	5c blue J. Davis, sia 1
5	140.00	58.50	10c Thomas Jefferson

Typographed

6	2.00	3.25	5c J. Davis (London print)
7	3.50	3.50	5c blue, sia 6 (local print)

Issues of 1863, Engraved

8	9.00	35.00	2c Andrew Jackson

Thick or Thin Paper

9	110.00	90.00	10c Jefferson Davis
10	600.00	300.00	10c blue, sia 9, (with rectangular frame)

Prices of 10 are for copies showing parts of lines on at least two sides of frame.

11	2.25	3.25	10c blue J. Davis, die A, sia 11c
11c	2.25	3.25	10c blue J. Davis, die A
12	2.25	3.25	10c blue J. Davis, die B, sia 11c

Dies A and B differ in that B has an extra line outside its corner ornaments.

13	7.00	40.00	20c George Washington

Issue of 1862, Typographed

14	23.50		1c John C. Calhoun (This stamp was never put in use.)

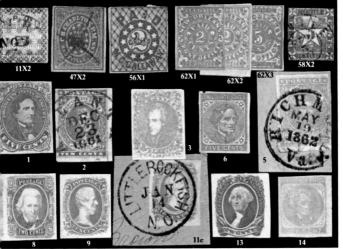

137

CANAL ZONE
(kā•nǎl zōn)

LOCATION—A strip of land ten miles wide, extending through the Republic of Panama, from the Atlantic to the Pacific Ocean.
GOVT.—A United States Government Reservation.
AREA—552.8 sq. mi.
POP.—44,650 (1970).

The Canal Zone, site of tne Panama Canal, was leased in perpetuity to the United States for a cash payment of $10,000,000 and a yearly rental ($1,930,000 a year since 1955). The cities of Panama and Colon remain under the authority of Panama, subject to certain U.S. jurisdiction.

100 Centavos = 1 Peso
100 Centesimos = 1 Balboa
100 Cents = 1 Dollar

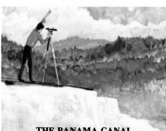

THE PANAMA CANAL

Today they call it one of mankind's greatest works, this fifty-mile canal. But less than a century ago Isthmus jungle stood where the canal now flows. Its tangled mass blocked the efforts of far-sighted men who sensed the time had come for a change; that sailing from Atlantic to Pacific by the route Magellan used (around Cape Horn) was too slow for the needs of a modern age.

Issues of 1904
Blue-black Handstamp, "CANAL ZONE," on Panama Nos. 72, 72c, 78 and 79.
Perf. 12, Unwmkd.

1	115.00	115.00	2c Map of Panama
2	55.00	50.00	5c Map of Panama
3	75.00	70.00	10c Map of Panama

Counterfeit "CANAL ZONE" overprints exist.

United States
Nos. 300, 319, 304, 306 and 307
Overprinted in Black

CANAL ZONE PANAMA

Wmkd. USPS **(191)**

4	6.00	5.50	1c Franklin
5	5.00	4.00	2c Washington
6	18.00	18.00	5c bl. Lincoln, sia U.S. 304
7	30.00	30.00	8c violet black M. Washington, sia U.S. 306
8	32.00	32.00	10c Webster

Issues of 1904-06 Unwmkd.

Black Overprint on Stamps of Panama.

CANAL ZONE

The first country to try its hand at digging a canal was France (1882). This attempt met with failure. When Theodore Roosevelt became president of the United States in 1901 he correctly sensed that a U. S. built canal would add to American prestige and might. Roosevelt moved to complete the project but was faced with mossback Congressmen who held back badly needed funds.

9	1.00	.65	1c Map of Panama
10	1.25	1.00	2c rose, sia 9

Overprinted "CANAL ZONE" in Black, "PANAMA" 15 mm. long and Bar in Red.

11	2.00	1.75	2c rose, sia 13

1.50	1.00	5c blue, sia 13
4.00	3.50	10c Map of Panama
5.00	4.00	8c in red on 50c Map of Panama."PANAMA" reading up and down

Nos. 11, 12 and 13 are overprinted, and 14 is surcharged on Panama Nos. 77, 78, 79 and 81.

While politicians haggled over where and how to dig the canal, Roosevelt acted to achieve his goal. He picked Panama, then a part of Colombia, as the site. When Colombia failed to ratify the project Panama revolted, gained its independence (1903) and gave the United States permanent use of a ten-mile-wide canal zone for which America now pays $1.93 million annually.

Panama No. 74 Overprinted "CANAL ZONE" in Regular Type and Surcharged. 13mm long "PANAMA" reading up on both sides.
Issue of 1905

550.00	550.00	8c in red on 50c bistre brown, sia 14

Issues of 1906

.35	.35	1c in blk. on 20c vio., sia 17
.55	.55	2c in black on 1p Map of Panama

Issues of 1905-06

16.00	15.00	8c in red on 50c Map of Panama
12.00	12.00	8c without period in red on 50c bistre brown, sia 20
5.50	5.00	8c in red on 50c Map of Panama."PANAMA" reading up and down

Stamps of Panama Overprinted "CANAL ZONE" in Black
Issue of 1906, Overprint Reading Up

21	4.50	4.00	2c Francisco de Córdoba

Issue of 1906-07, Overprint Reading Down

22	.75	.50	1c Vasco Núñez de Balboa
23	.75	.60	2c red & black Córdoba, sia 21
24	1.50	.65	5c Justo Arosemena
25	4.00	1.65	8c Manuel J. Hurtado
26	4.00	1.50	10c José de Obaldía

Overwhelming obstacles, including mud, earth slides, and disease faced the men who built the canal. Opened in 1914, it remains one of the United States greatest technological achievements. Roosevelt, often questioned about his alleged role in the Panamanian revolt that helped make it possible, once said, "If I had followed conventional, conservative methods, I should have submitted a dignified state paper...to the Congress and the debate would have been going on yet..."

Issue of 1909, Overprint Reading Down

27	4.00	1.75	2c vermilion and black Córdoba, sia 32
28	9.50	2.50	5c Arosemena
29	7.00	2.50	8c Hurtado
30	8.00	2..75	10c Obaldía

Issues of 1909-10
Type I Black Overprint Reading Up*

31	.75	.50	1c Balboa
31c	90.00		Booklet pane of six, handmade, perf. margins
32	1.00	.50	2c Córdoba
32c	55.00		Booklet pane of six, handmade, perf. margins

*Canal Zone overprints, types I-V, are shown in the Appendix.

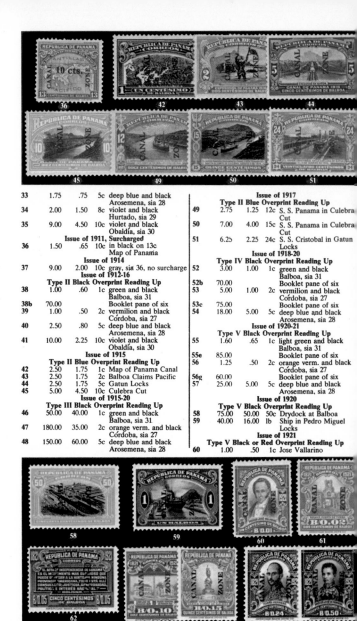

33	1.75	.75	5c	deep blue and black Arosemena, sia 28
34	2.00	1.50	8c	violet and black Hurtado, sia 29
35	9.00	4.50	10c	violet and black Obaldía, sia 30

Issue of 1911, Surcharged

36	1.50	.65	10c	in black on 13c Map of Panama

Issue of 1914

37	9.00	2.00	10c	gray, sia 36, no surcharge

Issue of 1912-16
Type II Black Overprint Reading Up

38	1.00	.60	1c	green and black Balboa, sia 31
38b	70.00			Booklet pane of six
39	1.00	.50	2c	vermilion and black Córdoba, sia 27
40	2.50	.80	5c	deep blue and black Arosemena, sia 28
41	10.00	2.25	10c	violet and black Obaldía, sia 30

Issue of 1915
Type II Blue Overprint Reading Up

42	2.50	1.75	1c	Map of Panama Canal
43	2.50	1.75	2c	Balboa Claims Pacific
44	2.50	1.75	5c	Gatun Locks
45	5.00	4.50	10c	Culebra Cut

Issue of 1915-20
Type III Black Overprint Reading Up

46	50.00	40.00	1c	green and black Balboa, sia 31
47	180.00	35.00	2c	orange verm. and black Córdoba, sia 27
48	150.00	60.00	5c	deep blue and black Arosemena, sia 28

Issue of 1917
Type II Blue Overprint Reading Up

49	2.75	1.25	12c	S. S. Panama in Culebra Cut
50	7.00	4.00	15c	S. S. Panama in Culebra Cut
51	6.25	2.25	24c	S. S. Cristobal in Gatun Locks

Issue of 1918-20
Type IV Black Overprint Reading Up

52	3.00	1.00	1c	green and black Balboa, sia 31
52b	70.00			Booklet pane of six
53	5.00	1.00	2c	vermilion and black Córdoba, sia 27
53c	75.00			Booklet pane of six
54	18.00	5.00	5c	deep blue and black Arosemena, sia 28

Issue of 1920-21
Type V Black Overprint Reading Up

55	1.60	.65	1c	light green and black Balboa, sia 31
55e	85.00			Booklet pane of six
56	1.25	.50	2c	orange verm. and black Córdoba, sia 27
56g	60.00			Booklet pane of six
57	25.00	5.00	5c	deep blue and black Arosemena, sia 28

Issue of 1920
Type V Black Overprint Reading Up

58	75.00	50.00	50c	Drydock at Balboa
59	40.00	16.00	1b	Ship in Pedro Miguel Locks

Issue of 1921
Type V Black or Red Overprint Reading Up

60	1.00	.50	1c	Jose Vallarino

68	69	70	71	73	74

0b	95.00			Booklet pane of six
1	1.00	.45	2c	"Land Gate"
1f	135.00			Booklet pane of six
2	2.75	1.20	5c	Bolivar's Tribute
3	4.00	1.50	10c	Municipal Building— 1821 and 1921
4	7.00	2.75	15c	Statue of Balboa
5	12.50	6.00	24c	Tomás Herrera
6	35.00	21.00	50c	José de Fabrega

Issue of 1924
Type III Black Overprint Reading Up

7	150.00	50.00	1c grn. Vallarino, sia 60

Issue of 1924, Black Overprint

8	2.35	1.65	1c Coat of Arms
9	1.80	.95	2c Coat of Arms

The 5c to 1b values were prepared but never issued.

Issue of 1924-25, Perf. 11

CANAL ZONE — United States Nos. 551 to 554, 557, 562, 564, 565, 566, 569, 570 and 571a Overprinted in Red or Black Letters "A" with Flat Tops.

Type A

70		.20	.20	½c Nathan Hale
71		.30	.20	1c Franklin
71e		12.00		Booklet pane of six
72		.30	.30	1½c yellow brown Harding, sia U.S. 553
73		1.35	.35	2c Washington
73a		16.00		Booklet pane of six

THEODORE ROOSEVELT (1858-1919)

I wish to preach, not the doctrine of ignoble ease, but the doctrine of the strenuous life. An 1899 speech

Tough, aggressive, and adventurous, Teddy Roosevelt lived the "strenuous life". He transformed himself from a frail and asthmatic child into the man who climbed the Matterhorn during his honeymoon and led the Rough Riders in the charge of San Juan Hill. The latter episode made him a popular hero, and as president he fought for the rights of the people against industrial monopolies and moneyed trusts. A fighter, Roosevelt was also a diplomat. His personal mediation ending the Russo-Japanese War in 1905 won him a Nobel Peace Prize. In 1912 he ran for a third term, saying "I feel as fit as a Bull Moose," and gave his maverick party its name. In that year, however, Woodrow Wilson was the new hero.
See Canal Zone Scott Nos. 74, 138, 150

74	3.50	2.00	5c Theodore Roosevelt
75	11.00	7.00	10c James Monroe
76	6.50	5.75	12c Grover Cleveland
77	4.50	4.00	14c American Indian
78	11.00	9.00	15c Statue of Liberty
79	6.00	5.00	30c Buffalo
80	8.75	7.50	50c lilac Amphitheater sia U.S. 570
81	50.00	30.00	$1 Lincoln Memorial

Issues of 1925-26

CANAL ZONE — United States Nos. 554, 555, 557, 562, 564, 565, 566, 567, 569, 570, 571a and 623 Overprinted in Black or Red

Type B. Letters "A" with Sharp Pointed Tops

75	76	77	78	79	81

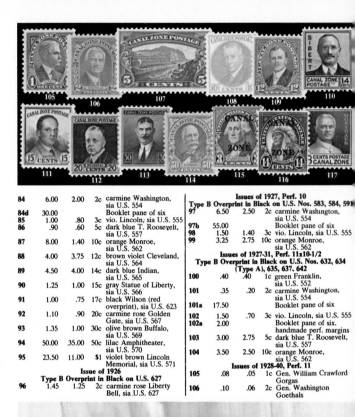

84	6.00	2.00	2c	carmine Washington, sia U.S. 554	
84d	30.00			Booklet pane of six	
85	1.00	.80	3c	vio. Lincoln; sia U.S. 555	
86	.90	.60	5c	dark blue T. Roosevelt, sia U.S. 557	
87	8.00	1.40	10c	orange Monroe, sia U.S. 562	
88	4.00	3.75	12c	brown violet Cleveland, sia U.S. 564	
89	4.50	4.00	14c	dark blue Indian, sia U.S. 565	
90	1.25	1.00	15c	gray Statue of Liberty, sia U.S. 566	
91	1.00	.75	17c	black Wilson (red overprint), sia U.S. 623	
92	1.10	.90	20c	carmine rose Golden Gate, sia U.S. 567	
93	1.35	1.00	30c	olive brown Buffalo, sia U.S. 569	
94	50.00	35.00	50c	lilac Amphitheater, sia U.S. 570	
95	23.50	11.00	$1	violet brown Lincoln Memorial, sia U.S. 571	

Issue of 1926
Type B Overprint in Black on U.S. 627

96	1.45	1.25	2c	carmine rose Liberty Bell, sia U.S. 627	

Issues of 1927, Perf. 10
Type B Overprint in Black on U.S. Nos. 583, 584, 591

97	6.50	2.50	2c	carmine Washington, sia U.S. 554	
97b	55.00			Booklet pane of six	
98	1.50	1.40	3c	vio. Lincoln, sia U.S. 555	
99	3.25	2.75	10c	orange Monroe, sia U.S. 562	

Issues of 1927-31, Perf. 11x10-1/2
Type B Overprint in Black on U.S. Nos. 632, 634
(Type A), 635, 637, 642

100	.40	.40	1c	green Franklin, sia U.S. 552	
101	.35	.20	2c	carmine Washington, sia U.S. 554	
101a	17.50			Booklet pane of six	
102	1.50	.70	3c	vio. Lincoln, sia U.S. 555	
102a	2.00			Booklet pane of six, handmade perf. margins	
103	3.00	2.75	5c	dark blue T. Roosevelt, sia U.S. 557	
104	3.50	2.50	10c	orange Monroe, sia U.S. 562	

Issues of 1928-40, Perf. 11

105	.08	.05	1c	Gen. William Crawford Gorgas	
106	.10	.06	2c	Gen. Washington Goethals	

BUILDERS OF THE PANAMA CANAL

Theodore Roosevelt needed men like himself to build the Panama Canal, tough men who would stick to the job. But before construction could begin, Panama, infested with yellow fever and malaria, had to be made safe for the workers. From 1904-06 Col. William Gorgas (1854-1920) made medical history with mosquito control in Panama. Breeding spots were found, oil poured on water, swamp grass burned, and in two years the diseases were under control.

Col. George Goethals

In 1907 Roosevelt picked an Army engineer, Col. George Goethals (1858-1928) and gave him absolute power in the Canal Zone. At the peak of activity 56,000 men toiled in the jungle heat. They dammed rivers, poured tons of concrete, and dug away mountains to cut through the continent. In spite of mud slides, which in seconds wiped out the work of weeks, Goethals drove his men on. On September 26, 1913 water poured into the Gatun Locks, and his job was done.

See Canal Zone Scott Nos. 105, 106, 117

Issues of 1933 , Perf. 11x10-1/2
Type B Overprint in Black on U.S. 720, 695

Issued for the twentieth anniversary of the opening of the Panama Canal. Also see No. 153.

Issues of 1939

United States
Nos. 803 and 805
Overprinted in Black

CANAL ZONE

Perf. 11x10-1/2

Panama Canal 25th Anniversary Issue
Perf. 11, Aug. 15

The Panama Canal was opened in 1914.

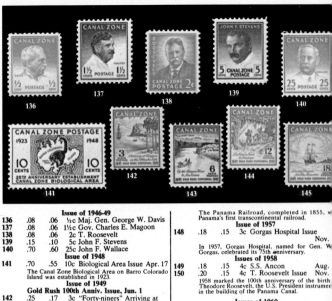

			Issue of 1946-49
136	.08	.06	½c Maj. Gen. George W. Davis
137	.08	.06	1½c Gov. Charles E. Magoon
138	.08	.06	2c T. Roosevelt
139	.15	.10	5c John F. Stevens
140	.70	.60	25c John F. Wallace

Issue of 1948

| 141 | .70 | .55 | 10c Biological Area Issue Apr. 17 |

The Canal Zone Biological Area on Barro Colorado Island was established in 1923.

Issue of 1949

Gold Rush 100th Anniv. Issue, Jun. 1

142	.25	.17	3c "Forty-niners" Arriving at Chagres
143	.30	.20	6c Journey in Bungo to Las Cruces
144	.60	.45	12c Las Cruces Trail to Panama
145	.85	.75	18c Departure for San Francisco

The gold rush of 1849 brought 90,000 settlers to California.

Issue of 1951

| 146 | 1.00 | .85 | 10c West Indian Laborers Aug. 15 |

Construction of the Panama Canal was accomplished with the aid of 31,071 West Indian laborers.

Issue of 1955

| 147 | .30 | .25 | 3c Panama Railroad Jan. 28 |

The Panama Railroad, completed in 1855, w Panama's first transcontinental railroad.

Issue of 1957

| 148 | .18 | .15 | 3c Gorgas Hospital Issue Nov. |

In 1957, Gorgas Hospital, named for Gen. W Gorgas, celebrated its 75th anniversary.

Issues of 1958

| 149 | .18 | .15 | 4c S.S. Ancon Aug. |
| 150 | .20 | .15 | 4c T. Roosevelt Issue Nov. |

1958 marked the 100th anniversary of the birth Theodore Roosevelt, the U.S. President instrumen in the building of the Panama Canal.

Issues of 1960

| 151 | .40 | .30 | 4c Boy Scout Issue Fet |

The Boy Scouts of America was founded in 19

| 152 | .10 | .08 | 4c Administration Bldg. Nov |

Coil Stamps

Perf. 10 Vertically

| 153 | .15 | .12 | 3c Goethals |

Perf. 10 Horizontally

| 154 | .18 | .15 | 4c dull rose lilac Admin. Blc sia 152 |

Issues of 1962

Coil Stamp, Perf. 10 Vertically

| 155 | .25 | .18 | 5c dp. bl. Stevens, sia 139 |

153	**156**	**157**	**158**

Perf. 11

.20 .18 4c Girl Scout Issue Mar. 12

The Girl Scouts of America was founded in 1902.

.18 .12 4c Thatcher Ferry Bridge Oct. 12

The Thatcher Ferry Bridge. spanning the Panama Canal, was opened in 1962.

.12 .06 6c Goethals Memorial Mar. 15

AIR POST STAMPS
Issue of 1929

Type I. Flag of "5" pointing up **15 15** Type II. Flag of "5" curved

Perf. 11
Regular Issue of 1928 Surcharged in Dark Blue

C1	3.50	2.75	15c (I) on 1c Gorgas
C2	30.00	22.50	15c (II) on 1c green, sia C1
C3	1.25	.90	25c on 2c Goethals

C1	**C3**	**C4**	**C5**	**C6**

C15	**C16**	**C17**

3.75	3.25	10c on 50c Blackburn
2.25	.60	20c on 2c Goethals

Issue of 1931-49

.25	.20	4c Gaillard Cut

Nos. C6-14: Gaillard Cut, sia C6

.18	.15	5c yellow green
.30	.15	6c yellow brown
.35	.12	10c orange
.50	.10	15c blue
.70	.20	20c red violet
1.00	.40	30c rose lake
1.35	.55	40c yellow
3.50	1.00	$1 black

Issue of 1939
Air Mail Anniversary Issue, Jul. 15

1.25	1.25	5c Douglas Plane over Sosa Hill
1.50	1.25	10c Plane and Map of Central America
1.65	.50	15c Clipper and Scene near Fort Amador
6.00	4.50	25c Clipper at Cristobal Harbor

C19	4.50	3.25	30c Clipper over Gaillard Cut
C20	15.00	12.00	$1 Pan American Clipper Landing

Nos. C15-C20 were issued for the 10th anniversary of Air Mail service and the 25th anniversary of the Panama Canal.

Issue of 1951
Nos. C21-C26: Globe and Wing, sia C23

C21	.25	.15	4c red violet	Jul. 16
C22	.30	.15	6c brown	Jul. 16
C23	.50	.20	10c Globe and Wing	Jul. 16
C24	2.25	1.25	21c blue	Jul. 16
C25	2.50	1.00	31c Globe and Wing	Jul. 16
C26	3.00	1.00	80c gray black	Jul. 16

Issue of 1958
Nos. C27-C31: Globe and Wing, sia C23

C27	.30	.25	5c yellow green	Aug. 16
C28	.35	.15	7c olive	Aug. 16
C29	1.50	.80	15c brown violet	Aug. 16
C30	2.00	.60	25c orange yellow	Aug. 16
C31	2.75	.90	35c dark blue	Aug. 16

C18	**C19**	**C20**

			Issue of 1961
C32	.75	.50	15c Emblem of U.S. Army, Caribbean School Nov. 21
			Issue of 1962
C33	.30	.25	7c Malaria Eradication Issue Sep. 24

Issue publicized the World Health Organization's drive to eradicate malaria.

Issues of 1963
Perf. 10-1/2x11

C34	.30	.15	8c carmine, sia C23 Jan. 7

Perf. 11

C35	.75	.55	15c Alliance for Progress Aug. 17

The Alliance for Progress, founded in 1961, aims to stimulate economic growth in Latin America.

"PANAMA CANAL" 19-20-1/2 mm. long
Issues of 1941-42, Perf. 11
Nos. CO1-CO14: Gaillard Cut, sia C6

CO1	1.50	.60	5c yellow green
CO2	2.25	.90	10c orange
CO3	2.50	1.00	15c blue
CO4	3.25	2.75	20c red violet
CO5	3.85	2.40	30c rose lake
CO6	5.00	2.75	40c yellow
CO7	6.25	3.65	$1 black

"PANAMA CANAL" 17 mm. long

CO8	50.00		5c light green
CO9	50.00		10c orange
CO10	55.00		20c red violet
CO11	25.00		30c rose lake

CO12	55.00		40c yellow
			Issue of 1947
			"PANAMA CANAL" 19-20-1/2 mm. long
CO14	2.75	1.50	6c yellow brown

Postage Due Stamps

Postage Due Stamps of the United States Overprinted in Black   CANAL ZONE

Issue of 1914, Perf. 12

Wmkd.   USPS   (190)

J1	7.00	3.00	1c Figure of Value
J2	20.00	7.00	2c rose carmine, design of J
J3	75.00	9.00	10c rose carmine, design of J

Issues of 1915
Type II Blue Overprint on Postage Due Stamps of Panama
Unwmkd

J4	2.00	1.10	1c olive brown, sia J7
J5	16.00	5.00	2c olive brown, sia J10
J6	8.50	4.00	10c Pedro J. Sosa

Surcharged in Red

J7	15.00	3.25	1c on 1c San Geronimo Ca Gate

No. J7 was intended to show a gate of San Lore Castle, Chagres, and is so labeled. By error the st actually shows the main gate of San Geronimo Ca Portobelo.

Issue of 1964
Panama Canal Golden Anniv. Issue, Aug. 15

C36	.25	.20	6c Jet over Cristobal
C37	.35	.20	8c Gatun Locks
C38	.60	.40	15c Madden Dam
C39	.80	.50	20c Gaillard Cut
C40	1.20	.85	30c Miraflores Locks
C41	2.75	1.85	80c Balboa

Issue of 1965, Jul. 15

C42	.15	.08	6c Canal Zone Seal and Jet Plane
C43	.18	.08	8c Canal Zone Seal and Jet Plane
C44	.30	.12	15c Canal Zone Seal and Jet Plane
C45	.40	.18	20c Canal Zone Seal and Jet Plane
C46	.60	.25	30c reddish brown and blk., sia C42
C47	1.60	.70	80c Canal Zone Seal and Jet Plane

Issue of 1968-70, Mar. 15

C48	.20	.12	10c dull orange and black, sia C42
C48a	.80		Booklet pane of four
C49	.50	.20	25c pale yellow, sia C42

Air Post Official Stamps

Air Post Stamps of 1931-41   OFFICIAL
Overprinted in Black   PANAMA CANAL

146

4.50	1.85	2c on 2c olive brown, sia J10
4.00	1.25	10c on 10c olive brown, sia J6

Issue of 1919
Surcharged in Carmine

40	6.00	3.00	2c on 2c Statue of Columbus
41	8.00	4.50	4c on 4c Capitol, Panama City

Issue of 1924
Type A Overprint in Black on U.S. Postage Due Stamps
Perf. 11

42	22.50	9.00	1c carmine rose, design of J14
43	10.00	4.00	2c deep claret, design of J14
44	40.00	15.00	10c Figure of Value

Issues of 1925

United States Postage Due Stamps
Nos. 552, 554 and 562 Overprinted Type A
and additional
Overprint
in Red or Blue

POSTAGE
DUE

45	15.00	4.00	1c Franklin
46	2.75	1.50	2c carmine Washington, blue overprint, sia U.S. 554
47	8.00	3.00	10c Monroe

Type B Overprint on U.S. Postage Due Stamps

49	1.50	1.00	2c carmine rose, design of J14
50	4.25	1.25	2c carmine rose, design of J14
20	20.00	3.00	10c carmine rose, design of J14

Issue of 1929-30
Canal Zone No. 107 Surcharged in Black

1	.45	.45	1c on 5c blue, sia J22

J22	1.25	.60	2c on 5c Gaillard Cut
J23	1.00	.85	5c on 5c blue, sia J22
J24	1.25	.75	10c on 5c blue, sia J22

Note: J23 does not have bars in lower corners.

Issue of 1932-41

J25	.05	.05	1c Canal Zone Seal
J26	.08	.08	2c claret, sia J25
J27	.12	.12	5c claret, sia J25
J28	.45	.45	10c claret, sia J25
J29	.35	.35	15c Canal Zone Seal

Overprints Types A and B are shown on page 141.

Official Stamps

Regular Issues of 1928-34
Overprinted in Black:

OFFICIAL

PANAMA	OFFICIAL
CANAL	PANAMA CANAL
Type I	Type II

Type I: "Panama" 10 mm. long
Type IA: "Panama" 9 mm. long

Issue of 1941, Perf. 11

O1	.20	.15	1c yellow green type I, sia 105
O2	.50	.25	3c deep violet type I, sia 117
O3		7.50	5c blue type II, sia 107
O4	1.15	.75	10c orange type I, sia 108
O5	1.75	.85	15c gray type I, sia 111
O6	2.25	1.00	20c olive brown type I, sia 112
O7	5.50	2.50	50c lilac type I, sia 114
O8		150.00	50c lilac type IA, sia 114

Issue of 1947

O9	1.65	1.10	5c deep blue type I, sia 139

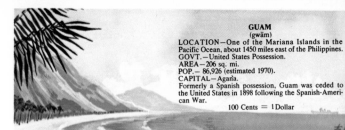

GUAM
(gwäm)
LOCATION—One of the Mariana Islands in the Pacific Ocean, about 1450 miles east of the Philippines.
GOVT.—United States Possession.
AREA—206 sq. mi.
POP.—86,926 (estimated 1970).
CAPITAL—Agaña.
Formerly a Spanish possession, Guam was ceded to the United States in 1898 following the Spanish-American War.

100 Cents = 1 Dollar

Issues of 1899, Perf. 12
United States Stamps Nos. 279, 267, 268, 280a, 281a, 282, 272, 282C, 283a, 284, 275, 276, and 276A

Overprinted **GUAM**

Wmkd. **USPS** (191)

Black Overprint

1	4.25	4.75	1c Benjamin Franklin
2	3.75	4.25	2c George Washington
3	20.00	22.50	3c purple Jackson, sia U.S. 253
4	18.00	20.00	4c Abraham Lincoln
5	5.75	5.25	5c blue Grant, sia U.S. 255
6	17.50	20.00	6c James A. Garfield
7	13.50	15.00	8c General Sherman
8	8.00	8.00	10c Daniel Webster, type I
9	900.00		10c brown Webster type II, sia 8
10	18.00	20.00	15c Henry Clay
11	35.00	40.00	50c orange Jefferson, sia U.S. 260

Red Overprint

12	50.00	62.50	$1 black Perry type I, sia U.S. 261
13	600.00		$1 black Perry type II, sia U.S. 261A

United States No. E5
Overprinted in Red **GUAM**

Wmkd. **USPS** (191)

E1	35.00	35.00	10c Messenger Running

Stamps overprinted "Guam" were superseded by the regular postage stamps of the United States in 1901

Guam Guard Mail
Local Postal Service
Issues of 1930
Perf. 11, Unwmkd.

Philippines
Nos. 290b and 291
Overprinted

M1	75.00	75.00	2c green Rizal, sia M7	Apr
M2	75.00	75.00	4c car. McKinley, sia M6	Apr

Perf. 12, Without Gum

M3	37.50	30.00	1c Seal of Guam	Jul
M4	27.50	25.00	2c Seal of Guam	Jul

Perf. 11, Unwmkd.

Philippines
Nos. 290b, 290 and 291
Overprinted in Black

M5	1.80	2.75	2c green Rizal, sia M7	Aug. 1st
M6	.55	2.75	4c William McKinley	Aug. 1st

Red Overprint

M7	.85	.85	2c José Rizal	Dec
M8	.85	.85	4c car., McKinley, sia M6	Dec
M9	2.25	2.25	6c deep violet Magellan, sia P1243	Dec
M10	1.65	1.65	8c orange brown Legaspi, sia P1244	Dec
M11	1.80	1.80	10c Gen. Henry W. Lawton	Dec

The local postal service was discontinued on April 8th 1931, and replaced by the service of the United States Post Office Department.

HAWAII
(hä.wiĕ)

ATION—A group of twenty islands in the Pacific
an, about two thousand miles southwest of San
cisco.

T.—Former Kingdom and Republic.

A—6,435 sq. mi.

— 748,575 (1970).

ITAL—Honolulu.

1893 an independent kingdom, from 1893 to 1898
ublic, the Hawaiian Islands were annexed to the
ed States in 1898 at the request of the inhabitants.
Territory of Hawaii achieved statehood in 1959.

100 Cents = 1 Dollar

es of early Hawaii stamps vary according to con-
n. Quotations for Nos. 1-18 are for fine copies.
fine to superb specimens sell at much higher
es, and inferior or poor copies sell at reduced
es, depending on the condition of the individual
men

Issue of 1851-52
Imperf.
Type-set, Pelure Paper, Unwmkd.

65,000.00	35,000.00	2c	Figure of Value
15,000.00	7500.00	5c	Figure of Value
8500.00	5000.00	13c	Figure of Value
17,000.00	8000.00	13c	Figure of Value

Issue of 1853
Thick White Wove Paper

385.00	250.00	5c	King Kamehameha III
145.00	160.00	13c	dark red King Kamehameha III, sia 7
1000.00	1200.00	5c	on 13c King Kamehameha III

HAWAII: FROM KINGDOM TO STATEHOOD

Long ago Polynesians in sea-faring canoes migrated to Hawaii and evolved a feudal society. By the time Captain Cook arrived in 1778, six of the main islands were united under the monarchy of King Kamehameha I. His descendants and other Hawaiians continued to rule until 1893. During this period a great many foreigners immigrated to Hawaii, making it a melting pot. The first company of Protestant missionaries arrived in 1820 from New England. Others followed and churches, schools, and news-papers were soon established. By 1893 the growth of American interests in the sugar and pineapple industries had led to the annexation movement. When Queen Liliuokalani assumed the throne the powerful "Committee of Safety" abolished the monarchy and appealed to the United States for annexation. When this failed the Re-public of Hawaii was established (in 1894) with Sanford B. Dole as its leader. Following the Spanish-American War the United States rec-ognized the strategic value of Hawaii for naval installations. Hawaii was annexed in 1898 and made a territory in 1900. In 1959 it became the 50th state.

799

	Issue of 1857, Thin White Wove Paper		
8	155.00	155.00	5c blue King Kamehameha III, sia 5
	Issue of 1861, Thin Bluish Wove Paper		
9	70.00	70.00	5c blue King Kamehameha III, sia 5
	Issue of 1868, Ordinary White Wove Paper		
10	15.00		5c blue King Kamehameha III, sia 5
11	125.00		13c dull rose King Kamehameha III, sia 7

Nos. 10 and 11 were never placed in use.

	Issue of 1859-60, Design of 12 Type-Set		
12	700.00	800.00	1c Figure of Value
13	575.00	375.00	2c light blue, bluish white paper
14	750.00	500.00	2c black, greenish blue paper
	Issue of 1863-64, Design of 12		
15	80.00	175.00	1c black, grayish paper
16	200.00	150.00	2c black, grayish paper
17	950.00	825.00	2c dark blue, bluish paper
18	260.00	400.00	2c black, blue gray paper
	Issue of 1864-65 Nos. 19-20: Design of 12		
19	120.00	225.00	1c black
20	135.00	185.00	2c black
21	125.00	125.00	5c Figure of Value
22	90.00	100.00	5c Figure of Value
	Issue of 1864, Design of 12		
23	50.00	225.00	1c black, laid paper
24	50.00	225.00	2c black, laid paper

	Issue of 1865, Design of 26		
25	75.00		1c dark blue, wove paper
26	65.00		2c Figure of Value, wove pap

Nos. 12 to 26 were type-set and were printed in se tings of ten different stamps.

	Issues of 1861-63 Horizontally Laid Paper		
27	75.00	65.00	2c King Kamehameha IV
	Vertically Laid Paper		
28	77.50	50.00	2c pale rose, sia 27
	Issue of 1869, Thin Wove Paper		
29	25.00	26.50	2c red, sia 27

No. 29 is a reissue. It was not issued for postal pu poses although cancelled copies and copies ove printed "CANCELLED" are known to exist.

	Issue of 1864-71 Perf. 12 Wove Paper		
30	3.00	3.00	1c Princess Victoria Kamamalu
31	3.50	3.00	2c King Kamehameha IV
32	12.00	6.50	5c King Kamehameha V
33	4.50	3.50	6c King Kamehameha V
34	13.50	6.00	18c Mataio Kekuanaoa

No. 32 has traces of rectangular frame lines surround the design. Nos. 39 and 52C have no such frame lin

HAWAII, TROPICAL PARADISE

From historic Diamond Head and Waikiki to Hawaii's western bird sanctuary the Aloha State is a tropic wonderland. Snow-capped volcanoes roll into lush green hills cut by mountain streams and waterfalls; spraying surf abounds in its Pacific waters. Hawaii's balmy climate, sand, and sea make it a mecca for tourists; its plant and marine life make it a laboratory for scientists.

		Issue of 1875
2.50	1.25	2c King David Kalakaua
13.00	8.00	12c Prince William Pitt Leleiohoku

See also Nos. 38, 43, 46.

		Issue of 1882
1.65	1.65	1c Princess Likelike (Mrs. Archibald Cleghorn)
15.00	7.00	2c King David Kalakaua
4.50	1.40	5c ultramarine, sia 32
7.50	7.00	10c King David Kalakaua
12.00	10.00	15c Queen Kapiolani

		Issue of 1883-86
1.10	1.00	1c green, sia 37
1.65	.60	2c rose, sia 35
5.50	2.50	10c red brown, sia 40
6.00	6.00	10c vermilion, sia 40
12.50	12.50	12c red lilac, sia 36
15.00	13.50	25c Statue of King Kamehameha I
35.00	30.00	50c King William Lunalilo
45.00	35.00	$1 Queen Emma Kaleleonalani

Reproduction and Reprint, Yellowish Wove Paper
Issue of 1886-89, Imperf.

85.00		2c orange vermilion, sia 27
12.50		2c carmine, sia 27

For reprint information, refer to the Appendix.

Issue of 1890-91, Perf. 12

1.60	.80	2c dull violet, sia 57
C 15.00	15.00	5c deep indigo, sia 57

Issues of 1893

	Issues of 1864 to 1891 Overprinted		Provisional GOVT. 1893	

Red Overprint

53	1.80	2.00	1c purple, sia 30
54	1.75	2.00	1c blue, sia 37
55	.80	.80	1c green, sia 37
56	2.50	3.00	2c brown, sia 35
57	.70	.70	2c Queen Liluokalani, (Mrs. John Dominis)
58	2.35	3.00	5c deep indigo, sia 32
59	1.85	1.65	5c ultramarine, sia 32
60	2.50	2.75	6c green, sia 33
61	2.50	3.00	10c black, sia 40
61B	*1500.00*		10c red brown, sia 40
62	2.35	2.85	12c black, sia 36
63	35.00	50.00	12c Prince William Pitt Leleiohoku
64	5.00	7.00	25c dark violet, sia 47

Black Overprint

65	17.00	16.00	2c rosy vermilion, sia 31
66	.50	.65	2c rose, sia 35
66C	*1500.00*		6c green, sia 33
67	4.50	4.75	10c vermilion, sia 40
68	3.00	3.25	10c King David Kalakaua
69	70.00	75.00	12c red lilac, sia 36
70	6.00	7.00	15c red brown, sia 41
71	7.00	7.50	18c dull rose, sia 34
72	12.00	12.50	50c red, sia 48
73	25.00	25.00	$1 rose red, sia 49

The islands' 900 species of flowering plants include violets which grow six feet tall. The sea also yields exotic treasure: 650 species of bright tropical fish swim in the waters around Hawaii. Sugar cane and pineapples are the chief export products, although coffee, rice, sisal, and cotton are also grown. The seven main islands are Hawaii, Maui, Oahu, Kauai, Molokai, Lanai, Niihau, and the uninhabited Kahooawe. Honolulu, the capital, is on Oahu.

PHILIPPINES
(fil·i·penz; -pinz)

LOCATION—A group of 7,100 islands and islets i the Malay Archipelago, north of Borneo, in the Nor Pacific Ocean.
GOVT.—U.S. Administration, 1898-1946.
AREA—115,748 sq. mi.
POP.—38,100,000 (1970).
CAPITAL—Quezon City.

The islands were ceded to the United States by Spai in 1898. On November 15, 1935, they were given the independence, subject to a transition period whic ended July 4, 1946. On that date the Commonweal became the "Republic of the Philippines."

100 Cents = 1 Dollar (1899)
100 Centavos = 1 Peso (1906)
Issued under American Dominion.

Regular Issues of the United PHILIPPINES
States Overprinted
Issue of 1899-1900, Perf. 12
Unwmkd.
Blk. Overprint on U.S. 260

212	60.00	50.00	50c Thomas Jefferson

Wmkd. USPS (191)

Blk. Overprint on U.S. Nos. 279, 267, 268, 281, 282C, 283, 284, 275

213	1.00	.50	1c yellow green Franklin, sia U.S. 246
214	.75	.50	2c orange red Washington type III, sia U.S. 248
214b	35.00	27.50	Booklet pane of six
215	1.50	1.10	3c purple Jackson, sia U.S. 2
216	1.60	.75	5c blue Garfield, sia U.S. 25
217	4.00	2.50	10c brown Webster type I, sia U.S. 282C
217A	25.00	5.00	10c orange brown Webster, type II, sia U.S. 283
218	5.00	3.00	15c olive green Clay, sia U.S. 2
219	18.00	13.00	50c orange Jefferson, sia U.S. 260

Issue of 1901
Blk. Overprint on U.S. Nos. 280b, 282 and 272

220	3.25	2.00	4c orange brown Lincoln, sia U.S. 254
221	4.00	3.75	6c lake Garfield, sia U.S. 256
222	4.50	2.50	8c violet brown Sherman, sia U.S. 257

Red Overprint on U.S. Nos. 276, 276A, 277, and 278

223	90.00	65.00	$1 black Perry type I, sia U.S. 276
223A	250.00	150.00	$1 black Perry type II, sia U.S. 276A
224	110.00	80.00	$2 dark blue Madison, sia U.S. 262
225	220.00	175.00	$5 dark green Marshall, sia U.S. 263

Issue of 1903-04
Black Overprint on U.S. Nos. 300-310

226	.60	.30	1c blue green Franklin, sia U.S. 300
227	1.50	1.00	2c carmine Washington, sia U.S. 301
227a			Booklet pane of six
228	6.00	5.75	3c Andrew Jackson
229	9.00	8.00	4c brown Grant, sia U.S. 303
230	2.00	.75	5c blue Lincoln, sia U.S. 304
231	6.50	6.00	6c brownish lake Garfield, sia U.S. 305
232	6.00	5.25	8c violet black M. Washington, sia U.S. 306
233	4.50	2.00	10c pale red brown Webster, sia U.S. 307
234	7.00	6.00	13c purple black Harrison, sia U.S. 308
235	7.50	4.50	15c olive green Clay, sia U.S. 309
236	25.00	8.75	50c orange Jefferson, sia U.S. 310

Issue of 1894

74	.85	.70	1c Coat of Arms
75	1.00	.50	2c View of Honolulu
76	1.80	.90	5c Statue of King Kamehameha I
77	2.00	2.00	10c Star and Palms
78	3.25	3.50	12c S. S. Arawa
79	5.75	5.75	25c Pres. Sanford Ballard Dole

Issue of 1899

80	1.00	.95	1c Coat of Arms
81	.85	.50	2c View of Honolulu
82	2.50	1.25	5c blue, sia 76

Official Stamps, 1896
Perf. 12

O1	8.50	8.50	2c Lorrin Andrews Thurston

Nos. O2-O5, sia O1

O2	8.50	8.50	5c black brown
O3	8.50	8.50	6c deep ultramarine
O4	8.50	8.50	10c bright rose
O5	8.50	8.50	12c orange
O6	8.50	8.50	25c Lorrin Andrews Thurston

The stamps of Hawaii have been replaced by those of the United States.

THE SPANISH-AMERICAN WAR

As a result of this brief war the United States acquired Guam, Puerto Rico, and the Philippines from Spain. On April 24, 1898, after relations with Spain had been strained by disagreements over the government of Cuba and the blow-up of the *Maine* in the Havana harbor, the United States declared war. One week later Commodore George Dewey destroyed the Spanish fleet in the Battle of Manila Bay, and in the months that followed U. S. forces captured Guantanamo, San Juan Hill, and Santiago. On August 12, during the invasion of Puerto Rico, an armistice was declared.

Philippines Scott No. 422

Red Overprint on U.S. Nos. 311-313

No.				
237	75.00	55.00	$1	black Farragut, sia U.S. 311
238	185.00	155.00	$2	dark blue Madison, sia U.S. 312
239	250.00	200.00	$5	dark green Marshall, sia U.S. 313

Issue of 1904
Black Overprint on U.S. 319

No.				
240	2.00	1.00	2c	carmine Washington, sia U.S. 319
240a	75.00			Booklet pane of six

Issues of 1906-10
Wmkd. Double-lined PIPS (191PI)

No.				
241	.20	.06	2c	José Rizal
241b	22.50			Booklet pane of six

José Rizal (1861-96), Philippine patriot and author, was exiled in 1887 and executed by the Spanish in 1896.

No.				
242	.30	.06	4c	William McKinley
242b	27.50			Booklet pane of six
243	.95	.15	6c	Fernando Magellan
244	1.10	.70	8c	Miguel Lopez de Legaspi
245	1.45	.10	10c	Gen. Henry W. Lawton
246	2.25	1.85	12c	Abraham Lincoln
247	2.35	.25	16c	Adm. William T. Sampson
248	3.00	.40	20c	George Washington
249	2.50	2.35	26c	Francisco Carriedo
250	3.75	1.60	30c	Benjamin Franklin
251	11.00	8.25	1p	Arms of Manila
252	10.00	1.00	2p	black, sia 251
253	24.00	9.50	4p	dark blue, sia 251
254	60.00	30.00	10p	Arms of Manila

Issue of 1909-13

No.				
255	3.65	2.65	12c	red orange Lincoln, sia 246
256	1.10	.40	16c	olive green Sampson, sia 247
257	5.00	1.35	20c	yellow Washington, sia 248
258	.90	.80	26c	blue green Carriedo, sia 249
259	7.25	3.85	30c	ultramarine Franklin, sia 250
260	13.50	3.85	1p	pale violet Manila Arms, sia 251
260A	30.00	1.35	2p	violet brown Manila Arms, sia 251

Issue of 1911
Wmkd. Single-lined PIPS (190PI)

No.				
261	.60	.10	2c	green Rizal, sia 241
261a	20.00			Booklet pane of six
262	2.50	.12	4c	car. lake McKinley, sia 242
262b	27.50			Booklet pane of six
263	1.35	.10	6c	deep violet Magellan, sia 243
264	4.00	.30	8c	brown Legaspi, sia 244
265	1.75	.08	10c	blue Lawton, sia 245
266	1.20	.18	12c	orange Lincoln, sia 246
267	1.75	.15	16c	olive green Sampson, sia 247
268	1.50	.15	20c	yellow Washington, sia 248
269	2.50	.30	26c	blue green Carriedo, sia 249
270	2.50	.50	30c	ultramarine Franklin, sia 250
271	10.00	.40	1p	pale violet Manila Arms, sia 251
272	12.00	.70	2p	violet brown Manila Arms, sia 251
273	160.00	14.00	4p	deep blue Manila Arms, sia 251
274	65.00	10.00	10p	deep green Manila Arms, sia 254

Wmk. 190   Wmk. 191

212   228   241   242   243   244   245   246   247   248   249   250   251   254   303

319-325

354

355

356

Issue of 1914						
275	5.50	.40	30c gray Franklin, sia 250			
Issue of 1914-23, Perf. 10						
276	1.00	.12	2c green Rizal, sia 241			
276a	22.50		Booklet pane of six			
277	1.00	.15	4c carmine McKinley, sia 242			
277a	27.50		Booklet pane of six			
278	8.00	6.00	6c light violet Magellan, sia 243			
279	9.00	4.00	8c brown Legaspi, sia 244			
280	7.00	.25	10c dark blue Lawton, sia 245			
281	17.00	1.85	16c olive green Sampson, sia 247			
282	6.00	1.00	20c orange Washington, sia 248			
283	14.00	1.30	30c gray Franklin, sia 250			
284	25.00	1.30	1p pale violet Manila Arms, sia 251			
Issue of 1918-26, Perf. 11						
285	3.50	1.35	2c green Rizal, sia 241			
285a	80.00		Booklet pane of six			
286	6.00	1.10	4c carmine McKinley, sia 242			
286a	85.00		Booklet pane of six			
287	10.00	.55	6c deep violet Magellan, sia 243			
287A	40.00	6.00	8c light brown Legaspi, sia 244			
288	12.00	1.00	10c dark blue Lawton, sia 245			
289	24.00	1.00	16c olive green Sampson, sia 247			
289A	12.50	3.65	20c orange Washington, sia 248			
289C	10.00	5.25	30c gray Franklin, sia 250			
289D	20.00	5.50	1p pale violet Manila Arms, sia 251			
Issue of 1917-25						
Perf. 11, Unwmkd.						
290	.10	.05	2c yellow green Rizal, sia 241			
290e	5.00		Booklet pane of six			
291	.10	.05	4c carmine McKinley, sia 242			
291b	1.75	1.50	Booklet pane of six			
292	.30	.08	6c deep violet Magellan, sia 243			
292c	27.50		Booklet pane of six			

293	.20	.12	8c yellow brown Legaspi, sia 2
294	.20	.08	10c deep blue Lawton, sia 245
295	.30	.15	12c red orange Lincoln, sia 2
296	9.00	.15	16c light olive green Sampson, sia 247
297	.35	.10	20c orange yellow Washingto sia 248
298	.55	.50	26c green Carriedo, sia 249
299	.50	.10	30c gray Franklin, sia 250
300	17.00	1.00	1p pale violet Manila Arms, sia 251
301	13.00	.60	2p violet brown Manila Arms, sia 251
302	9.00	.25	4p blue Manila Arms, sia 25
Issue of 1923-26			
303	.75	.15	16c Adm. George Dewey
304	27.00	3.65	10p deep green Manila Arms sia 254
Issue of 1926			
Perf. 12, Unwmkd.			
319	.35	.25	2c Legislative Palace
320	.35	.35	4c Legislative Palace
321	.80	.75	16c Legislative Palace
322	.85	.65	18c Legislative Palace
323	1.25	1.10	20c Legislative Palace
324	1.00	.70	24c Legislative Palace
325	15.00	12.50	1p Legislative Palace

This issue commemorates the opening of the Legislative Palace at Manila.

Coil Stamp of 1928
Perf. 11 Vertically

326	2.00	2.00	2c green Rizal, sia 241

Issue of 1925-31
Imperf., Unwmkd.

340	.12	.12	2c green Rizal, sia 241
341	.20	.20	4c carmine McKinley, sia 2

358

359

357

368

369

360

52	1.75	1.75	6c deep violet Magellan, sia 243
53	1.50	1.50	8c yellow brown Legaspi, sia 244
54	2.00	2.00	10c deep blue Lawton, sia 245
55	2.75	2.75	12c red orange Lincoln, sia 246
56	2.00	2.00	16c olive bistre Dewey, sia 303
57	2.00	2.00	20c yellow Washington, sia 248
48	2.00	2.00	26c blue green Carriedo, sia 249
49	2.25	2.25	30c gray Franklin, sia 250
50	6.00	6.00	1p violet Manila Arms, sia 251
51	13.00	13.00	2p violet brown Manila Arms, sia 251
52	22.50	22.50	4p dp. blue Manila Arms, sia 251
53	50.00	47.50	10p deep green Manila Arms, sia 254

Issue of 1932, Perf. 11

54	.75	.35	2c Mayon Volcano
55	.50	.35	4c Post Office, Manila
56	.75	.75	12c Pier No. 7, Manila Bay

No. 357 was intended to show a view of Pagsanjan Falls, and is so labeled. By error the stamp actually shows a view of Vernal Falls in Yosemite National Park, California.

384	.05	.05	4c Woman and Carabao
385	.09	.06	6c La Filipina
386	.12	.12	8c Pearl Fishing
387	.22	.20	10c Fort Santiago
388	.18	.15	12c Salt Spring
389	.18	.12	16c Magellan's Landing
390	.25	.06	20c "Juan de la Cruz"
391	.35	.35	26c Rice Terraces
392	.35	.35	30c "Blood Compact", 1565
393	2.00	1.85	1p Barasoain Church, Malolos
394	3.75	1.75	2p Battle of Manila, 1898
395	3.75	3.75	4p Montalban Gorge
396	8.00	2.25	5p George Washington

Commonwealth Issue

397	.10	.08	2c "The Temples of Human Progress"
398	.15	.12	6c "The Temples of Human Progress"
399	.25	.20	16c "The Temples of Human Progress"
400	.45	.45	36c "The Temples of Human Progress"

357	12.50	8.50	18c Vernal Falls
358	1.00	.80	20c Rice Planting
359	1.50	1.00	24c Rice Terraces
360	1.50	1.15	32c Baguio Zigzag

Stamps of 1917-25, Surcharged.

368	2.25	.50	1p (in orange) on 4p Arms of Manila
369	4.00	.90	2p (in red) on 4p Arms of Manila

Issue of 1934, Perf. 11-1/2, 12

380	.18	.18	2c Baseball Players
381	.35	.35	6c Tennis Player
382	.70	.70	16c Basketball Players

The issue honors the Tenth Far Eastern Championship Games.

Issues of 1935, Perf. 11

383	.05	.04	2c José Rizal

401	.70	.70	50c "The Temples of Human Progress"

The Philippine Commonwealth was inaugurated on Nov 15, 1935.

Issues of 1936 Perf. 12

402	.08	.08	2c José Rizal
403	.12	.10	6c José Rizal
404	.50	.50	36c José Rizal

1936 marked the 75th anniversary of the birth of José Rizal.

Perf. 11

408	.06	.06	2c Pres. Manuel L. Quezon
409	.12	.10	6c Pres. Manuel L. Quezon
410	.18	.15	12c Pres. Manuel L. Quezon

Issued for the first anniversary of the Commonwealth. Stamps show Manuel L. Quezon (1878-1944), first President of the Philippines.

Issues of 1936
Perf. 12

402	.08	.08	2c José Rizal
403	.12	.10	6c José Rizal
404	.50	.50	36c José Rizal

1936 marked the 75th anniversary of the birth of Jose Rizal.

Perf. 11

408	.06	.06	2c Pres. Manuel L. Quezon
409	.12	.10	6c Pres. Manuel L. Quezon
410	.18	.15	12c Pres. Manuel L. Quezon

Issued for the first anniversary of the Commonwealth. Stamps show Manuel L. Quezon (1878-1944), first President of the Philippines.

Issue of 1936-37
Stamps of 1935 Overprinted in Black:

COMMON-
WEALTH   COMMONWEALTH
a   *b*

Perf. 11

Nos. 411, 413, and 418 are overprinted with type "a".
Nos. 412, 414-417, 419-424 are overprinted with type "b".

411	.06	.04	2c rose Rizal, sia 383
411a	1.00	.90	Booklet pane of six
412	.75	.40	4c yellow green Woman, sia 384
413	.25	.10	6c dk. brn. La Filipina, sia 385
414	.35	.30	8c violet Pearl Fishing, sia 386
415	.18	.06	10c rose carmine Ft. Santiago, sia 387
416	.18	.08	12c black Salt Spring, sia 388
417	.25	.20	16c dark blue Magellan's Landing, sia 389
418	.70	.50	20c light olive green "Juan de la Cruz", sia 390
419	.60	.45	26c indigo Rice Terraces, sia 391
420	.25	.15	30c orange red "Blood Compact", sia 392
421	.90	.30	1p red orange and black Church, sia 393
422	5.00	2.50	2p bistre brown and black Manila Bay, sia 394
423	10.00	2.00	4p blue and black Montalban Gorge, sia 395
424	1.75	1.65	5p green and black Washington, sia 396

Issues of 1937

425	.06	.06	2c Map of Philippines
426	.15	.10	6c Map of Philippines
427	.20	.10	12c Map of Philippines
428	.30	.12	20c Map of Philippines
429	.50	.50	36c Map of Philippines
430	.65	.35	50c Map of Philippines

Issue commemorates the 33rd Eucharistic Congress

		Perf. 11
3.75	2.50	10p Arms of Manila
2.00	1.85	20p Arms of Manila

Issues of 1938-40, Perf. 11

Stamps of 1935 Overprinted in Black

COMMON-WEALTH	COMMONWEALTH
a	*b*

Nos. 433, 435, and 440 are overprinted with type "a". Nos. 434, 436-439, 441-446 are overprinted with type "b".

.08	.05	2c rose Rizal, sia 383
1.00	.90	Booklet pane of six
.60	.50	4c yellow green Woman, sia 384
.08	.08	6c dk. brown La Filipina. sia 386
.10	.10	8c violet Pearl Fishing, sia 386
.10	.06	10c rose car. Ft. Santiago, sia 387
.10	.09	12c black Salt Spring, sia 388
.18	.10	16c dark blue Magellan's Landing, sia 389
.20	.10	20c light olive green "Juan de la Cruz", sia 390
.25	.30	26c indigo Rice Terraces, sia 391
1.45	.85	30c orange red "Blood Compact", sia 392
.50	.25	1p red orange and black Church, sia 393
3.00	1.00	2p bistre brown and black Manila Bay. sia 394
30.00	25.00	4p blue and black Montalban Gorge, sia 395
4.00	4.00	5p green and black Washington, sia 396

Foreign Trade Week Issue

Stamps of 1917-37 Surcharged in Red, Violet or Black:

FIRST FOREIGN   **TRADE WEEK**

2 CENTAVOS

MAY 21-27, 1939

Type a: on 449

FIRST FOREIGN TRADE WEEK   **50** CENTAVOS **50**

FIRST FOREIGN TRADE WEEK

MAY 21-27, 1939

6 CENTAVOS **6**   MAY 21-27, 1939

Type b: on 450   Type c: on 451

.10	.08	2c (in red) on 4c yellow green, sia 384
.20	.20	6c (in violet) on 26c blue green, sia 249
1.00	.90	50c (in black) on 20p henna brown, sia 432

Commonwealth Fourth Anniv. Issue, 1939-40

1939

.10	.08	2c Triumphal Arch
.15	.10	6c Triumphal Arch
.25	.10	12c Triumphal Arch
.10	.06	2c Malacañan Palace

456	.15	.10	6c Malacañan Palace
457	.25	.08	12c Malacañan Palace
			1940
458	.10	.08	2c Quezon Inauguration
459	.15	.12	6c Quezon Inauguration
460	.30	.15	12c Quezon Inauguration

Nos. 452-460 were issued to commemorate the fourth anniversary of the Commonwealth.

Issue of 1941, Perf. 11x10-1/2

461	.05	.04	2c José Rizal

Issue of 1941-43, Perf. 11

462	.12	.06	2c green Rizal, sia 461

462b	.80	.70	Booklet pane of six

This stamp was issued in booklet panes and all copies have straight edges.

Further printings were made in 1942 and 1943 in different shades from the first supply of stamps sent to the islands.

No. 462 was privately overprinted in red or black "PPC V-PEX Oct. 20, 21, 22, 1945 To Commemorate First Anniv. Leyte D-Day" in seven lines by the Philippine Philatelic Club.

464   482   488   497

Issue of 1944, Perf. 11, 11x10-1/2

VICTORY   Handstamped in Violet on the Following Stamps of 1935-41:

463	150.00	100.00	2c rose Rizal 411 (sia 383)
463a	900.00		Booklet pane of six
463B	600.00		2c rose Rizal 433 (sia 383)
464	2.00	2.00	2c José Rizal 461
465	20.00	20.00	4c yellow green Woman 384
466	500.00	300.00	6c dk. brown La Filipina 385
467	75.00	60.00	6c yellow green Quezon 409
468	300.00	200.00	6c dk. brown La Filipina 413 (sia 385)
469	60.00	55.00	6c car. Triumphal Arch 453
470	250.00	150.00	6c orange Malacanan Palace 456
471	80.00	80.00	6c dark green Quezon Inauguration 459
472	10.00	10.00	8c violet Pearl Fishing 436 (sia 386)
473	50.00	35.00	10c rose carmine Ft. Santiago 415 (sia 387)
474	65.00	50.00	10c rose carmine Ft. Santiago 437 (sia 387)
475	125.00	80.00	12c ultramarine Quezon 410
476	600.00	400.00	12c bright blue Triumphal Arch 454
477	100.00	80.00	12c purple Quezon Inauguration 460
478	375.00		16c dark blue Magellan's Landing 389
479	200.00	100.00	16c dark blue Magellan's Landing 417 (sia 389)
480	100.00	100.00	16c dark blue Magellan's Landing 439 (sia 389)
481	20.00	15.00	20c light olive green "Juan de la Cruz" 440 (sia 390)
482	100.00	100.00	30c orange red "Blood Compact" 420
483	150.00	100.00	30c orange red "Blood Compact" 442 (sia 392)
484	1200.00		1p red orange & black Church 443 (sia 393)

Issues of 1945, Perf. 11

Stamps of 1938-40 with additional Overprint in Black:

VICTORY   **VICTORY**
a   b

Nos. 485, 487, and 492 are Overprinted with Type "a".
Nos. 486, 488-491, 493 and 494 are Overprinted with Type "b".

485	.08	.06	2c rose Rizal, sia 383
486	.10	.08	4c yel. grn. Woman, sia 38‖
487	.12	.10	6c golden brown La Filipina, sia 385
488	.18	.18	8c Pearl Fishing
489	.20	.15	10c rose carmine Ft. Santiago, sia 387
490	.28	.18	12c black Salt Spring 438 sia 388
491	.35	.15	16c dark blue Magellan's Landing, sia 389
492	.40	.12	20c light olive green "Juan de la Cruz", sia 390
493	.55	.50	30c orange red "Blood Compact", sia 392
494	1.70	.40	1p red orange & black Church, sia 393

Nos. 431-432 Overprinted in Black   **VICTORY**

495	27.50	10.00	10p gray Manila Arms, sia 431
496	22.50	13.00	20p henna brown Manila Arms, sia 432

Issue of 1946, Perf. 11x10-1/2

497	.10	.06	2c José Rizal

Succeeding issues, released by the Philippine Republic on and after July 4, 1946, are listed in *Scott Standard Postage Stamp Catalogue.*

Air Post Stamps

Madrid-Manila Flight Issue of 1926, May 13 Perf. 11, Unwmkd.

Regular Issue of 1917-26 Overprinted in Red (R) or Violet (V)

C1	3.50	3.25	2c José Rizal (R)
C2	4.00	3.75	4c Pres. Wm. McKinley (V‖
C3	9.50	7.50	6c Fernando Magellan (R)
C4	11.00	8.50	8c orange brown (V), sia 24‖
C5	11.00	8.50	10c deep blue (R), sia 245
C6	11.50	11.00	12c Abraham Lincoln (V)
C7	575.00	575.00	16c light olive green (V), sia 247
C8	575.00	575.00	16c olive bistre (R), sia 247
C9	11.50	11.00	16c olive green (V), sia 303
C10	11.50	11.00	20c orange yellow (V), sia 24‖
C11	11.50	11.00	26c Francisco Carriedo (V‖
C12	11.50	11.00	30c gray (V), sia 250
C13	175.00	130.00	2p violet brown (R), sia 25‖
C14	300.00	235.00	4p dark blue (R), sia 253
C15	550.00	400.00	10p deep green (V), sia 254

C1   C2   C3   C6   C11

REPUBLIC OF THE PHILIPPINES, ASIA'S YOUNG DEMOCRACY

The Philippine islands, discovered by Magellan in 1521, were controlled by Spain for three hundred years before the islanders revolted and declared their independence in 1898. The Spanish-American War of that year, however, doomed this first attempt at becoming a republic. During that brief conflict Spain was driven out of the archipelago and control of the Philippines fell to the United States.

Guerilla war broke out again in 1899, this time against the United States. Led by Emilio Aguinaldo, it continued until 1905.

Even with the cessation of hostilities the Philippines continued to demand independence and in 1934 the United States declared 1946 as freedom year. The Japanese occupation of World War II failed to halt freedom plans and on July 4, 1946 the Philippines became an independent nation.

The Republic consists of more than 7,000 mountainous islands. The official languages are Filipino (taken from Tagalog), English, and Spanish. The native people are mainly of Malay stock, but Spanish, Chinese, American and other immigrants have produced an ethnically mixed population.

Perf. 10			
Same Overprint on No. 284			

7 65.00 40.00 1p pale violet (V), sia 251

This issue honors the flight of Spanish aviators Gallarza and Loriga from Madrid to Manila.

London-Orient Flight Issue of 1928, Nov. 9
Perf. 11
Unwmkd.

Regular Issue
of 1917-25
Overprinted in Red

L.O.F.

1928

8	.40	.40	2c green, sia 241
9	.50	.50	4c carmine, sia 242
0	1.75	1.75	6c violet, sia 243
1	1.85	1.85	8c orange brown, sia 244
2	1.85	1.85	10c deep blue, sia 245
3	2.50	2.50	12c red orange, sia 246
4	2.25	2.25	16c olive green, sia 303
5	3.00	3.00	20c George Washington
6	6.25	6.25	26c blue green, sia 249
7	6.25	6.25	30c gray, sia 250

Perf. 12			
Same Overprint on No. 271			
Wmkd. Single-lined PIPS (190PI)			

C28 16.00 16.00 1p Arms of Manila

Stamp honors air flight from London to Manila.

Issue of 1932, Sep. 27
Perf. 11, Unwmkd.
Nos. 354-360 Overprinted

ROUND-THE-WORLD FLIGHT
VON GRONAU
1932

C29	.45	.45	2c yellow green, sia 354
C30	.50	.50	4c Post Office, Manila
C31	.80	.80	12c orange, sia 356
C32	4.00	4.00	18c red orange, sia 357
C33	2.25	2.25	20c Rice Planting
C34	2.25	2.25	24c Rice Terraces
C35	2.25	2.25	32c olive brown, sia 360

In 1932, Captain Wolfgang von Gronau visited the Philippines during his historic round-the-world flight.

C25

C28

C30

C34

C33

C43   C46   C47   C53   C56

Issues of 1933, Apr. 11

Regular Issue
of 1917-25
Overprinted

F.REIN

MADRID-MANILA

FLIGHT-1933

C36	.40	.40	2c green, sia 241
C37	.50	.50	4c carmine, sia 242
C38	.60	.60	6c deep violet, sia 243
C39	1.65	1.65	8c orange brown, sia 244
C40	1.35	1.25	10c dark blue, sia 245
C41	1.00	1.00	12c orange, sia 246
C42	1.00	1.50	16c olive green, sia 303
C43	1.00	1.00	20c George Washington
C44	1.50	1.50	26c green, sia 249
C45	1.85	1.85	30c gray, sia 250

Issue honors the 1933 Madrid-Manila flight of the
Spanish aviator Fernando Rein y Loring.

No. 290b
Overprinted

| C46 | .55 | .50 | 2c José Rizal | May 26 |

Regular Issue
of 1932
Overprinted

C47	.10	.08	4c Post Office, Manila
C48	.35	.18	12c orange, sia 356
C49	.35	.30	20c yellow, sia 358
C50	.40	.35	24c deep violet, sia 359
C51	.55	.45	32c olive brown, sia 360

Issue of 1935, Dec. 2
Nos. 387 and 392 Overprinted in Gold

P.I-U.S.

INITIAL FLIGHT

December-1935

| C52 | .25 | .25 | 10c rose carmine, sia 387 |
| C53 | .50 | .50 | 30c "Blood Compact" |

Issued for the December 2-5 flight of the Chi
Clipper from Manila to San Francisco, Californ

Issue of 1936, Sep. 6

Regular Issue
of 1917-25
Surcharged
in Various Colors

MANILA-MADRID

ARNACAL

FLIGHT-1936

2 CENTAVOS 2

C54	.08	.06	2c (in blue) on 4c car., sia 24
C55	.15	.12	6c (in violet) on 12c red orange, sia 246
C56	.30	.30	16c (in black) on 26c Carried

Issued for the 1936 Manila-Madrid flight made
aviators Antonio Arnaiz and Juan Calvo.

Issue of 1939, Feb. 17

Regular Issue
of 1917-37
Surcharged in
Black or Red

**FIRST
AIR MAIL
EXHIBITION**

Feb 17 to 19,1939

8 CENTAVOS 8

| C57 | .85 | .55 | 8c (in black) on 26C Carried |
| C58 | 2.75 | 2.50 | 1p (in red) on 10p Manila Arms |

The Philippines held its first Air Mail Expositi
from February 17-19, 1939.

C59	.90	.70	8c Moro Vinta and Clipper
C60	1.00	.55	20c Moro Vinta and Clipper
C61	1.50	1.00	60c Moro Vinta and Clipper
C62	.70	.65	1p Moro Vinta and Clipper

Issue of 1944, Dec. 3

VICTORY   Hand Stamped in Violet on C47

| C63 | *700.00 450.00* | | 4c rose carmine, sia 355 |

C57   C58   C59-C62

THE SIEGE OF THE PHILIPPINES: 1941-45

Japan's World War II invasion of the Philippines began ten hours after the surprise attack on Pearl Harbor of December 7, 1941. On January 2, 1942 Manila fell before a Japanese land invasion and Allied forces under the command of General Douglas A. MacArthur retreated to Bataan and Corregidor.

On February 22 MacArthur transferred his headquarters to Australia by order of President Franklin D. Roosevelt. In April Bataan succumbed, but troops under General Jonathan Wainwright remained at Corregidor, an island fortress in Manila Bay. Though vastly outnumbered and low on supplies, the heroic army kept Japan's navy out of Manila Bay until May 6, 1942 when the fall of Corregidor ended all organized Philippine resistance to the Japanese.

925

More than two years after this defeat, on October 9, 1944, MacArthur returned to the Philippines and invaded Leyte. The Battle of Leyte Gulf (October 23-25) ended with three Japanese units in retreat. Soon afterward the Allies were victorious at Mindoro and Luzon. When Manila was liberated on February 25, 1945 the general had fulfilled his famous promise, "I shall return."

See U.S. Scott Stamp Nos. 925, 1424

Special Delivery Stamps			
Issue of 1901, Perf. 12			

United States No. E5
Overprinted in Red **PHILIPPINES**

Wmkd. Double-lined PIPS (191PI)

22.00	21.00	10c dark blue, sia U.S. E5	

Issue of 1906
Wmkd. Double-lined PIPS (191PI)

8.00	5.50	20c ultramarine, sia E3	

Special Printing of 1907
Red Overprint of E1 on U.S. No. E6

350.00		10c ultramarine, sia U.S. E6	

Issue of 1911
Wmkd. Single-lined PIPS (190PI)

6.00	1.25	20c Special Delivery Messenger	

Issue of 1916, Perf. 10

32.50	10.00	20c deep ultramarine, sia E3	

Issue of 1919, Perf. 11, Unwmkd.

45	.25	20c ultramarine, sia E3	
.45	.25	20c dull violet, sia E3	

Issue of 1931, Imperf.

6.50	6.50	20c Special Delivery Messenger	

Issue of 1939, Perf. 11

E5 Overprinted
in Black **COMMONWEALTH**

E7	.30	.30	20c blue violet, sia E3

Issue of 1944

VICTORY Handstamped in Violet on E5b and E7

E8	100.00	90.00	20c dull violet, sia E3
E9	75.00	60.00	20c blue violet, sia E3

Issue of 1945

No. E7
with additional
Overprint
in Black **VICTORY**

E10	.60	.60	20c Special Delivery Messenger

Official Special Delivery Stamp
Perf. 11, Unwmkd.

E5b Overprinted **O. B.**

EO1	.65	.55	20c dull violet, sia E3

E3	E6	E10

Postage Due Stamps

Issue of 1899, Design of U.S. J33
Perf. 12

Postage Due Stamps of the United States Nos. J38 to J44 Overprinted in Black

PHILIPPINES

Wmkd. USPS (191)

J1	1.45	1.10	1c deep claret
J2	1.45	1.10	2c deep claret
J3	1.75	1.65	5c deep claret
J4	3.25	3.25	10c deep claret
J5	25.00	22.50	50c deep claret

Issue of 1901

J6	3.50	3.50	3c deep claret
J7	25.00	25.00	30c deep claret

Issue of 1928, sia J10
Perf. 11, Unwmkd.

J8	.12	.12	4c brown red
J9	.15	.15	6c brown red
J10	.15	.15	8c Post Office Clerk
J11	.18	.18	10c brown red
J12	.20	.20	12c brown red
J13	.25	.25	16c brown red
J14	.18	.18	20c brown red

Issue of 1937
No. J8 Surcharged in Blue   **3 CVOS. 3**

J15	.20	.12	3c (3 cvos. 3 in blue) on 4c brown red, sia J10

Issue of 1944, sia J10

VICTORY   Handstamped in Violet on Nos. J8-J14

J16	40.00	4c brown red
J17	30.00	6c brown red
J18	35.00	8c brown red
J19	30.00	10c brown red
J20	30.00	12c brown red
J21	55.00	16c brown red
J22	35.00	20c brown red

Official Stamps

Regular Issue of 1926 Overprinted in Red   **OFFICIAL**

Issue of 1926, Perf. 12
Unwmkd.

O1	1.65	1.65	2c green and black, sia 319
O2	1.65	1.50	4c carmine and blk., sia 320
O3	4.25	2.50	18c lt. brown and blk., sia 322
O4	3.25	1.65	20c orange and black, sia 323

Note: Prior to 1926, stamps used for official business handstamped "OB" or "Official Business." For information on these stamps, refer to the Appendix.

Regular Issue of 1917-26 Overprinted   **O. B.**

Issue of 1931, Perf. 11

O5	.06	.04	2c green, sia 241
O6	.08	.05	4c carmine, sia 242
O7	.10	.08	6c deep violet, sia 243
O8	.10	.08	8c yellow brown, sia 244
O9	.40	.12	10c deep blue, sia 245
O10	.25	.15	12c red orange, sia 246
O11	.25	.10	16c light olive green, sia 30
O12	.30	.10	20c orange yellow, sia 24
O13	.45	.45	26c green, sia 249
O14	.40	.35	30c gray, sia 250

Issues of 1935
Same Overprint on Regular Issue of 1935

O15	.06	.04	2c rose, sia 383
O16	.06	.05	4c yellow green, sia 384
O17	.10	.06	6c dark brown, sia 385
O18	.12	.12	8c Pearl Fishing
O19	.15	.06	10c rose carmine, sia 387
O20	.20	.15	12c black, sia 388
O21	.20	.15	16c dark blue, sia 389
O22	.20	.15	20c light olive green, sia 39
O23	.40	.35	26c indigo, sia 391
O24	.45	.40	30c orange red, sia 392

Same Overprint on Overprinted Issue of 1936-3

O25	.08	.04	2c rose, sia 383
O26	1.00	.75	20c light olive green, sia 39

Issue of 1938-40, Perf. 10
Regular Issue of 1935 Overprinted in Black:

O.   B.   **O.   B.**

COMMON-WEALTH   COMMONWEALTH

a   *b*

Nos. O27, O29, and O34 are overprinted with type "a".
Nos. O28, O30-O33, O35 and O36 are overprinted with type "b".

O27	.08	.04	2c rose, sia 383
O28	.10	.08	4c yellow green, sia 384
O29	.15	.06	6c dark brown, sia 385
O30	.15	.10	8c violet, sia 386
O31	.17	.10	10c rose, sia 387
O32	.18	.18	12c black, sia 388
O33	.25	.12	16c dark blue, sia 389
O34	.35	.35	20c light olive green, sia 39
O35	.45	.45	26c indigo, sia 391
O36	.40	.40	30c "Blood Compact"

Issue of 1941, Perf. 11x10-1/2
Unwmkd.

Regular Stamp of 1941 Overprinted in Black   **O.   B.**

c

O37	.04	.04	2c Rizal

Issue of 1944, Perf. 11, 11x10-1/2

VICTORY   Handstamped in Violet on the Following:

O38	150.00	75.00	2c rose O27 (sia 383)
O39	5.00	3.00	4c apple green O37
O40	20.00	17.50	4c yellow green. O16 (sia 384
O40A	1750.00		6c dark brown O29 (sia 385
O41	200.00		10c rose car. O31 (sia 387)
O42	1000.00		20c lt. olive grn. O22 (sia 39
O43	1750.00		20c lt. olive grn. O26 (sia 39

Issue of 1946, Perf. 11x10-1/2
Black Overprint of O37 on No. 497

O44	.06	.05	2c sepia, sia 497

J10   O18   O34   O36   O37

PUERTO RICO
(pwĕr′tŭ rē′kō)
(Porto Rico)

When Christopher Columbus discovered this island of green mountains and fertile valleys in 1493, it was the only time he set foot on what is now U. S. territory. Soon afterwards gold was found in the Puerto Rican mountains, and in 1508 Juan Ponce de León brought settlers to the island and became its first governor. The gold, however, was soon exhausted and the colonists were plagued by hurricanes and pirates. Finally, at the islanders' request, Spain fortified the island with impregnable fortresses that withstood foreign attack until the United States invaded Puerto Rico during the Spanish-American War of 1898. At this short war's conclusion Puerto Rico became an American possession. Since 1917 its people have been U. S. citizens.

LOCATION — A large island in the West Indies, east of Hispaniola.
GOVT. — Former Spanish possession.
AREA — 3,435 sq. mi.
POP. — 2,689,932 (1970).
CAPITAL — San Juan.
Spanish issues of 1855-71 for Puerto Rico were also used by Cuba.

Issued Under American Dominion

Issues of 1898, Imperf.
Unwkd.

1000.00		5c Ponce Issue

Counterfeits of Nos. 200-201 exist.

| 100.00 | 125.00 | 5c Coamo Issue |

There are ten varieties in the setting. The stamps bear the control mark "F. Santiago" in violet.

Issue of 1899, Perf. 12

United States
Nos. 279a, 267, 281a,
272 and 282C
Overprinted in Black
at 36° degree angle

Wmkd. **USPS** (191)

| 1.00 | .50 | 1c Benjamin Franklin |
| 1.00 | .25 | 2c George Washington |

212	1.50	1.00	5c Ulysses S. Grant
213	5.50	4.50	8c William T. Sherman
214	3.00	2.25	10c Daniel Webster

Issue of 1900

United States Stamps
Nos. 279a and 267
Overprinted Diagonally
in Black

| 215 | 1.00 | .60 | 1c yel. grn. Franklin, sia 210 |
| 216 | 1.00 | .50 | 2c car. Washington, sia 211 |

Postage Due Stamps
Issue of 1899, Perf. 12

United States
Nos. J38, J39 and J42
Overprinted in Black
at 36° degree angle

Wmkd. (191)

J1	3.50	3.00	1c deep claret, design of J2
J2	3.50	3.00	2c Figure of Value
J3	25.00	17.50	10c deep claret, design of J2

Stamps of Puerto Rico have been replaced by those of the United States.

THE UNITED NATIONS

We, the peoples of the United Nations, determined to save succeeding generations from the scourge of war, which twice in our lifetime has brought untold sorrow to mankind, and to reaffirm faith in fundamental human rights, in the dignity and worth of the human person . . . **have resolved to combine our efforts to accomplish these aims. Preamble to the Charter of the United Nations.**

The guns of World War II shattered the world's hopes for a lasting peace through the League of Nations, but before the war ended California's San Francisco Opera House saw the birth of a new organization pledged to the preservation of world peace. On June 26, 1945, following two months of deliberation, delegates to the fifty-nation San Francisco Conference unanimously adopted a Charter for the new United Nations.

The Charter created s principal organs which wor to achieve international peac and human dignity: the Ge eral Assembly, the Securi Council, the Trusteeshi Council, the Internation Court of Justice, the Eco nomic and Social Counc and the Secretariat. Th latter is headed by the chie administrative officer of th U.N., the Secretary Genera Four men have thus far hel this post: Trygve Lie of No way, Dag Hammarskjöld o Sweden, U Thant of Burma and Kurt Waldheim of Austri

164

Although it cannot legislate in a strict sense, the General Assembly wields important power in crucial ways—through diplomacy and international debate. Including representatives from all 127 member nations, this "world parliament" provides a forum where disputes may be solved with words instead of guns. The spotlight of world opinion is perpetually brought to bear upon its sessions, in which nations of the world present their views on such questions as the cessation of nuclear testing, disarmament and arms control, and the peaceful uses of outer space.

The Security Council consists of fifteen members, five of which are permanent (China, France, the U.S.S.R., the United Kingdom, and the United States).

The U.N.'s most powerful organ, it has "the primary responsibility for the maintenance of international peace and security." In 1950, for example, during the Korean crisis, the General Assembly created the U.N. Emergency Force, but when North Korean forces crossed the 38th parallel into South Korea only the Security Council was authorized to deploy U.N. troops into the troubled area.

Throughout the world, other U.N. "emergency" forces combat foes to peace and security. In 1950, simultaneous to the creation of a military force, the General Assembly also established the U.N. Korean Reconstruction Agency (UNKRA), a crash relief program for South Korea. The U.N. Relief and Work Agency for Arab Refugees from Palestine (UNRWA), also established in 1950, continues to provide aid to the war-torn Middle East. Through the programs of special agencies such as UNESCO (see p. 169), UNICEF (see p. 173), and the World Health Organization, the United

Nations fights poverty and disease to fulfill its peace-promoting mission. In the words of Secretary-General U. Thant, "These evils (poverty, disease, hunger and illiteracy) are not only affronts to human dignity; each intensifying the other, they menace the stability of Governments, aggravate tensions, threaten international peace."

United Nations
Regular Issue of 1951, Unwmkd.
Perf. 13x12-1/2, 12-1/2x13, 12-1/2x13-1/2

1	.04	.04	1c Peoples of the World
2	.04	.04	1½c U.N. Headquarters
3	.12	.08	2c "Peace, Justice, Security"
4	.15	.08	3c U.N. Flag
5	.15	.12	5c U.N. Children's Fund
6	.80	.50	10c Peoples of the World
7	.50	.40	15c U.N. Flag
8	1.75	.90	20c World Unity
9	1.50	1.25	25c U.N. Flag
10	15.00	6.00	50c U.N. Headquarters
11	2.50	1.75	$1 "Peace, Justice, Security"

Issues of 1952
Perf. 12

12	.85	.65	5c U.N. 7th Anniv. Issue Oct. 24

1952 marked the seventh anniversary of the signing of the U.N. Charter at the Veterans War Memorial Building, San Francisco (shown)

Perf. 13-1/2x14

13	.50	.30	3c Human Rights Day Issue Dec. 10
14	1.50	.70	5c Human Rights Day Issue Dec. 10

The Universal Declaration of Human Rights was adopted in 1948. It has frequently been honored on U.N. stamps.

Perf. 12-1/2x13

15	.50	.30	3c Refugee Issue	Apr. 24
16	3.50	1.50	5c Refugee Issue	Apr. 24

Issued to publicize "Protection for Refugees."

Perf. 13

17	.75	.35	3c UPU Issue	Jun. 16
18	3.00	1.50	5c UPU Issue	Jun. 16

Issued to honor the Universal Postal Union (UPU). The stamps show an envelope, a map, and the U.N. emblem.

Perf. 13x12-1/2				
.50	.40	3c	Technical Assistance Issue	Oct. 24
2.25	1.00	5c	Technical Assistance Issue	Oct. 24

Issued to publicize United Nations' activities in the field of technical assistance, these stamps depict gearwheels and the U.N. emblem.

Perf. 12-1/2x13				
.50	.40	3c	Human Rights Day Issue	Dec. 10
2.50	1.00	5c	Human Rights Day Issue	Dec. 10

Issues of 1954				
.50	.40	3c	FAO Issue	Feb. 11
2.50	1.10	8c	FAO Issue	Feb. 11

The purpose of the U.N. Food and Agriculture Organization (FAO) is to combat hunger in the world. The stamps show a stalk of wheat.

25	.60	.40	3c ILO Issue	May 10
26	4.75	1.25	8c ILO Issue, inscribed "OIT"	

The International Labor Organization (ILO) was created in 1919. It is the only surviving major organization from the League of Nations. The stamps show an anvil with the U.N. emblem.

Perf. 14				
27	5.50	2.50	3c U.N. Day Issue	Oct. 25
28	.50	.50	8c U.N. Day Issue	Oct. 25

On October 24, 1954, the United Nations celebrated the ninth anniversary of the ratification of its charter. The stamps show the U.N. European Office in Geneva, Switzerland.

29	27.50	5.00	3c Human Rights Day Issue	Dec. 10
30	1.00	1.00	8c Human Rights Day Issue	Dec. 10

		Issues of 1955		
		Perf. 13-1/2x14		
31	4.00	1.00	3c ICAO Issue	Feb. 9
32	1.25	1.00	8c ICAO Issue,	
			inscribed "OACI"	

The charter of the International Civil Aviation Organization (ICAO), ratified in 1947, dates from 1944, and is older than the U.N. Charter. The stamps show a symbol of flight.

33	2.00	1.00	3c UNESCO Issue	May 11
34	.50	.50	8c UNESCO Issue	May 11

This issue honors the United Nations Educational, Scientific, and Cultural Organization (UNESCO), created in November, 1946. Stamps show the UNESCO emblem.

35	4.50	1.25	3c U.N. 10th Anniv. Issue	Oct. 24
36	.25	.25	4c U.N. 10th Anniv., Spanish inscription	
37	.50	.40	8c U.N. 10th Anniv., French inscription	

Nos. 35-37 are inscribed with the first words of the U.N. Charter, which was ratified 10 years before these stamps were issued.

Wmkd., Wavy Lines (309)
Imperf.

38	110.00	45.00	Souvenir sheet of three, sia 35-37	
38a	25.00	12.00	3c deep plum, sia 35	
38b	25.00	12.00	4c dull green, sia 36	
38c	25.00	12.00	8c bluish black, sia 37	

No. 38 contains imperforate, watermarked varieties of Nos. 35-37, with marginal inscription in deep plum.

Perf. 14x13-1/2

39	.25	.25	3c Human Rights Day Issue	Dec. 9
40	1.25	.85	8c Human Rights Day Issue	Dec. 9

Issues of 1956
Perf. 14

41	.75	.40	3c ITU Issue	Feb. 17
42	1.00	.75	8c ITU Issue, inscribed "UIT"	

The International Telecommunication Union (ITU) is the oldest of the U.N. agencies. Its prototype dates from 1865. The stamps show symbols of telecommunication.

43	.20	.20	3c WHO Issue	Apr. 6

44	1.50	.90	8c WHO Issue, inscribed "OMS"	

This issue honors the World Health Organization (WHO), whose constitution was ratified in April, 1948. The stamps show the globe and a caduceus.

45	.10	.10	3c U.N. Day Issue	Oct. 24
46	.50	.35	8c U.N. Day, French inscription	

The 11th anniversary of the United Nations was celebrated on October 24, 1956. The stamps depict a General Assembly meeting.

47	.10	.08	3c Human Rights Day Issue,	Dec.
48	.20	.15	8c Human Rights Day Issue,	Dec.

Issues of 1957

49	.10	.08	3c WMO Issue	Jan.
50	.20	.15	8c WMO issue, Agency Name in French	

Stamps, showing a weather balloon, honor the 10th anniversary of the World Meteorological Organization (WMO).

Perf. 14x12-1/2

51	.10	.10	3c U.N. Emergency Force	
52	.20	.15	8c U.N. Emergency Force	Apr.

Nos. 51 and 52 Re-engraved

53	.10	.10	3c light blue, sia 51	Apr.-May
54	.55	.50	8c rose carmine, sia 52	Apr.-M

The U.N. Emergency Force was honored in 1957 for its peace-keeping operations during the Suez Canal crisis. Stamps show the badge of the Force. Nos. 53 and 54 have lightly shaded backgrounds. The lettering on the stamps is more distinct than on Nos. 51 and 52, as there is a line around each letter.

Perf. 12-1/2x13

55	.10	.07	3c Security Council Issue	Oct.
56	.20	.15	8c Security Council, French inscription	

The five permanent members of the 11-member Security Council are China, France, the U.S.S.R., the United Kingdom, and the United States. The stamps show the U. N. emblem and the globe.

Perf. 14

57	.10	.07	3c Human Rights Day Issue	Dec.
58	.20	15	8c Human Rights Day Issue	Dec.

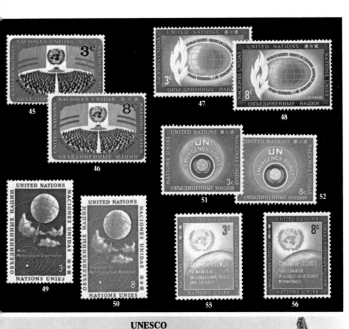

UNESCO

UNESCO, the United Nations Educational, Scientific, and Cultural Organization, seeks to nurture the growth of knowledge in order to improve the material and spiritual lot of man. One of its constitutional tasks is to assure "the conservation and protection of the world's inheritance of books, works of art, and monuments of history and science." To fulfill this pledge the organization led a world-wide fight in 1961 to save Egypt's Nubian monuments from floods caused by the building of the Aswan Dam. Working with its member nations, UNESCO also seeks to eliminate illiteracy by fostering the creation of suitable educational opportunities for adults.

See U. N. Scott Stamp Nos. 33-34, 134-136

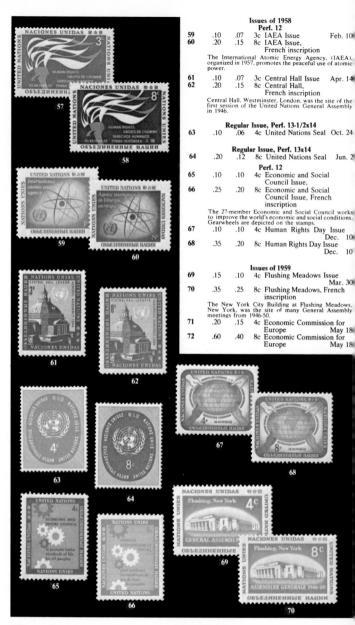

Issues of 1958
Perf. 12

59	.10	.07	3c IAEA Issue	Feb. 10
60	.20	.15	8c IAEA Issue, French inscription	

The International Atomic Energy Agency, (IAEA), organized in 1957, promotes the peaceful use of atomic power.

61	.10	.07	3c Central Hall Issue	Apr. 14
62	.20	.15	8c Central Hall, French inscription	

Central Hall, Westminster, London, was the site of the first session of the United Nations General Assembly in 1946.

Regular Issue, Perf. 13-1/2x14

63	.10	.06	4c United Nations Seal	Oct. 24

Regular Issue, Perf. 13x14

64	.20	.12	8c United Nations Seal	Jun. 2

Perf. 12

65	.10	.10	4c Economic and Social Council Issue,	
66	.25	.20	8c Economic and Social Council Issue, French inscription	

The 27-member Economic and Social Council works to improve the world's economic and social conditions. Gearwheels are depicted on the stamps.

67	.10	.10	4c Human Rights Day Issue	Dec. 10
68	.35	.20	8c Human Rights Day Issue	Dec. 10

Issues of 1959

69	.15	.10	4c Flushing Meadows Issue	Mar. 30
70	.35	.25	8c Flushing Meadows, French inscription	

The New York City Building at Flushing Meadows, New York, was the site of many General Assembly meetings from 1946-50.

71	.20	.15	4c Economic Commission for Europe	May 18
72	.60	.40	8c Economic Commission for Europe	May 18

	.20	.15	4c	Trusteeship Council Issue Oct. 23
	.45	.30	8c	Trusteeship Council, French inscription

The Trusteeship Council supervises the administration of Trust territories held by U.N. members. The figure on the stamps was adapted from Rodin's "Age of Bronze."

	.12	.10	4c	World Refugee Year Dec. 10
	.30	.20	8c	World Refugee Year, French inscription

The World Refugee Year of July 1, 1959-June 30, 1960 publicized the work of the office of the U.N. High Commissioner for Refugees.

Issues of 1960
Perf. 14

	.12	.10	4c	Chaillot Palace Issue Feb. 29
	.30	.20	8c	Chaillot Palace, French inscription

The Chaillot Palace in Paris was the site of General Assembly meetings in 1948 and 1951.

Perf. 13x13-1/2

	.12	.10	4c	ECAFE Issue Apr. 11
	.30	.20	8c	ECAFE Issue, French inscription

The Economic Commission for Asia and the Far East (ECAFE) is a regional commission of the Economic and Social Council.

Perf. 13-1/2

	.12	.10	4c	World Forestry Issue Aug. 29
	.30	.20	8c	World Forestry, French inscription

The Fifth World Forestry Congress was held in Seattle, Washington from Aug. 29-Sep. 10, 1960.

Perf. 11

	.10	.08	4c	U.N. Day Issue Oct. 24
	.20	.15	8c	U.N. Day, French inscription

The U.N. Day Issue of 1960 notes the 15th anniversary of the United Nations. Stamps show U.N. Headquarters and the Preamble to the U.N. Charter.

Imperf.

	5.00	3.50		Souvenir Sheet of two, sia 83-84
5a	2.00	1.25	4c	blue, sia 83
5l	2.00	1.25	8c	gray, sia 84

No. 85 contains imperforate varieties of Nos. 83 and 84 with marginal inscription in dark gray.

71

72

73

74

75

76

77

78

79

80

81

82

83

84

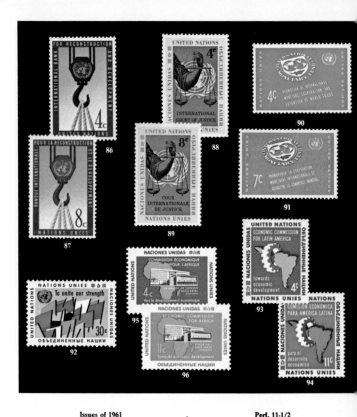

Issues of 1961

88	.12	.10	4c World Court Issue Feb. 13
89	.30	.20	8c World Court, French inscription

The 15-member International Court of Justice is, according to the U.N. Charter, "the principal judicial organ of the U.N."

90	.12	.10	4c Intl. Monetary Fund Issue Apr. 17
91	.25	.20	7c Intl. Monetary Fund, French inscription

The International Monetary Fund, organized in 1945, is the sister organization of the World Bank.

Regular Issue, Perf. 11-1/2

92	.65	.45	30c Abstract Group of Flags Jun. 5

Perf. 13-1/2

93	.30	.20	4c Economic Commission for Latin America Sep. 18
94	.90	.60	11c Economic Comm. for Latin America, Spanish inscription

This issue honors the Economic Commission for Latin America, a regional commission of the Economic and Social Council.

95	.20	.15	4c Economic Comm. for Africa French inscription Oct. 24
96	.55	.35	11c Economic Comm. for Africa

The Economic Commission for Africa is a regional commission of the Economic and Social Council.

97	.10	.08	3c UNICEF Issue Dec. 4
98	.40	.20	4c UNICEF, Spanish inscription
99	.50	.40	13c UNICEF, French inscription

1961 marked the 15th anniversary of the United Nations International Children's Emergency Fund (UNICEF). The stamps show a mother bird feeding her young and the seal of UNICEF.

Issues of 1962
Perf. 14-1/2x14

100	.20	.15	4c Urban Development Feb. 28
101	.40	.30	7c Urban Development, French inscription

Issued to publicize U.N. programs in the areas of housing and urban development, these stamps show a family and symbolic buildings.

Perf. 14x14-1/2

102	.20	.15	4c WHO—Malaria Issue Mar. 30
103	.55	.35	11c WHO—Malaria Issue Mar. 30

Issued in connection with the World Health Organization's international campaign to eradicate malaria.

Regular Issue

104	.15	.08	1c "Peace" May 25

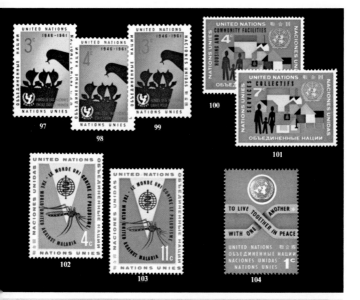

UNICEF

The United Nations Childrens Fund (UNICEF) began as an emergency force to provide aid to homeless orphans of war-ravaged countries after World War II. In 1950 when the crash relief program in Europe was nearing completion, the General Assembly made UNICEF a permanent part of the U. N.

Since then UNICEF's goal has been to eliminate the threat of hunger and sickness to children in underdeveloped areas of the world. The Fund has launched massive health campaigns to eradicate disease and improve nutrition. In addition, UNICEF still provides emergency aid in times of flood, earthquake, drought, and war. Maintained by voluntary contributions and governed by a thirty-nation executive board, UNICEF is currently helping 112 countries fill the urgent needs of their children in the hope that these stamps will be the peace-makers of the future.

See Scott Stamp Nos. 5, 97-99, 161-163

105	.06	.05	3c U.N. Flag	May 25
			Perf. 12	
106	.50	.30	5c Hands, "U.N.," and Globe	
			Perf. 12-1/2	
107	.22	.18	11c U.N. Emblem Over Globe	
			Perf. 11-1/2	
108	.25	.20	5c Hammarskjöld Issue	Sep. 17
109	1.50	.65	15c Hammarskjöld Issue	Sep. 17

Issued on the first anniversary of the death of Dag
Hammarskjöld, Secretary General of the United Nations
from 1953-1961. The stamps show a flag at half-mast
at U.N. Headquarters.

110	.35	.20	4c Congo Operation Issue	
				Oct. 24
111	1.50	.60	11c Congo Operation, French inscription	

Issued for United Nations Day, 1962, these stamps note
the 1960-63 United Nations Operation in the Congo.

Perf. 14x13-1/2

112	.20	.15	4c Peaceful Use of Outer Space	
				Dec. 3
113	.55	.35	11c Peaceful Use of Outer Space, French inscription	

Issued to promote the Committee on the Peaceful
Uses of Outer Space, these stamps show a globe in the
universe with a palm frond.

Issues of 1963
Perf. 11-1/2

114	.25	.15	5c Development Decade	Feb. 4
115	.55	.45	11c Development Decade, French inscription	

The U.N. Development Decade Issue honors the U.N.
Conference on the Application of Science and Technology for the Benefit of the Less Developed Areas
held at Geneva from February 4-20.

116	.25	.15	5c Freedom From Hunger	
				Mar. 22
117	.55	.45	11c Freedom From Hunger, French inscription	

Issued to publicize the Food and Agricultural Organization's "Freedom from Hunger" campaign, these
stamps show stalks of wheat.

118	1.25	.85	25c UNTEA Issue	Oct. 1

Issued for the first anniversary of the United Nations
Temporary Executive Authority (UNTEA) in West
New Guinea (West Irian).

Perf. 13

119	.25	.15	5c General Assembly Hall	
				Nov. 4
120	.55	.40	11c General Assembly Hall, French inscription	

Since October, 1955, all sessions of the General Assembly have been held in the General Assembly Hall
(shown), U.N. Headquarters, New York.

121	.20	.15	5c Human Rights Day 15th Anniversary Issue	Dec. 10
122	.60	.40	11c Human Rights Day 15th Anniv. Issue, inscribed "15e ANNIVERSAIRE."	

Issues of 1964

123	.20	.15	5c IMCO Issue	Jan. 13
124	.50	.40	11c IMCO Issue, inscribed "OMCI"	

The Inter-Governmental Maritime Consultative Organization (IMCO), ratified in 1958, is the youngest U.N.
special agency. The stamps depict ships at sea with
the IMCO emblem.

Regular Issue
Perf. 13-1/2

125	.04	.04	2c Map of World	May 29
			Perf. 11-1/2	
126	.14	.12	7c U.N. Emblem	May 29
127	.20	.18	10c Three Men & Globe	May 29

Jordan Scott No. 386

DAG HAMMARSKJÖLD (1905-1961)

In 1953 Swedish diplomat and scholar Dag Hammarskjöld became the second Secretary-General of the United Nations. The son of Sweden's World War I prime minister, Hammarskjöld began his long career as a national and international public servant at the age of twenty-five when he was secretary of a government committee on unemployment.

Hammarskjöld, a nonpartisan but controversial Secretary-General, undertook many missions in the cause of peace. In 1955 he went to Peking to secure the release of American prisoners. The U. N. peace-keeping force he sent to the Middle East after the Suez crisis of 1956 earned him the ire of Great Britain. In 1961, while flying to Africa to negotiate a cease-fire in the Congo crisis, Hammarskjöld was killed in a plane crash. He was posthumously awarded the 1961 Nobel Prize for Peace.

See U. N. Scott Stamp Nos. 108-109

"Single Form" by Barbara Hepworth
This twenty-one foot abstract sculpture is a memorial to Dag Hammarskjöld. It stands outside the Secretariat building.

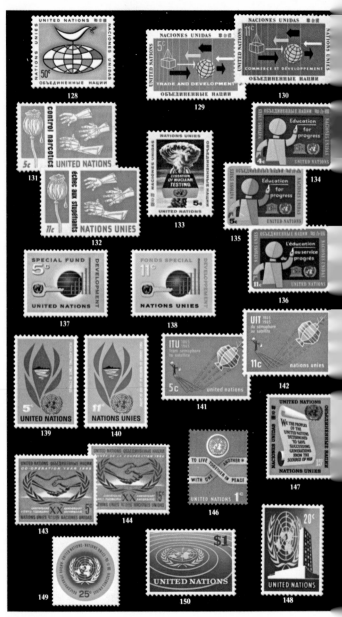

176

| 28 | 1.00 | .90 | 50c Stylized Globe and "Peace Dove" Mar. 6 |

Perf. 13

| 29 | .15 | .12 | 5c Trade and Development Jun. 15 |
| 30 | .50 | .40 | 11c Trade and Development, French inscription |

This issue commemorates the U.N. Conference on Trade and Development held at Geneva from March 23-June 15, 1964.

Perf. 12

| 31 | .15 | .12 | 5c Control Narcotics Sep. 21 |
| 32 | .60 | .40 | 11c Control Narcotics, French inscription |

Issued to honor international efforts and achievements under U.N. auspices to control narcotics.

Perf. 11x11-1/2

| 33 | .15 | .12 | 5c Test Ban Treaty Issue Oct. 23 |

Issued in connection with the signing of the nuclear test ban treaty, which resolved to end all nuclear explosions in the atmosphere, outer space, and underwater.

Perf. 12-1/2

34	.12	.10	4c UNESCO Education Issue Dec. 7
35	.15	.12	5c UNESCO Education Issue Dec. 7
36	.40	.30	11c UNESCO Education, French inscription

Issued to publicize the UNESCO world campaign for universal literacy and for free compulsory primary education.

Issues of 1965
Perf. 13-1/2x13

| 47 | .15 | .12 | 5c Special Fund Issue Jan. 25 |
| 48 | .40 | .30 | 11c Special Fund, French inscription |

The Special Fund aims to speed economic growth and social advancement in low-income countries.

Perf. 11-1/2

| 49 | .12 | .10 | 5c Peace-Keeping Force on Cyprus Mar. 4 |
| 40 | | .30 | .25 | 11c Peace-Keeping Force on Cyprus, French inscription |

Issued to honor the United Nations Peace-Keeping Force on Cyprus.

| 41 | .20 | .15 | 5c ITU Issue May 17 |
| 42 | .35 | .30 | 11c ITU, French inscription |

The International Telecommunications Union (ITU) celebrated its 100th anniversary in 1965.

Perf. 14x13-1/2

43	.20	.15	5c Intl. Cooperation Year Jun. 26
44	.30	.25	15c Intl. Cooperation Year, French inscription
45	.90	.90	Souvenir sheet of two, sia 143 and 144

Issue notes the 20th anniversary of the U.N. and honors the International Cooperation Year.
No. 145 contains one each of Nos. 143-144, with dark blue and ochre marginal inscription and ochre edging.

Regular Issue of 1965-66
Perf. 13-1/2

| 46 | .03 | .03 | 1c "Peace" Sep. 20 |

Perf. 14

| 47 | .30 | .25 | 15c Preamble, U.N. Charter Oct. 25 |

Perf. 12

| 48 | .40 | .35 | 20c U.N. Headquarters Oct. 25 |

Perf. 14

| 49 | .50 | .45 | 25c U.N. Emblem Sep. 20 |

Perf. 11-1/2

| 40 | 2.00 | 1.80 | $1 U.N. Emblem Mar. 25 |

Issues of 1965
Perf. 12

51	.10	.08	4c World Population Issue Nov. 29
52	.12	.10	5c World Population Issue Nov. 29
53	.30	.22	11c World Population, French inscription

Showing fields and people, these stamps emphasize the importance of the problems caused by the world's population growth.

151

152

153

154

155

156

157

Issues of 1966
Perf. 11-1/2

| 154 | .15 | .10 | 5c World Federation of U. N. Assns. Issue Jan. 31 |
| 155 | .45 | .40 | 15c World Fed. of U.N. Assns. Issue, French inscription |

Issued to honor the World Federation of United Nations Associations, these stamps show the globe with the flags of U.N. members.

Perf. 12-1/2x12

| 156 | .20 | .15 | 5c WHO Headquarters Issue May 26 |
| 157 | .30 | .22 | 11c WHO Headquarters, French inscription |

The World Health Organization (WHO) opened its new headquarters in Geneva in 1966.

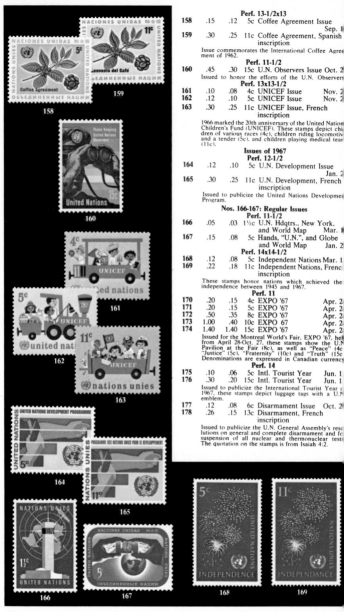

Perf. 13-1/2x13

158	.15	.12	5c Coffee Agreement Issue
			Sep. 1
159	.30	.25	11c Coffee Agreement, Spanish inscription

Issue commemorates the International Coffee Agreement of 1962.

Perf. 11-1/2

| 160 | .45 | .30 | 15c U.N. Observers Issue Oct. 2 |

Issued to honor the efforts of the U.N. Observers.

Perf. 13x13-1/2

161	.10	.08	4c UNICEF Issue	Nov. 2
162	.12	.10	5c UNICEF Issue	Nov. 2
163	.30	.25	11c UNICEF Issue, French inscription

1966 marked the 20th anniversary of the United Nations Children's Fund (UNICEF). These stamps depict children of various races (4c), children riding locomotive and a tender (5c), and children playing medical team (11c).

Issues of 1967
Perf. 12-1/2

164	.12	.10	5c U.N. Development Issue
			Jan. 2
165	.30	.25	11c U.N. Development, French inscription

Issued to publicize the United Nations Development Program.

Nos. 166-167: Regular Issues
Perf. 11-1/2

| 166 | .05 | .03 | 1½c U.N. Hdqtrs., New York, and World Map Mar. 1 |
| 167 | .15 | .08 | 5c Hands, "U.N.", and Globe and World Map Jan. 2 |

Perf. 14x14-1/2

| 168 | .12 | .08 | 5c Independent Nations Mar. 1 |
| 169 | .22 | .18 | 11c Independent Nations, French inscription |

These stamps honor nations which achieved their independence between 1945 and 1967.

Perf. 11

170	.20	.15	4c EXPO '67	Apr. 2
171	.20	.15	5c EXPO '67	Apr. 2
172	.50	.35	8c EXPO '67	Apr. 2
173	1.00	.40	10c EXPO 67	Apr. 2
174	1.40	1.40	15c EXPO '67	Apr. 2

Issued for the Montreal World's Fair, EXPO '67, held from April 28-Oct. 27, these stamps show the U.N. Pavilion at the Fair (8c), as well as "Peace" (4c), "Justice" (5c), "Fraternity" (10c) and "Truth" (15c). Denominations are expressed in Canadian currency.

Perf. 14

| 175 | .10 | .06 | 5c Intl. Tourist Year | Jun. 1 |
| 176 | .30 | .20 | 15c Intl. Tourist Year | Jun. 1 |

Issued to publicize the International Tourist Year of 1967, these stamps depict luggage tags with a U.N. emblem.

| 177 | .12 | .08 | 6c Disarmament Issue Oct. 2 |
| 178 | .26 | .15 | 13c Disarmament, French inscription |

Issued to publicize the U.N. General Assembly's resolutions on general and complete disarmament and for suspension of all nuclear and thermonuclear tests. The quotation on the stamps is from Isaiah 4:2.

ART AT THE UNITED NATIONS

The glass and marble Secretariat building on New York's East River — itself an architectural masterpiece — also houses a large and varied international art collection. The art objects, whether paintings, tapestries, or sculptures, are donated to the U.N. by its member nations, although in some cases the U.N. commissions special works. Most notable of the special commissions is the stained glass panel which the Russian painter Marc Chagall designed in memory of the former U.N. Secretary-General Dag Hammarskjöld.

The United Nations publicizes its art acquisitions by its "Art at the U.N." series of postage stamps. One such acquisition is a section of a third century mosaic given by the Tunisian Republic. Just north of the Secretariat building stands the "Peace Bell" presented to the U.N. in 1954 by the United Nations Association of Japan in the name of the People of Nippon. The bell, housed in an open pagoda of cypress, was cast from contributed coins and other metals.

See U. N. Scott Stamp Nos. 179, 180, 183-184, 201-204

Henrik Starcke Statue in U.N. Trusteeship Council chamber.

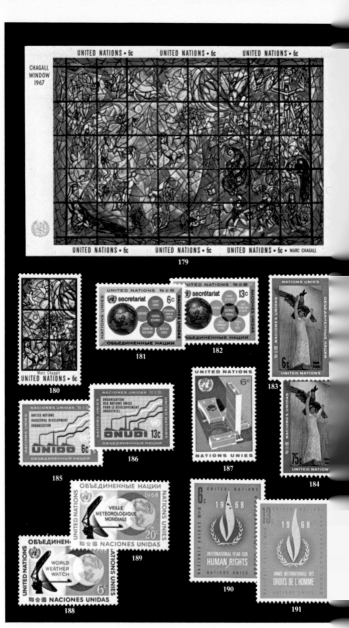

180

Rouletted 9

79   .75   .60   Art at U.N. Issue. Miniature Sheet of Six (179a-179f)   Nov. 17

No. 179 is divisible into six 6c stamps each rouletted on three sides and imperf. on the fourth side. Each stamp shows a different portion of the U.N.'s stained glass window by Russian artist Marc Chagall and each is a different size as follows: 179a, 41x46 mm.; 179b, 24x46 mm.; 179c. 41x33-1/2 mm.; 179d, 36x33-1/2 mm.; 179e, 29x33-1/2 mm.; 179f, 41-1/2x47 mm. "United Nations 6c" appears at the top of Nos. 179a-179c, and at the bottom of Nos. 179d-179f. No. 179f includes the name "Marc Chagall."

Perf. 12-1/2x13-1/2

80   .20   .08   6c Art at U.N. Issue   Nov. 17

No. 180 depicts "The Kiss of Peace" by Marc Chagall (1899-).

Issues of 1968
Perf. 11-1/2

81   .12   .08   6c U.N. Secretariat   Jan. 16
82   .26   .15   13c Secretariat, French inscription

Issued to honor the U.N. Secretariat, these stamps show the chief U.N. departments and the globe.

83   .12   .08   6c Art at U.N. Issue   Mar. 1
84   1.50   .85   75c Art at U.N. Issue   Mar. 1

The Henrik Starcke statue depicted on these stamps represents mankind's search for freedom and happiness.

Perf. 12

85   .12   .08   6c Industrial Development   Apr. 18
86   .26   .15   13c Industrial Development French inscription

Issued to publicize the U.N. Industrial Development Organization.

Regular Issue, Perf. 13-1/2

87   .12   .08   6c U.N. Headquarters   May 31

Perf. 13x13-1/2

88   .12   .08   6c World Weather Watch   Sep. 19
89   .40   .25   20c World Weather Watch, French inscription

The World Weather Watch was instituted by the World Meteorological Organization in 1968. Stamps show radarscope and globes.

Perf. 12-1/2

90   .60   .50   6c Intl. Human Rights Year Issue   Nov. 22
91   .35   .35   13c Intl. Human Rights, French inscription

Issues of 1969
Perf. 13-1/2

92   .12   .06   6c UNITAR Issue   Feb. 10
93   .26   .15   13c UNITAR, French inscription

Issued to publicize the United Nations Institute for Training and Research (UNITAR).

Perf. 14

94   .12   .06   6c U.N. Bldg., Santiago   Mar. 14
95   .30   .15   15c U.N. Bldg., Santiago, Spanish inscription

The U.N. Building in Santiago, Chile is the seat of the U.N. Economic Commission for Latin America and of the Latin American Institute for Economic and Social Planning.

Regular Issue, Perf. 13-1/2

196   .26   .13   13c "U.N." and U.N. Emblem   Mar. 14

Perf. 11-1/2

97   .20   .18   6c Intl. Law Comm.   Apr. 21
98   .35   .30   13c Intl. Law Commission, French inscription

Issued for the 20th anniversary session of the U.N. International Law Commission.

Perf. 13

99   .12   .06   6c Labor and Development   Jun. 5
200   .40   .30   20c Labor and Development, French inscription

Issued to publicize "Labor and Development" and to honor the International Labor Organization (ILO), established in 1919.

192

193

194

195

196

197

198

199

200

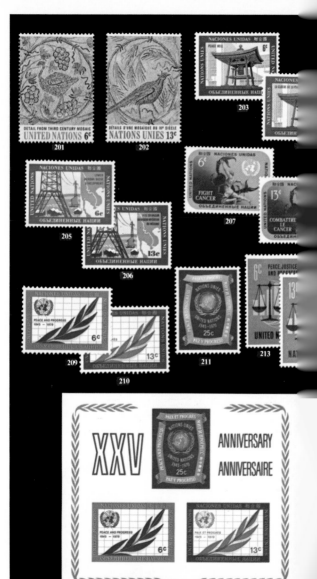

			Perf. 14	
201	.12	.06	6c Art at U.N. Issue	Nov. 21
202	.26	.20	13c Art at U.N. Issue, French inscription	Nov. 21

The ostrich and pheasant details on these stamps are from a third century Tunisian mosaic. The complete mosaic depicts the "Four Seasons" and the "Genius of the Year."

Issues of 1970 Perf. 13-1/2x13

203	.12	.06	6c Art at U.N. Issue	Mar. 13
204	.50	.35	25c Art at U.N. Issue, French inscription	

A gift of the Japanese, the Peace Bell shown on Nos. 203-204 was cast from contributed coins and other metals.

205	.12	.06	6c Mekong Basin Project	Mar. 13
206	.26	.13	13c Mekong Basin Project, French inscription	

The Lower Mekong Basin development project in Southeast Asia has been undertaken under U.N. auspices. Stamps show power lines, the Mekong River, and a map of the Delta.

207	.12	.06	6c "Fight Cancer"	May 22
208	.26	.13	13c "Fight Cancer," French inscription	

Issued to publicize the fight against cancer in connection with the 10th International Cancer Congress of the International Union Against Cancer, which was held in Houston, Texas from May 22-29.

Perf. 11-1/2

209	.30	.35	6c U. N. 25th Anniversary Issue	Jun. 26
210	.35	.35	13c U. N. 25th Anniversary, French inscription	Jun. 26
211	.65	.60	25c U. N. 25th Anniversary	Jun. 26

			Imperf.	
212	1.00	1.00	Souvenir sheet of three, sia 209-211	
212a	.12	.10	6c sia 209	
212b	.26	.20	13c sia 210, French inscription	
212c	.50	.35	25c sia 211	

Nos. 209-212 were issued for the 25th anniversary of the United Nations. No. 212 contains imperforate varieties of Nos. 209-211, with a blue marginal inscription and a gold border.

213	.20	.18	6c "Peace, Justice and Progress"	Nov. 20
214	.40	.35	13c "Peace, Justice and Progress," French inscription	

Issued in connection with the 25th anniversary of the United Nations, these stamps show an olive branch, the scales of justice and a progress symbol.

Issues of 1971
Perf. 13

215	.12	.06	6c Sea-Bed Issue	Jan. 25

Issued to publicize peaceful uses of the sea bed.

Perf. 13x12-1/2

216	.12	.06	6c Support for Refugees	Mar. 12
217	.26	.13	13c Support for Refugees	Mar. 12

The International Support for Refugees Issue shows a sculpture by Kaare K. Nygaard entitled "Refugees."

Perf. 14

218	.26	.13	13c World Food Program	Apr. 13

Issued to publicize the U.N. World Food Program.

Perf. 11-1/2

219	.40	.20	20c UPU Headquarters, Bern	May 28

The new headquarters of the Universal Postal Union (UPU) are at Bern, Switzerland.

UNIRO

A refugee who flees from a Communist-dominated country such as Hungary in 1956...a refugee escaping from today's tension-ridden border between Israel and Jordan...anyone made homeless by the ravages of war and strife is helped by the services of the United Nations International Refugee Organization. Since its ratification on August 20, 1948, UNIRO has operated under a constitution which accepts full responsibility for material aid to refugees, social and health services, reparation, and resettlement. Its transfer to an agency of the United Nations High Commissioner for Refugees in 1955 made it a permanent U. N. committee. Since then it has offered constant aid to those who relocate in a strange land to seek a new life.

See U. N. Scott Stamp Nos.
15-16, 75-76, 216-217

183

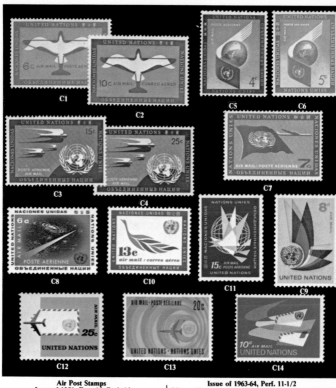

Air Post Stamps
Issue of 1951, Dec. 14, Perf. 14

C1	.40	.30	6c	Plane and Gull
C2	.50	.35	10c	Plane and Gull
C3	1.50	.75	15c	Swallows and U.N. Emblem
C4	3.50	2.00	25c	Swallows and U.N. Emblem

Issue of 1957, May 27, Perf. 12-1/2x14
C5	.10	.08	4c	Wing and Globe

Issue of 1959, Feb. 9, Perf. 12-1/2x13-1/2
C6	.15	.10	5c	Wing and Globe

Perf. 13-1/2x14
C7	.25	.15	7c	U.N. Flag and Plane

Issue of 1963-64, Perf. 11-1/2
C8	.12	.10	6c	Outer Space	Jun. 17
C9	.16	.12	8c	U.N. Emblem	Jun. 17

Perf. 12-1/2x12
C10	.26	.22	13c	Bird of Laurel Leaves	Jun. 17

Perf. 11-1/2x12, 12x11-1/2
C11	.30	.25	15c	"Flight Across Globe"	May 1
C12	.50	.40	25c	Jet Plane and Envelope	May 1

Issue of 1968, Apr. 18, Perf. 13
C13	.40	.25	20c	Jet Plane and U.N. Emblem

Issue of 1969, Apr. 21
C14	.20	.10	10c	Wings, Envelopes and U.N. Emblem

Offices in Geneva, Switzerland
Regular Issue of 1969-70
Perf. 13

1	.03	.03	5c	U.N. Headquarters, New York and World Map Oct. 4

Perf. 12-1/2x12

2	.05	.04	10c	U.N. Flag Oct. 4

Perf. 11-1/2

3	.10	.08	20c	Three Men and Globe, French inscription Oct. 4
4	.15	.12	30c	U.N. European Office, Geneva Oct. 4
5	.25	.20	50c	Opening Words, U.N. Charter Oct. 4
6	.30	.25	60c	U.N. Emblem over Globe Apr. 17, 1970

Perf. 13

7	.35	.25	70c	"U.N." and U.N. Emblem Sep. 22, 1970

Perf. 11-1/2x12

8	.38	.35	75c	"Flight Across Globe" Oct. 4, 1969

Perf. 13-1/2x14

9	.40	.35	80c	U.N. Headquarters and Emblem, French inscription Sep. 22, 1970

Perf. 13

10	.45	.40	90c	Abstract Group of Flags, French inscription Sep. 22, 1970

Perf. 14

11	.50	.45	1fr.	U.N. Emblem Oct. 4, 1969

Perf. 12x11-1/2

12	1.00	.85	2fr.	Stylized Globe and "Peace Dove," Sep. 22, 1970

Perf. 11-1/2

13	1.50	1.35	3fr.	Statue by Henrik Starcke Oct. 4, 1969

Perf. 12

14	5.00	4.50	10fr.	"Peace, Justice, Security", French-English inscription Apr. 17, 1970

Issues of 1971, Perf. 13

15	.15	.12	30c	Seabed Issue, French inscription Jan. 5

See U.N. No. 215

Perf. 13x12-1/2

16	.25	.20	50c	Support for Refugees, French inscription Mar. 12

See note after U. N. Nos. 216-17.

Perf. 14

17	.25	.20	50c	World Food Program, French inscription Apr. 13

See note after U.N. Nos. 216-17.

Perf. 11-1/2

18	.38	.35	75c	UPU Headquarters, Bern, French inscription May 28

See note after U.N. No. 219.

Australia to Zanzibar

Animals to Zoology

Astronauts and Aviation

Autos

How to Be a Happy Stamp Collector

At first glance stamp collecting may se
like a maze of colors, shapes, and mystify
symbols; but look a little closer and yo
see that...

Anything and almost everything you
is found on stamps, from animals to as
nauts...from famous works of art to sp
...from safaris to far-off lands to music
flowers.

Above all stamps capture the spirit a
preserve the history of famous peop
places, things . . . To look at them is to ta
a journey into the far-distant and ne
distant past . . . to relive the exciting d
of chivalry and buccaneers, explorers a
kings . . . man's first landing on the mo

A great way to start your journey into
magic world of stamps is to read stamp ca
logues and use stamp albums to mount yo
stamps. On one colorful album page you
imagine a visit to Africa. On another
can travel to the Old Wild West of

To ~Z

...ited States and retrace the route of the
...neers and Pony Express riders.

...ecoming a stamp collector is easy and
...fun...Here are a few tips to get you
...rted—

...elect a subject you like—anything! Per-
...ps you'd like to collect the stamps you've
...t seen in this book...or fashion...theater
...dogs...U.S.A....Canada...It can be
...y country—any topic—you have the
...rld to choose from!

...Now start to save stamps from mail de-
...ered to your home. (Here's a special tip:
...remove bits of envelope from the stamp,
...ak it in cold water for fifteen minutes, or
...til the water has softened the gum on the
...ck of the stamp. Take one edge of the
...ached paper, bend it back, and peel it
...ay!)

...f you're fortunate enough to travel in
...untries other than your own, be sure to
...tain that nation's latest issues before you
...ve. Frequent your post office and buy
...e new issues at actual face value. Ask
...ends and relatives to save stamps for you
...Barter with other collectors...Join a

Austria to Zululand

Brazil

Birds

Butterflies

Belgium

Make Your Own Magic World

Canada

China

Children

Cards

stamp club...Start corresponding with a p[en]
pal living in the country whose stamps y[ou]
want to collect...

Before long you will have a collection [of]
your own . . . one that you will want to ca[ta]
logue and mount in a beautiful stamp albu[m].

Your first stamps will probably be mode[rn]
commemoratives. These stamps, issued [to]
honor famous people and events, are ea[sy]
to identify and catalogue.

First, pick up your stamp with *star*
tongs. These handy gadgets, shaped li[ke]
tweezers, keep fingerprints off your stam[ps].

Examine the stamp. Look at its year a[nd]
place of issue, its color and denominatio[n].

Now flip through your stamp catalogue [to]
locate the year and country in questio[n].
Search the listings for a stamp that lo[oks]
like yours . . . is the same color, has t[he]
same design, and shows the same denomin[a]
tion. Look for the Scott number that appe[ars]
with this listing. Once you've found it y[ou]
have catalogued your stamp!

Next, find a space in your album for t[he]
stamp. You are now ready to mount it.

Dominican Republic

With Stamps You Really Like

Dance

Explorers

Do's and Don'ts of Mounting Stamps

on't paste stamps on album pages...
y are fragile!
o use the best peelable hinges you can
. Follow these directions:

n diagram A we have folded a hinge,
nmed side out, one quarter from the end
lightly moistened it as shown. Fasten
glued side to the back of the stamp near
top just below the perforation as shown
diagram B. Then moisten the tip of the
ge and fasten squarely in position on the
um page.

ow that you've put your first stamps
our first album (easy, wasn't it) you've
bably discovered that stamp collecting
Educational and enjoyable— a marvel-
way to explore the world...to thrill to
wonders of nature. Stamps also offer you

Education

Flags

Ecuador

France

Flowers

Gambia

Geography

Greece

Germany

a chance to make new *friends*. As you [?]lect and exchange stamps you will meet [?] people, and develop lasting friendships [?] will grow over the years.

Getting to Know Stamps

The more you explore the magic w[?] of stamps, the more you will find ther[?] to learn about them, for stamps have [?] intriguing history. The first postage st[?] was the famous "Penny Black". Sales of [?] 1840 stamp—which pictures Queen Vict[?]—were intended to provide the British g[?]ernment with enough money to insure [?] effective, rapid means of mail delivery. [?] idea caught on and before long coun[?] round the world were issuing postage sta[?] To date approximately 272,000 diffe[?] stamps have appeared. In the United Sta[?] the first general issues appeared in 1[?] For 47 years afterward all U.S. Stamps w[?] privately printed, but on July 1, 1894 [?] printing of stamps became a function of [?] Treasury Department.

Italy

Heroes

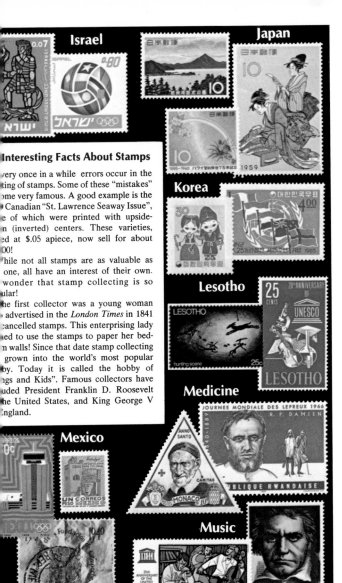

Interesting Facts About Stamps

...very once in a while errors occur in the ...ting of stamps. Some of these "mistakes" ...ome very famous. A good example is the ... Canadian "St. Lawrence Seaway Issue", ...e of which were printed with upside-...n (inverted) centers. These varieties, ...ed at $.05 apiece, now sell for about ...00!

...hile not all stamps are as valuable as ...one, all have an interest of their own. ...wonder that stamp collecting is so ...ular!

...he first collector was a young woman ...advertised in the *London Times* in 1841 ...cancelled stamps. This enterprising lady ...ed to use the stamps to paper her bed-...n walls! Since that date stamp collecting ...grown into the world's most popular ...by. Today it is called the hobby of ...ngs and Kids". Famous collectors have ...uded President Franklin D. Roosevelt ...he United States, and King George V ...ngland.

Napoleon

Norway

Olympics

Oldenburg

Postal History

Local libraries can provide you with wealth of interesting information ab stamps — their history and lore.

Invaluable are publications such as *Lin Stamp News, Mekeel's News, Minkus Sta Journal, National Stamp News, Scott Mon Journal, Stamps Magazine,* and *West Stamp Collector,* for they improve y knowledge about stamps.

THE ANATOMY OF A U.S. STAMP

While just about every topic in the wo is shown on stamps, most stamps are co posed of but six parts: design, printi paper, watermark, glue, and separation.

The *design process* begins when t government authorizes a new stamp, incl ing a subject and a value. Proposed sketch are submitted, one design is picked a greatly enlarged. Illustrators and graph artists work from this enlargement prepare finished art. The completed is turned over to an engraver whose job is to reproduce the art in metal, which called a die. The master die is transfer to a press die by using transfer rolls und great pressure, and the *printing proce* begins.

Paintings

REPUBLIQUE DE HAUTE VOLTA
90¢
QUENTIN METSYS (1466-1530)
PRÊTEUR ET SA FEMME

REPUBLIQUE DU NIGER
200F
POSTE AÉRIENNE
AUTOPORTRAIT · VAN GOGH (1853-1890)

REPUBLIQUE FRANÇAISE
1,00
P. GAUGUIN

Panama

PANAMA
CORREOS
1c

Most United States stamps are printed
the *engraved intaglio* method, which
means they are produced from steel or
copper plates. Other methods used are
typography (letterpress printing) and *lithography*, which is close to the engraved method but was at one time printed from stone
or transfer image.

Three basic kinds of *paper* are used: laid
paper, wove paper, and granite paper.
Sometimes the paper is *watermarked;* sometimes it is not.

Glue or *"gum"* is put on the backs of
stamps to allow the user to affix them to
his letters. (Note: stamps with full original
glue generally sell for more than those from
which the glue is gone.)

Stamps are generally issued in sheets or
coils (for use in vending machines). Individual stamps are *separated* from the sheet
or coil in one of three basic ways. Of these
perforating is the most popular. In this process bits of paper between the stamps are
punched out in a line of holes. This leaves
tiny bridges of paper holding the stamps
together. *Rouletting* is a type of separation
in which the paper is cut but no bits are removed. *Imperforate* refers to an early form
of separation in which the stamps were cut
apart with scissors.

Poland

POLSKA
3.40 zł

POLSKA
2.50 zł
150 ROCZNICA
SMIERCI
TADEUSZA
KOSCIUSZKI

Qatar

1 QATAR

QATAR SCOUTS
POSTAGE
5 QATAR

Queens

POSTES
£1

4d
ARTIST UNKNOWN c.1575 · HARRISON

Quixote

REPUBLICA DEL ECUADOR
MIGUEL DE CERVANTES
1547 · SAAVEDRA · 1947

REPUBLICA DEL ECUADOR
5

Romance

MAURITIUS 15

FRANCAISE .85
M. CHAGALL

Religion

RÉPUBLIQUE FRANÇAISE
0.60
7ᵉ CENTENAIRE
NOTRE-DAME DE PARIS

POSTA ROMANA

Rarities

The world's rarest and most valuab[le] stamp is an 1856 British Guiana "One Cen[t] Black on Magenta," which recently sold [at] auction for the unbelieveable but actu[al] price of $280,000. The stamp, which w[as] issued by the former British colony duri[ng] a shortage of regular issues, had for yea[rs] been impossible to find.

While not everyone can afford ra[re] stamps, you should always take good ca[re] of your collection, for stamps in fine cond[i]tion are always much more valuable th[an] those in poor condition. Uncancelled (mi[nt]) stamps which are well-centered, with ev[en] margins and all perforations intact, are m[ost] highly prized.

Stamp Semantics

Did you ever wonder where the term pos[t]age stamp originated? Long ago whe[n] people carried mail from one destinatio[n] to another, mail stations were called post[s]. *Postage* referred to the charge for carryi[ng] this mail. The letters themselves were seale[d] with wax which was *stamped* with a seal [or] ring design to identify the sender.

Romania

4ᵈ ENGLAND WINNERS
World Cup 1966

GRENOBLE 1968
JOCURILE OLIMPICE DE IARNA
52
2.30 LEI
A ROMANA

Sports

LIRE 15
SAN MARINO

SCAUTISMO
POSTE ITALIANE L.50

Jamborette 1961 20c+5
SURINAME

Scouting

80 cts
ESPANA

JUEGOS OLIMPICOS MEJICO 1968
CORREOS
ESPAÑA 1.50 PTAS

1 PTA
CORREOS
DIA MUNDIAL DEL SELLO 1965
ESPAÑA

Spain

194

Tchad

The word *philately* was coined shortly after the advent of postage stamps. Taken from the Greek, the term means "the love of tax-free things" and refers to the fact that stamps indicate the sender has paid for the transportation of a letter.

Treasure Hunting in the Magic World of Stamps

Sometimes luck pays off and collectors find rare stamps by accident. W. T. Robey did. In 1918 Robey, a clerk in a Washington brokerage house, bought a sheet of U. S. air mail stamps for $24.00, and then discovered that the stamps, which showed a "Jenny" airplane, had inverted centers. In 1971 a single stamp from this sheet sold at a New York auction for $36,000.

Unusual Types of Stamps

Everyone is familiar with air mail stamps and regular stamps used to post letters, but did you know that stamps have been used to tax potatoes, wine and beer? That there are hunting stamps and newspaper stamps? That the English Stamp Act helped bring about the American Revolutionary War?

Varieties of Stamps

Sometimes two stamps look almost alike but are not. They are different varieties. Experienced collectors learn to tell such varieties apart by measuring the number of perforations in a length of 20 millimeters

Writers

Xylophone

Wallis and Futuna

...by finding out if the stamp was printed by rotary press or flat press (stamps printed by rotary press are longer or wider than stamps printed by flat press).

Watermarks

Watermarks are formed in the paper-making process of a stamp. They are the design, lettering, or overall pattern created in the paper fibres, and can often be seen if you hold a stamp up to bright light. Sometimes the only way to distinguish between two stamps is to find out which one has a watermark.

X-Rays and Stamps

X-ray equipment is presently being used by a few leading dealers to test the authenticity of stamps and coins. These tests are an invaluable means of protecting collectors from stamp forgeries.

While volumes have been written about stamps, nothing can match the beauty and variety of the stamps themselves. No matter what type of stamps you choose to collect, you will find that stamps are educational, inspiring, enjoyable, and entertaining. From *Australia* and *architecture* all the way to *Zambia* and *zebras*, stamps offer you a fun-filled way to utilize your leisure time.

Youth

Yugoslavia

Zoology

Zambia

FIRST-DAY COVERS

FIRST PONY EXPRESS

EIGHTIETH ANNIVERSARY

1860   1940

*Commemorating the Eightieth Anniversary
of the Pony Express. Left St. Joseph, Mo.
April 3, 1860. Arrived at San Francisco, Calif.
on April 14th. Distance 1966 Miles in 11 Days.*

FIRST DAY COVER

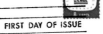

FIRST
DAY
OF
ISSUE

U.S. MAIL

Inaugurating the
UNITED STATES POSTAL SERVICE
JULY 1, 1971

Collecting of first-day covers is a
rapidly expanding part of philately. These
covers are envelopes bearing a new stamp
cancelled on the first-day of issue at the
post office designated to conduct the first-
day ceremonies.

For each new stamp or postal stationery
issue, the Postal Service designates one
post office where the item is first placed
on sale. This post office generally is related
to the subject being commemorated, and it
is the only one permitted to sell the stamps
on the first-day of issue. Other post offices
place them on sale the following day.

The date and place of issue are announced through the press and on post
office bulletin board posters. About six
weeks prior to the issue date, collectors
can send self-addressed plain or cacheted
envelopes inside another envelope to "First-
Day Cover," care of the postmaster at the
designated city together with money order
or certified check remittance for the
stamps to be affixed. Personal checks or
cash should not be submitted.

The Postal Service does not provide
cacheted envelopes (envelopes which carry
a design or cachet at the left of the envelope). These can be purchased from stamp
dealers and some department stores or
stationery stores.

The Postal Service services first-day
covers as an accommodation only to collectors. For that reason, only a reasonable

450th *Anniversary*
OF THE INTRODUCTION OF
SHEEP
TO THE NORTH AMERICAN CONTINENT

First Day of Issue

LAS VEGAS, NV
JUN
19
1971

UNITED STATES

AMERICA'S WOOL

FIRST DAY OF ISSUE

Wildlife
conservation

Fleetwood

OFFICIAL FIRST DAY COVER
AUTHORIZED BY
NATIONAL WILDLIFE FEDERATION
WASHINGTON, DC.

AVERY ISLAND, LA
JUN
12
1971
70513

WILDLIFE CONSERVATION
UNITED STATES
8¢
FIRST DAY OF ISSUE

First Day of Issue

PORTLAND HEAD LIGHT
COLONIAL LIGHTHOUSE AUTHORIZED BY
GEORGE WASHINGTON

PINE TREE STATE
150TH ANNIVERSARY
Maine
Statehood
1820-1970

PORTLAND, ME
JUL
9
1970

MAINE STATEHOOD
FIRST DAY OF ISSUE

umber — 200 or less — will be serviced. Dealers and others requiring more than 00 covers should be present at the first-day city or make arrangement through private organizations which provide this service for a fee.

All requests for first-day covers must e postmarked by the day of issue. Covers submitted too late will be returned. Requests with improper remittances also will e returned.

Collectors who receive covers damaged n the mail should immediately return them o the designated post office for replacement.

The Postal Service makes every effort o provide quality and speedy first-day service, but the volume of requests sometimes causes delays. Between 400,000 and 600,000 first-day covers are serviced on the average new issue. However, certain stamps are even more popular. The 10¢ Moon Landing, Airmail stamp had 8,700,000 first-day covers.

Servicing the average first-day takes upwards of 50 persons working several weeks. Elaborate local or state ceremonies are usually held on the first-day.

One of the most widely seen ceremonies was a brief one conducted by astronaut David Scott on the moon, August 2, 1971, when he cancelled the twin stamps issued to mark a decade of space achievements.

HOW TO START A STAMP CLUB

For years collectors throughout the world have been forming stamp clubs to add extra pleasure to their hobby. Starting a stamp club is an ambitious, but gratifying task that can more than repay your time and effort. If you have the interest and are willing to spend the time to organize a club, this article will tell you how.

Three basics should be considered: desire, knowledge, and resources. A sincere desire for companionship in stamps and the benefits of group effort helps to insure success. Knowledge offers you the necessary "know-how", and resources the tools for an effective organization.

DESIRE

The successful stamp club does not just happen overnight. Time should be devoted to careful planning of its organization. The individual, or more appropriately several collectors, must have a genuine desire to form a club, and be willing to devote enough time to it to insure success. They must also want to truly help their fellow hobbyists, for those who set up clubs for self-esteem or profit seldom experience the success and satisfaction of the devoted organizer.

KNOWLEDGE

One need not be a professional collector to organize a stamp club. Basic knowledge may be gained by reading the philatelic press and some well-known works about the hobby. With this acquired knowledge a beginner will have some "know-how" to pass on to other collectors through a planning session. It is helpful but not necessary to have a professional with stamp experience among the organizers. The combined thoughts of several beginning collectors can produce enough information for a start.

RESOURCES

Having the desire and some of the "know-how", the next step is to obtain club resources, which are the ingredients of physical organization. Here are the eight main steps.

1. Get members. Your first club need not be a large one to be successful. If possible, try to find a few experienced collectors, but remember that a group of beginners can trigger additional response from other new enthusiasts.

2. Seek publicity. Since you probably cannot afford to advertise for members you must rely on the philatelic and general press to promote your club and arouse interest in prospective members. School newspapers, area shopping guides, company magazines, and news bulletins will usually respond to your timely request.

You should also tell your local newspapers about your meetings as they are planned, highlighting a specific time, place, and program schedule. Most local newspapers will cooperate, especially if a personal contact is made. Publicity may also be sought from the philatelic press or the bulletins of nearby clubs. One particularly helpful hint is to be sure press releases are well-written, typed, and double-spaced. While this fact may appear minor, copy-ready releases are more acceptable to a busy editor.

3. Provide an adequate home. Whether a youth club or adult organization, the club must have a meeting place. A good location would be one which is available for little or no cost. Many clubs meet in church or school halls, the YMCA, museums, or libraries, or meetings might be rotated among members' homes.

4. Establish rules of order. Any club meeting should be organized. The founding members may or may not make a written outline of rules for procedures and goals. Flexibility is the key to a well-written charter, by-laws, or constitution. Club progress may well be delayed by a strict set of by-laws.

5. Elect officers. These should be duly elected, providing guidance, leadership, and planning for the group. Adequate control but not dominance is a key factor of effective leadership.

6. Consider a publication. While a newsletter in the club's early stages may seem premature, it is a good way to unite club members and attract others. Size and printing method are of little importance, except that cost should be kept to a minimum. The contents, however, should be interesting, informative, and should promote club activity and unity. Many clubs frequently have a simple newsletter released prior to scheduled meetings.

7. Plan club meetings. Collectors generally prefer brief business meetings followed by special programs, such as films, slide shows, collection exhibits, or panel discussions. These can be of great interest and value to members. Group discussions are particularly good for younger collectors. Possible topics range from stamp design to proper care of a collection. An exchange of ideas among many can be just as interesting as a speaker.

8. Don't forget collecting. The hobby is still stamp collecting, and club members should be given opportunities to swap stamps, buy and sell, or perhaps stage a general club auction. Reputable dealers should be encouraged as members and their offerings made known before and after meetings.

Using the above as a guide, the young or young-at-heart can start a successful stamp club. Enthusiasm is both essential and contagious. Sharing one's knowledge with others is a satisfying experience, and in the vast world of stamps there is much to share.

Philately has added value when it is a group effort . . . and a stamp club is one way to assure more pleasure, knowledge, and inspiration from the world's most popular hobby.

ADDENDA — UNITED STATES

Issues of 1971
Perf. 11

1433 .16 .05 8c John Sloan Issue   Aug. 2
Issued to honor John Sloan (1871-1951), American painter. Stamp shows his work "The Wake of the Ferry".

Decade of Space Achievements Issue, Aug. 2

1434 .16 .05 8c Earth, Sun, Landing
                   Craft on Moon
1434a .32   Pair, sia 1434-1435
1435 .16 .05 8c Lunar Rover and Astronauts
Stamps honor a decade of space achievements and the Apollo 15 mission of July 26-August 7.

1436 .16 .05 8c Emily Dickinson Issue   Aug. 28
Emily Dickinson (1830-86), American poet.

1437 .16 .05 8c San Juan Issue   Sep. 12
Issued for the 450th anniversary of the founding of San Juan, Puerto Rico. Stamp shows the Sentry Box at Morro Castle.

Perf. 10-1/2x11

1438 .16 .05 8c Prevent Drug Abuse   Oct.
Issued for Drug Abuse Prevention Week, Oct. 3-
1439 .16 .05 8c CARE Issue   Oct.
Perf. 11
Historic Preservation Issue, Oct. 29

1440 .16 .05 8c Decatur House, Washington, D.
1441 .16 .05 8c Whaling Ship Charles W. Morga
1442 .16 .05 8c Cable Car, San Francisco, Cal.
1443 .16 .05 8c San Xavier del Bac Mission, Ari
1443a .64 .20   Block of four, sia 1440-1443
Perf. 10-1/2x11
Christmas Issue, Nov. 10

1444 .16 .03 8c Adoration of the Shepherds,
                  by Giorgione
1445 .16 .03 8c Partridge in a Pear Tree,
                  by Jamie Wyeth
The design of 1444 is from a painting in the Nation Gallery of Art, Washington, D.C.

ADDENDA — UNITED STATES

Issues of 1972

Perf. 11

1446   .16   .05   8c Sidney Lanier   Feb. 3
  Sidney Lanier (1842-1881), poet, musician, lawyer, educator.

Perf. 10-1/2x11

1447   .16   .05   8c Peace Corps   Feb. 11
  The act creating the Peace Corps, a volunteer program operating in underdeveloped countries in all parts of the globe, was passed by Congress in 1961.

National Parks Centennial

Perf. 11

1448	.04	.03	2c multi., sia 1451a Apr. 5
1449	.04	.03	2c multi., sia 1451a Apr. 5
1450	.04	.03	2c multi., sia 1451a Apr. 5
1451	.04	.03	2c multi., sia 1451a Apr. 5
1451a	.16	.08	Block of four, Cape Hatteras

Perf. 11

1452   .12   .06   6c Wolf Trap Farm   Jun. 26

Perf. 11

1453   .16   .05   8c Yellowstone   Mar. 1

Perf. 11

1454   .30   .15   15c Mt. McKinley   Jul. 28
  Yellowstone, created in 1872, was the first national park. Cape Hatteras National Seashore in North Carolina consists of 45 square miles of beach land. Wolf Trap Farm Park, 117 acres, is near Vienna, Virginia. Mt. McKinley National Park in Alaska, 3,020 square miles, was created in 1917.

Perf. 11

1455   .16   .05   8c Family Planning   Mar. 18
  Issue focuses attention on family planning.

Air Post Stamps

Issues of 1972

Perf. 11

C84   .22   .11   11c City of Refuge   May 3
  The City of Refuge National Park, 180 acres on the island of Hawaii, preserves Polynesian temples and royal tombs.

1446

1447

1451a

1452

1454

1455

1453

C84

ADDENDA — UNITED NATIONS

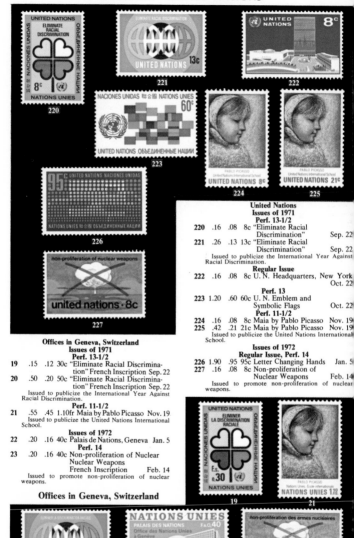

United Nations
Issues of 1971
Perf. 13-1/2

220	.16	.08	8c "Eliminate Racial Discrimination"	Sep. 22
221	.26	.13	13c "Eliminate Racial Discrimination"	Sep. 22

Issued to publicize the International Year Against Racial Discrimination.

Regular Issue

222	.16	.08	8c U. N. Headquarters, New York	Oct. 22

Perf. 13

223	1.20	.60	60c U. N. Emblem and Symbolic Flags	Oct. 22

Perf. 11-1/2

224	.16	.08	8c Maia by Pablo Picasso	Nov. 19
225	.42	.21	21c Maia by Pablo Picasso	Nov. 19

Issued to publicize the United Nations International School.

Issues of 1972
Regular Issue, Perf. 14

226	1.90	.95	95c Letter Changing Hands	Jan. 5
227	.16	.08	8c Non-proliferation of Nuclear Weapons	Feb. 14

Issued to promote non-proliferation of nuclear weapons.

Offices in Geneva, Switzerland
Issues of 1971
Perf. 13-1/2

19	.15	.12	30c "Eliminate Racial Discrimination" French Inscription	Sep. 22
20	.50	.20	50c "Eliminate Racial Discrimination" French Inscription	Sep. 22

Issued to publicize the International Year Against Racial Discrimination.

Perf. 11-1/2

21	.55	.45	1.10fr Maia by Pablo Picasso	Nov. 19

Issued to publicize the United Nations International School.

Issues of 1972

22	.20	.16	40c Palais de Nations, Geneva	Jan. 5

Perf. 14

23	.20	.16	40c Non-proliferation of Nuclear Nuclear Weapons French Inscription	Feb. 14

Issued to promote non-proliferation of nuclear weapons.

Offices in Geneva, Switzerland

A GLOSSARY of BASIC PHILATELIC TERMS

Approvals: Stamps sent to a collector for examination. Approvals must be bought or returned to the dealer within a specific time.

Bisect: Half of a stamp used to pay postage of half the face value of the original stamp. This variety must appear on its original cover with the cancellation or postmark covering the cut.

Block: An unsevered group of stamps at least two stamps wide and two stamps high.

Booklet pane: A small pane of stamps especially printed and cut to be sold in booklets.

Cachet: A special handstamp or printed device on a cover to denote the special circumstances in which it was mailed.

Cancellation: A mark placed on a stamp by a postal authority to prevent its reuse.

Cancelled to Order: (CTO) Stamps which are cancelled by the postal authorities without being sent through the mails. They are normally less desirable than stamps which have served their postal function.

Coils: Stamps issued in rolls for use in affixing or vending machines.

Color Changeling: A stamp whose color has been changed, either accidentally or intentionally.

Commemoratives: Stamps which honor anniversaries, important people, or special events. Commemoratives are usually sold for a specific length of time.

Compound Perforations: A stamp with perforations of different sizes on different sides.

Condition: The state of a stamp in regard to centering, color, freshness, cancellation, and other related characteristics.

Cover: The entire wrapping or envelope in which a letter has been sent through the mail.

Cut Square: An envelope stamp cut out with a square margin.

Definitives: Regular issues of stamps as distinct from commemoratives.

Die: The original steel engraving from which the plates for printing stamps are made.

Encased Postage Stamps: Stamps inserted into small cases and circulated as currency.

Errors: Stamps with accidental mistakes in color, paper, inscription, watermark, etc. Errors also include bicolored stamps with inverted centers.

Essays: Designs submitted in stamp form but not accepted for issuance.

First Day Cover: A cover bearing a new stamp and cancelled on the first day of sale, usually at an officially designated location.

Flat Press Stamps Stamps printed on the ordinary flat-bed press, as distinguished from a rotary press.

Freaks: Stamps which show conspicuous deviations from the normal caused by shifted perforations, heavy inking, color shifts, or similar accidents during production. Not errors.

Grill: Parallel rows of small pyramids impressed or embossed on the stamp in order to break the fibers of the paper so that the cancellation ink will soak in and make washing for reuse impossible.

Gum: The adhesive on the back of an unused stamp.

Hinges: Small strips of paper gummed on one side and used by collectors to mount their stamps.

Imperforate: Stamps without perforations. They must be separated with scissors and are usually collected in pairs to prove their authenticity.

India Paper: A soft, thin silky appearing wove paper usually used for proof impressions.

Inverted Center: A stamp with the center printed upside down in relation to the rest of the design.

Laid Paper: A paper showing alternate light and dark parallel lines when held to the light or immersed in benzine.

Locals: Stamps issued for use in restricted areas either by governments or private carriers.

Margin: The border outside the printed design of a stamp, or the similar border of a pane of stamps.

Overprint: Any word, inscription, or device placed on a stamp to alter its use or locality, or to serve a special purpose.

Packet: A selection of stamps in a sealed envelope.

Pair: Two unsevered stamps.

Pane: A portion of the original sheet as cut for sale at the post offices.

Part-Perforate: A stamp which has perforations on one, two or three sides.

Pen Cancel: A cancellation applied to the stamp with pen and ink.

Perforations: Line of small cuts or holes placed between two rows of stamps to facilitate separation.

Plate: The actual object from which the stamps are printed.

Plate Number Block: A block of stamps with sheet margin showing a plate number or numbers. Often it is known simply as a plate block.

Postal Stationery: Envelopes, postcards, wrappers, etc. which have nonadhesive stamps embossed or printed on them.

Postmark: A mark struck upon envelopes, generally to indicate the name of the post office, date of mailing, etc.

Precancels: Stamps with cancellations applied before the mailing of the article on which they prepay postage.

Proofs: Trial printings of a stamp made from the original die or the plate.

Provisionals:	Stamps issued prior to the regular issues or to meet a temporary shortage of regular stamps.
Reissue:	An official printing of a stamp, or stamps, that had been discontinued.
Remainders:	Stocks of stamps on hand after the issue has been discontinued.
Reprints:	Impressions from the original plates, blocks, or stones taken after the issuance of the stamps to post offices has ceased and their postal use has been voided.
Revenue Stamps:	Stamps issued for use in collecting special taxes on documents, proprietary articles, products, etc.
Rotary Press Stamps:	Stamps printed on a rotary type press from curved plates as compared to stamps printed from flat plates on a flat bed press. They will be slightly larger in one direction than flat press stamps.
Rouletting:	Short consecutive cuts in the paper between rows of stamps to facilitate separation.
Se-tenant:	An unsevered pair of stamps which differ in value, design, or surcharge.
Sheet:	Complete unseparated group of stamps as originally printed.
Special Printings:	Stamps of current design reissued, usually on a better grade of paper and in brilliant colors.
Stampless Cover:	An envelope without stamps generally bearing a postmark and

	sometimes notations such "Paid", "Paid 10".
Straight Edge:	The imperforate side of a sta which is otherwise perforate.
Strip:	Three or more unsevered sta forming a vertical or horizon row.
Surcharge:	An overprint which alters or states the face value or denom tion of the stamp to which i applied.
Tête-bêche:	Stamps printed upside down in lation to each other.
Tied On:	A stamp is "tied on" when the cellation or postmark exte from the stamp to the envel
Topicals:	Area of philately in which emp sis is on the subject portrayed stamps rather than the sta themselves.
Unused:	A stamp with or without orig gum which has no cancellation other evidence of postal duty.
Used:	A stamp which has done po duty as evidenced by the c cellation.
Want List:	A list of stamp numbers or ph telic items needed for a collect
Watermark:	A design or pattern incorpora into the paper during its m ufacture.
Wove Paper:	A paper of uniform text throughout, showing no light dark patterns when held to light or immersed in benzine.

INDEX of U.S. Commemorative Issues

UNITED STATES PRESIDENTS AND VICE-PRESIDENTS

President	Term of Office	Vice-President
1. George Washington	Apr. 30, 1789 — Mar. 3, 1797	John Adams
2. John Adams	Mar. 4, 1797 — Mar. 3, 1801	Thomas Jefferson
3. Thomas Jefferson	Mar. 4, 1801 — Mar. 3, 1809	Aaron Burr (1801-05)
		George Clinton (1805-09)
4. James Madison	Mar. 4, 1809 — Mar. 3, 1817	George Clinton (1809-12)
		Elbridge Gerry (1813-14)
5. James Monroe	Mar. 4, 1817 — Mar. 3, 1825	Daniel Tompkins
6. John Quincy Adams	Mar. 4, 1825 — Mar. 3, 1829	John Calhoun
7. Andrew Jackson	Mar. 4, 1829 — Mar. 3, 1837	John Calhoun (1829-32)
		Martin Van Buren (1833-37)
8. Martin Van Buren	Mar. 4, 1837 — Mar. 3, 1841	Richard Johnson
9. William H. Harrison	Mar. 4, 1841 — Apr. 4, 1841	John Tyler
10. John Tyler	Apr. 6, 1841 — Mar. 3, 1845	— — —
11. James Knox Polk	Mar. 4, 1845 — Mar. 3, 1849	George Dallas
12. Zachary Taylor	Mar. 4, 1849 — Jul. 9, 1850	Millard Fillmore
13. Millard Fillmore	Jul. 10, 1850 — Mar. 3, 1853	— — —
14. Franklin Pierce	Mar. 4, 1853 — Mar. 3, 1857	William King
15. James Buchanan	Mar. 4, 1857 — Mar. 3, 1861	John Breckinridge
16. Abraham Lincoln	Mar. 4, 1861 — Apr. 15, 1865	Hannibal Hamlin (1861-65)
		Andrew Johnson (1865)
17. Andrew Johnson	Apr. 15, 1865 — Mar. 3, 1869	
18. Ulysses Simpson Grant	Mar. 4, 1869 — Mar. 3, 1877	Schuyler Colfax (1869-73)
		Henry Wilson (1873-77)
19. Rutherford B. Hayes	Mar. 4, 1877 — Mar. 3, 1881	William Wheeler
20. James Abram Garfield	Mar. 4, 1881 — Sep. 19, 1881	Chester Arthur
21. Chester Alan Arthur	Sep. 19, 1881 — Mar. 3, 1885	— — —
22. Grover Cleveland	Mar. 4, 1885 — Mar. 3, 1889	Thomas Hendricks
23. Benjamin Harrison	Mar. 4, 1889 — Mar. 3, 1893	Levi Morton
24. Grover Cleveland	Mar. 4, 1893 — Mar. 3, 1897	Adlai Stevenson
25. William McKinley	Mar. 4, 1897 — Sep. 14, 1901	Garret Hobart (1897-99)
		Theodore Roosevelt (1901)
26. Theodore Roosevelt	Sep. 14, 1901 — Mar. 3, 1909	
		Charles Fairbanks (1905-09)
27. William Howard Taft	Mar. 4, 1909 — Mar. 3, 1913	James Sherman
28. Woodrow Wilson	Mar. 4, 1913 — Mar. 3, 1921	Thomas Marshall
29. Warren G. Harding	Mar. 4, 1921 — Aug. 2, 1923	Calvin Coolidge
30. Calvin Coolidge	Aug. 3, 1923 — Mar. 3, 1929	
		Charles Dawes (1925-29)
31. Herbert Clark Hoover	Mar. 4, 1929 — Mar. 3, 1933	Charles Curtis
32. Franklin D. Roosevelt	Mar. 4, 1933 — Apr. 12, 1945	John Garner (1933-41)
		Henry Wallace (1941-45)
		Harry Truman (1945)
33. Harry S. Truman	Apr. 12, 1945 — Jan. 20, 1953	
		Alben Barkley (1949-53)
34. Dwight D. Eisenhower	Jan. 20, 1953 — Jan. 20, 1961	Richard Nixon
35. John F. Kennedy	Jan. 20, 1961 — Nov. 22, 1963	Lyndon Johnson
36. Lyndon Baines Johnson	Nov. 22, 1963 — Jan. 20, 1969	— — —
		Hubert Humphrey (1965-69)
37. Richard Milhous Nixon	Jan. 20, 1969 —	Spiro Agnew

POSTMASTERS GENERAL OF THE UNITED STATES

1775 Benjamin Franklin, Pa.	1852 Samuel D. Hubbard, Conn.	1884 Frank Hatton, Iowa
1776 Richard Bache, Pa.	1853 James Campbell, Pa.	1885 Wm. F. Vilas, Wis.
1782 Ebenezer Hazard, N. Y.	1857 Aaron V. Brown, Tenn.	1888 Don M. Dickinson, Mich.
1789 Samuel Osgood, Mass.	1859 Joseph Holt, Ky.	1889 John Wanamaker, Pa.
1791 Timothy Pickering, Pa.	1861 Horatio King, Maine	1893 Wilson S. Bissell, N. Y.
1795 Joseph Habersham, Ga.	1861 Montgomery Blair, D. C.	1895 William L. Wilson, W. Va.
1801 Gideon Granger, Conn.	1864 William Dennison, Ohio	1897 James A. Gary, Md.
1814 Return J. Meigs, Jr., Ohio	1866 Alexander W. Randall, Wis.	1898 Charles Emory Smith, Pa.
1823 John McLean, Ohio	1869 John A. J. Creswell, Md.	1902 Henry C. Payne, Wis.
1829 William T. Barry, Ky.	1874 Jas. W. Marshall, N. J.	1904 Robert J. Wynne, Pa.
1835 Amos Kendall, Ky.	1874 Marshall Jewell, Conn.	1905 Geo. B. Cortelyou, N. Y.
1840 John M. Niles, Conn.	1876 James N. Tyner, Ind.	1907 Geo. von L. Meyer, Mass.
1841 Francis Granger, N. Y.	1877 David McK. Key, Tenn.	1909 Frank H. Hitchcock, Mass.
1841 Charles A. Wickliffe, Ky.	1880 Horace Maynard, Tenn.	1913 Albert S. Burleson, Tex.
1845 Cave Johnson, Tenn.	1881 Thomas L. James, N. Y.	1921 Will H. Hays, Ind.
1849 Jacob Collamer, Vt.	1882 Timothy O. Howe, Wis.	1922 Hubert Work, Colo.
1850 Nathan K. Hall, N. Y.	1883 Walter Q. Gresham, Ind.	1923 Harry S. New, Ind.

1929 Walter F. Brown, Ohio	1947 Jesse M. Donaldson, Ill.	1965 Lawrence F. O'Brien, Mas
1933 James A. Farley, N. Y.	1953 Arthur E. Summerfield, Mi.	1968 W. Marvin Watson, Tex.
1940 Frank C. Walker, Pa.	1961 J. Edward Day, Calif.	1969 Winton M. Blount, Ala.
1945 Robert E. Hannegan, Mo.	1963 John A. Gronouski, Wis.	1972 Elmer T. Klassen, Mass.

THE FRANKLIN AND WASHINGTON DEFINITIVES OF 1908-22

Beginning in 1908 and continuing to 1922, all regular issues except 479-80 portrayed Washington or Franklin. Series showing Washington (as on Scott 332, 333) and Franklin (as on Scott 331, 414, 547) are as follows:

331-42, 422-3	Double line Wmk.	Perf. 12	462-78	Unwmkd.	Perf.
343-47	Double line Wmk.	Imperf.	481-85	Unwmkd.	Impe
348-56	Double line Wmk. Coil Stamps		486-97	Unwmkd.	Coil Stam
357-66	Bluish Paper	Perf. 12	498-518, 523-4	Unwmkd.	Perf.
374-82, 405-7,			519	Double line Wmk.	Perf.
414-21	Single line Wmk.	Perf. 12	525-530	Offset Printing	Perf.
383-4, 408-9, 459	Single line Wmk.	Imperf.	531-35	Offset Printing	Impe
385-96, 410-13,			536	Offset Printing	Perf. 1
441-58	Single line Wmk. Coil Stamps		538-41	Rotary Press	Perf. 11×
424-40	Single line Wmk.	Perf. 10	542	Rotary Press	Perf. 10×
460	Double line Wmk.	Perf. 10	543	Rotary Press	Perf.
461	Single line Wmk.	Perf. 11	544-46	Rotary Press	Perf.

The illustrated examples which follow will aid collectors in identifying various 2c and 3c issues of 1908-22 showing Washington, sia 333. Illustrations reproduced by permission of H. L. Lindquist.

Two Cent Types
Numerals in Lower Corners

Type I. There is one shading line in the first curve of the ribbon above the left "2" and one in the second curve of the ribbon above the right "2".

The bottom of the toga has a faint outline.

The top line of the toga rope, from the button to the front of the throat, is also very faint.

The shading lines at the face terminate in front of the ear with little or no joining, to form a lock of hair.

Used on both flat and rotary press printings.

Type Ia. The design characteristics are similar t type I except that all of the lines of the design ar stronger.

The toga button, toga rope and rope shading line are heavy. The latter characteristics are those o type II, which, however, occur only on impression from rotary plates.

Used only on flat plates 10208 and 10209.

Type II. Shading lines in ribbons as on type I.

The toga button, rope, and rope shading lines are heavy.

The shading lines of the face at the lock of hair end in a strong vertical curved line.

Used on rotary press printings only.

Type III. Two lines of shading in the curves of the ribbons.

Other characteristics similar to type II.

Used on rotary press printings only.

Collectors are warned against copies of Type III (Nos. 455, 488, 492 and 540) which have had one line of shading scraped off to resemble Type II (Nos. 454, 487, 491 and 539).

Type IV. Top line of the toga rope is broken. The shading lines in the toga button are so arranged that the curving of the first and last form "ΠID".

The line of color in the left "2" is very thin and usually broken.

Used on offset printings only.

Type V. The top line of the toga is complete.

There are five vertical shading lines in the toga button.

The line of color in the left "2" is very thin and usually broken.

The shading dots on the nose and lip are as indicated on the diagram.

Used on offset printings only.

Type Va. Characteristics are the same as type V except in the shading dots of nose. The third row of dots from the bottom has four dots instead of six. The overall height of type Va is 1/3 mm. less than type V.

Used on offset printings only.

Type VI. General characteristics are the same as type V, except that the line of color in the left "2" is very heavy.

Used on offset printings only.

Type VII. The line of color in the left "2" is invariably continuous, clearly defined, and heavier than in type V or Va, but not as heavy as in type VI.

An additional vertical row of dots has been added to the upper lip.

Numerous additional dots have been added to the hair on top of the head.

Used on offset printings only.

Three Cent Types

Type I. The top line of the toga rope is weak and the rope shading lines are thin. The fifth line from the left is missing.

The line between the lips is thin.

Used on both flat plate and rotary press printings.

Type II. The top line of the toga rope is strong and the rope shading lines are heavy and complete.

The line between the lips is heavy.

Used on both flat plate and rotary press printings.

Type III. The top line of the toga rope is strong but the fifth shading line is missing as in type I.

Center shading line of the toga button consists of two dashes with a central dot.

The "P" and "O" of "POSTAGE" are separated by a line of color.

The frame line at the bottom of the vignette is complete.

Used on offset printings only.

Type IV. The shading lines of the toga rope are complete.

The second and fourth shading lines in the toga button are broken in the middle and the third line is continuous with a dot in the center.

The "P" and "O" of "POSTAGE" are joined.

The frame line at the bottom of the vignette is broken.

Used on offset printings only.

Two Cent Washington Types
of 1923-29 sia 554

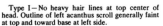

Type I—No heavy hair lines at top center of head. Outline of left acanthus scroll generally faint at top and toward base at left side.

Type II—The heavy hair lines at top center of head; two being outstanding in the white area. Outline of left acanthus scroll very strong and clearly defined at top (under left edge of lettered panel) and at lower curve (above and left of numeral oval).

Luminescence on U. S. Stamps

Quantities of various stamps were overprinted, starting in 1963, with a phosphorescent coating for tests in sorting and canceling first-class mail by use of ultraviolet light. These "phosphor-tagged" varieties are listed as Nos. 1035b, 1036b, 1044b, 1044c, 1045a, 1046a, 1055a, 1057b, 1208a, 1209a, 1213b, 1213c, 1225a, 1229a, 1240a, 1254a-1257a, 1276a, 1282a, 1283a, 1284a, 1285a, 1314a, 1315a, 1316a, 1317a, 1318a, 1319a, 1320a, 1321a, 1322a, 1363a, C59a, C62a-C63a, C64b, C64c, C65a, C67a. Complete listings for these varieties are found in Volume I of *Scott's Standard Postage Stamp Catalogue.*

The entire printings of Nos. 1238, 1280-1281,

1286-1288, 1298-1299, 1303-1305, 1323-1340, 1342-1362, 1364-1370, and C69-C75 and all following listings, unless otherwise noted, were coated with a luminescent overprint.

Two kinds of phosphor-coating have been used: For airmail stamps, calcium silicate, which glows orange red. For surface-mail stamps, zinc orthosilicate, which glows yellow green.

Overexposure to shortwave ultraviolet light can burn the eyes. Manufacturers advise caution in using ultraviolet lamps and suggest the use of either ordinary optical glasses or sunglasses as protective devices.

Canal Zone Overprints of 1909-21
"Canal Zone" Reading Up.

Illustrations of Types I to V are considerably enlarged and do not show actual spacing between lines of overprint.

Type I Overprint: "C" with serifs both top and bottom. "L", "Z" and "E" with slanting serifs.

Type II Overprint: "C" with serif at top only. "L" and "E" with vertical serifs. Inner oval of "O" tilts to left.

Type III Overprint: Similar to Type I but letters appear thinner, particularly the lower bar of "L", "Z" and "E". Impressions are often light, rough and irregular.

Type IV Overprint: "C" thick at bottom. "E" with center bar same length as top and bottom bars.

Type V Overprint: Smaller block type 1-3/4 mm. high. "A" with flat top.

Hawaii Reprints and Specimen Stamps

Reprints of 5 and 6

5c. Originals have two small dots near the left side of the square in the upper right corner. These dots are missing in the reprints.

13c. The bottom of the 3 of 13 in the upper left corner is flattened in the originals and rounded in the reprints. The "t" of "Cts" on the left side is as tall as the "C" in the reprints, but shorter in the originals.

On August 19, 1892, the remaining supply of reprints was overprinted in black "REPRINT". The reprints (both with and without overprint) were sold at face value.

Specimen Stamps

In 1885 the Postmaster General wished to have on sale complete sets of Hawaii's stamps as far back as the issues of 1861-63, but was unable to find either the stone from which Nos. 27 and 28, or the plate from which No. 29 was printed. He therefore sent a copy of No. 29 to the American Bank Note Company, with an order to engrave a new plate like it and print 10,000 stamps therefrom, of which 5,000 were overprinted "Specimen" in blue.

The original No. 29, was printed in sheets of 15 (5x3), but the plate of these "Official Imitations" was made up of 50 stamps (10x5). Later, in 1887, the original die for No. 29 was discovered, and after retouching, a new plate was made and 37,500 stamps were printed. These, like the originals, were printed in sheets of 15. They were delivered during 1889 and 1890. In 1892 all remaining unsold in the Post Office were overprinted "Reprint".

No. 29 is red in color, and printed on very thin white wove paper. No. 50 is orange vermilion in color, on medium, white to buff paper. In No. 50 the vertical line on the left side of the portrait touches the horizontal line over the label "Elua Keneta", while in the other two varieties. Nos. 29 and 51, it does not touch the horizontal line by half a millimeter. In No. 51 there are three parallel lines on the left side of the King's nose, while in No. 29 and No. 50 there are no such lines. No. 51 is carmine in color and printed on thick, yellowish to buff wove paper.

It is claimed that both Nos. 50 and 51 were available for postage, although not made to fill a postal requirement.

Philippine Official Stamps

"Officers purchasing stamps for government business may, if they so desire, overprint them with the letters 'O.B.' either in writing with black ink or by rubber stamps but in such a manner as not to obliterate the stamp that postmasters will be unable to determine whether the stamps have been previously used". C. M. Cotterman, Director of Posts, December 26, 1905.

Beginning with January 1, 1906, all branches of the Insular Government of the Philippines used postage stamps to prepay postage instead of franking them as before. Some officials used manuscript, some utilized the typewriting machines, some made press-printed overprints, but by far the larger

number provided themselves with rubber stamps. The majority of these read "O.B." but other forms were: "OFFICIAL BUSINESS" or "OFFICIAL MAIL" in two lines, with variations on many of these.

These "O.B." overprints are known on U. S. 1899-1901 stamps; on 1903-06 stamps in red and blue; on 1906 stamps in red, blue, black, yellow and green.

"O.B." overprints were also made on the centavo and peso stamps of the Philippines, per order of May 25, 1907.

Beginning in 1926 the stamps were overprinted and issued by the Government, but some post offices continued to handstamp "O.B."

INDEX OF STORY SUBJECTS

Page numbers which appear below in bolder type denote a story about the subject. Lighter type face numbers indicate a reference to the subject.

GIANT POSTERS 30" x 40" EACH

SPACE

FOUR INTERESTING TOPICS • 35 ENLARGED STAMP REPRODUCTIONS

Make colorful decorations in your home, office, or workshop. Posters also might be cut apart so individual stamp reproductions may decorate cabinets, containers, doors, etc.

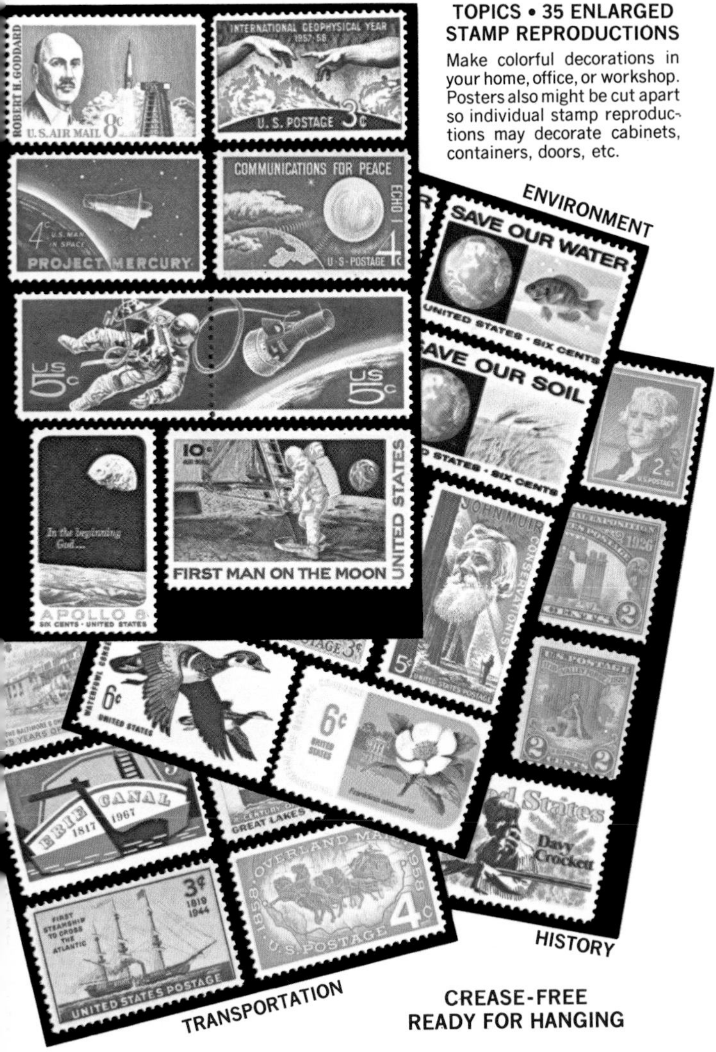

ENVIRONMENT

HISTORY

TRANSPORTATION

CREASE-FREE READY FOR HANGING

STAMPS – A NATION'S

This motion picture brings to the audience the beauty and meaning found in postage stamps. It portrays stamps as they reflect our nation's history and heritage. Featuring the Apollo Eleven "Moon Landing" stamp, the film shows seldom-seen processes from the first hand-engraved impression of a single stamp through the procedures that result in the final printing of millions. Creative photography set against an original music score brings life to numerous stamps that have become a part of our national tradition. The 19-minute 16mm color and sound film is a mixture of beauty and subtle humor of interest to both "Stamp Users" as well as advanced philatelists.

For free loan mail request to
National Audio Visual Center (GSA), Washington, D. C. 20409

Include individual name, organization name, address, city, state, zip code

Please indicate preferred and alternate dates

(For purchase include check or money order for $78.00)

CALLING CARDS

SPECIALTY COLLECTING

Most people begin to collect stamps by purchasing new issues. In time, however, they begin to specialize in an area which opens new horizons of enjoyment. Stamp collecting is a personal hobby, and no two stamp collections are ever entirely alike. A collector should carefully and creatively explore each of the following areas to determine which specialties offer him the greatest satisfaction.

BLOCKS OF FOUR

Many collectors prefer to save blocks consisting of four mint stamps, since these are more plentiful than other blocks also described here.

PLATE BLOCKS

Plate block collecting is one of the ol areas in U. S. stamp collecting. Plates u in the production of postage stamps poss serial numbers for identification. Th appear on each corner of a sheet of stam After the sheet is cut into four panes distribution, the plate number identi which portion of the original sheet pane occupied and by which plate it printed. Known as plate blocks, th stamps with the serial number are eage collected. Because the length of effec use of printing plates does vary, some pla soon wear out. The relatively scarce pa printed by these short-lived plates assiduously sought by plate block collecte

BOOKLET PANES

Stamp booklets were first issued in 18 On the average, only two new book panes are issued a year. Most philatel collect entire unsevered panes or en booklets (as sold in post offices).

The collecting of booklet panes or plate, "ZIP," and "Mail Early" blocks immensely popular because these c lector's items are simple and easy to loca All are available when issued at face va at most local post offices.

COVERS

Covers cancelled on the first day of iss of a postage stamp are collected enthusia cally by most philatelists. (See pp. 197-19 In addition, many people collect an versary, dedication, first flight, nav space, and other types of covers.

"MR. ZIP" BLOCKS

One of the successful projects devised to increase postal efficiency is the Zone Improvement Plan, known as ZIP Code. This geographically keyed system of numbers helps postal clerks route the ever-increasing volume of mail more quickly. A "Mr. ZIP" cartoon with slogan was inaugurated with the Sam Houston Issue released January 10, 1964. The cartoon and slogan with adjoining block of four have since been readily collected.

"MAIL EARLY IN THE DAY" BLOCKS

The earlier in the day mail is deposited the faster it is processed. The slogan "MAIL EARLY IN THE DAY" was included in a margin of sheets of the 6¢ Flag and White House stamp released on January 24, 1968. This inscription appears on the selvage midway between the plate and ZIP blocks. Most philatelists collect the slogan in blocks of six stamps.

SOUVENIR CARDS

From 1938 to 1939 the Post Office Department Philatelic Truck toured the country distributing souvenir sheets which pictured the White House. These were the forerunners of modern souvenir cards. Now issued at philatelic exhibitions in which the government participates, souvenir cards bear reproductions of U. S. stamps which have been made postally invalid by enlargement or by alteration to remove denomination, country name, and reference to postage. This new aspect of collecting now has thousands of avid followers and is the most exciting innovation in many years.

With so many variations open to the U. S. collector, the stamp enthusiast works in a field of infinite possibilities in which to expand the pleasure and value of his hobby.

SOUVENIR PAGE ORDER FORM

Here is your order form for subscribing to the new Souvenir Page service offered for the first time by the United States Postal Service. Just fill in the information requested below and send the completed form, along with your remittance, to: Philatelic Automatic Distribution Service, Philatelic Sales Unit, Washington, D. C. 20036.

PLEASE PRINT OR TYPE

_____

LAST NAME, FIRST NAME AND MIDDLE INITIAL OR NAME OF FIRM

_____

STREET NO., STREET NAME OR P.O. BOX NO., ETC.

_____

CITY NAME   STATE   ZIP CODE

SOUVENIR PAGES

NAME OF ITEM REQUESTED   ☐ $10.00
                                ☐ $25.00
                                ☐ $50.00
QUANTITY REQUESTED   DEPOSIT ENCLOSED

_____

SUBSCRIBER'S SIGNATURE   DATE SIGNED

SEND NOW FOR FREE PHILATELIC AIDS

A prospectus of the current Postal Service Stamp Program as well as an instruction sheet on obtaining First Day Covers may be obtained free of charge by writing the Philatelic Affairs Division, U. S. Postal Service, Washington, D. C. 20260. Please enclose a self-addressed stamped envelope with your request.

Souvenir Pages
with
First-Day Cancellations

WE'RE TESTING A NEW SERVICE

LIMITED OFFERING

A new computerized Philatelic Automatic Distribution Service is now being tested with a limited offering of Souvenir Pages cancelled on the first day of issue.

Collectors can receive automatically each new issue stamp on Souvenir Pages. The 8x10-1/2 inch pages, suitable for insertion in an album or for framing, are souvenir versions of the stamp announcements which appear in post office lobbies. They are printed on heavier paper and come with stamp affixed and cancelled with the Official First-Day Postmark.

Each Souvenir Page is 50¢ plus cost of the affixed stamp. However, the collector merely deposits $10 with his initial order. Each month he automatically receives pages with cancelled stamps issued the previous month, and the cost is subtracted from his subscription deposit. He will be notified whenever his account needs replenishing.

The new Philatelic Automatic Distribution Service is being inaugurated in 1972 on a pilot basis.

★ Guaranteed refund policy: Any subscriber can cancel his subscription on 30-day notice and receive a refund of the unused portion.

Orders for the Souvenir should be sent to Philatelic Automatic Distribution Service, Philatelic Sales Unit, Dept. 10, Washington D. C. 20036.

SPECIAL PHILATELIC ITEMS AVAILABLE

Quantity	Items	Value
	1971 Stamp Folder for 24 commemorative and special stamps issued in 1971. Similar to the 1971 Mini-Album, but has plastic strips for mounting stamps. Includes stamps. At $3.00	
	Space Folders. Twin Space Achievement stamps with first-day cancellations in colorful souvenir folders. Set of three folders at $3.00	
	Historic Stamp Posters. (See page 217 for details). Space, Environment, History and Transportation at $1.50 each or complete set of four at $5.00	
	Stamps and Stories Book. Paper bound edition at $2.00.	
	Stamps and Stories Book. Cloth bound edition at $5.95.	
	Souvenir Pages. Deposit $10.00 (No Postage and Handling Charges)	

MAIL TO:
Philatelic Sales Unit
Washington, D. C. 20036

Value of Items Ordered	
Postage and Handling Charges	.50
Grand Total	

PLEASE PRINT OR TYPE

Name _____

Address _____

City _____ State _____ Zip Code _____

SEND FOR LIST OF AVAILABLE U. S. STAMPS

For a complete listing of all mint U. S. stamps currently on sale at face value, send request, accompanied by a self-addressed stamped envelope, to: Philatelic Sales Unit, Washington, D. C. 20036.